MEDICAL PSYCHOLOGY

MEDICAL
PSYCHOLOGY

BY PAUL SCHILDER

Translator and Editor

DAVID RAPAPORT

Austen Riggs Center, Inc.
Stockbridge, Massachusetts

International Universities Press, Inc.
New York   New York

CONTENTS

5

TRANSLATOR'S FOREWORD

Schilder's *Medizinische Psychologie* is presented here in translation, three decades after it was written, both for its value as a historical document and its inherent value, which the decades have not dissipated.

It is a historical document first in the sense that it gives an "overview" of the common frontiers of neurological, psychiatric and psychologic knowledge in the beginning of the third decade of this century, and secondly in the sense that it represents the sweep of the most catholic thinker in the history of psychiatry.

Yet its interest is not primarily that of a historical document. Progress of knowledge has neither turned it into a classic nor fossilized it. Advances have shown up its weak spots, torn gaps into it, and frayed it; but its essential points hold up, and it still remains a pioneering endeavor. It speaks at once to the experimental and clinical psychologist, to the clinical and theoretical psychiatrist and psychoanalyst, and to the clinical and research neurologist and neuropsychiatrist—a feat unequalled in the literature. It is hoped that it will reach the advanced student in all these fields. To those students who proceed to clinical practice it can give a broader frame of reference than any other volume available; to those who go on to research and teaching, it opens vistas into broad areas of the field which are still uncharted, and presents hypotheses which to this day have remained untested, though vital and stimulating.

The *Medizinische Psychologie* was meant as an advanced textbook, yet not as a textbook of easy reading. Nor does it conform to the textbook custom of presenting only "tested knowledge." Neither was possible in 1923, when it was written. No canon existed then in these fields which could have served as the basis for judging safely "tested knowledge" and the safe limit of inference. It is very questionable whether we have such canons in the field even today.

7

The volume presents a broad selection of experimental and clinical observations, and their conceptualization. This selection itself, aiming at the essential and valid at a time when the knowledge and concepts were so new, was most difficult. This becomes particularly clear in some of Schilder's representations of Freud's views. Moreover, bodies of observation and theory stood isolated, and Schilder made the first single-handed attempt to relate them to each other. How insightful and successful he was in the field of the theory of thinking, I have tried to indicate in a Memorial Lecture which is reprinted as an Appendix. There is no doubt that the newness of the task gave free reign to Schilder's creative ingenuity and insight, so that in some ways we have still not quite caught up with what he saw or sensed. Neither is there doubt about the arbitrariness, looseness, and haphazardness of his presentation, qualities hardly avoidable in an early attempt at synthesis of data and concepts so elusive and indefinite. And yet Schilder's quests for relationships, and his finds, are more instructive than his arbitrary connections are misleading; and his conjectures are more stimulating than his recounts of information, many of which could not help becoming commonplace, trite, and boring.

*   *   *

To unburden this volume, the last of its seven sections (entitled "Affect and Experience") is omitted here. In its thirty-odd pages Schilder touched on such diverse topics as love and eroticism, homosexuality, social structure, affects in neuroses and psychoses, psychology of religion, of science, of esthetics, and the physician's relation to psychology, including discussions of psychosomatics; it is no wonder that the thirty years have wreaked more havoc here than in the rest of the volume. The loss which this omission entails is that Schilder's awareness of the sociocultural factor in personality development and pathology does not become clear in this volume. Yet, without extensive annotations, the omitted text would not have made it clear either. The interested reader will find this awareness in Schilder's *Goals and Desires of Man,* and *Psychoanalysis, Man, and Society.*

For purposes of clarification, some explanatory footnotes have been added, particularly where the American reader would not be familiar with what Schilder took for granted with his audience. The footnoting will be found to be quite uneven; of all the points of unclear reference, I have attempted to clarify only those which seemed particularly important in their bearing upon Schilder's thinking. The footnotes are consecutively numbered, Schilder's own being marked by an asterisk.

To ease the pure mechanics of reading, the gaps in Schilder's bibliography—the German original being complete neither in its coverage nor in its items—have been as much as possible filled in; bibliographic reference numbers, absent in the original, have been introduced. In a few instances it was not possible to identify the author or find the study referred to. In more instances it was difficult—in spite of a study of the originals—to be sure to which of an author's several studies Schilder meant to refer. Students more closely familiar than I with the fields of knowledge in question will readily discern the mistakes I have made in providing references.

Since the volume speaks to such a varied audience, and it is hoped will reach the advanced medical student, psychology student, and student of psychoanalysis, a further footnoting of the text was undertaken. The purpose of this footnoting was to indicate: (a) Schilder's other contributions to a topic; (b) up-to-date standard reference books on it; (c) specific new developments; (d) references to refuting or corroborating evidence; and (e) those ideas which are either salient to Schilder's thinking or anticipate later developments of significance in the field.

This multiple definition of the purpose of these footnotes again made it inevitable that they lack consistency by any single standard. Yet a guiding idea was systematically adhered to: to offer the reader reference-points to aid him in assessing the origins and present place of Schilder's material and views, particularly when they lie outside the reader's narrower field. Schilder's erudition and versatility were scarcely matched by anyone, even in 1923, and less so today since the luxuriant growth of information and the compartmentalization of the field. It would be blind not to acknowledge that the distribution of my own information, or lack of it, and predilections over the various fields, has influenced these footnotes. I have stressed those points where Schilder faced problems and anticipated theoretical solutions of psychoanalytic

ego-psychology; I have tried also to call attention to relations with
what might be called present-day "neuropsychology," particularly
Hebb's work.

* * *

Any broad present-day view would insist that the soma and
the nervous system, the id-impulses, the ego-self-organization, the
conscience-superego organization, the socio-cultural, and the situational dynamics, are all indispensable aspects of the study of
human behavior. Yet investigators focus usually on one, or at
best on one pair, of these. This is not simply a defect of our
present-day scene; it is in the nature of our human situation,
well characterized by the saying that we are learning more and
more about less and less. Indeed, the field is getting so broad that
mastery of information and concepts in more than a limited segment of it seems to exceed human capacity.

It is human nature to invest what one studies with an excessive importance. If the subject-matter of the study *is* human
nature—a loaded subject-matter, to say the least—the investment
of the aspect one studies and comprehends, and the devaluation of
that studied and comprehended by others, grows to the emotional
proportions of factional, philosophical, and religious fervor, mili-
tating against synthesis.

It seems difficult to be involved in the anatomy, physiology,
and pathology of the nervous system, and still be interested in
psychology—though Adrian, Penfield, and McCulloch have shown
such interest, and Lashley, Kluever, Koehler, Morris Bender and
Teuber, and Hebb have tried for some integration. But the complexities of the psychological dynamics reflected in concepts like
the ego and the id nowhere enter these syntheses. In Schilder's
thought, they do enter equally the treatment of the parapraxes of
the brain-injured, the preparatory phases of normal thought,
and the thought disorders of functional (neurotic and psychotic)
origin.

It seems difficult to be involved with the vicissitudes of id-
drives and still be concerned with the apparatuses of the ego—
perception, motility, memory, etc. Hartmann, Kris and Loewenstein, Klein, Mittelmann, have shown that it is possible. In turn,
those investigators interested primarily in the ego and in adapta-

tion (Adler, Horney, etc.) were little interested in either the id or the apparatuses. In Schilder's thought, these all appear so interwoven in their neural, drive, and adaptive aspects, that it is fair to say that his assumptions have not yet been listened to; even less have they been put to the test.

One could go down the line with further examples: how the interest in psychosomatic phenomena somehow tends to lose touch with or make shallow the understanding of neural, id, ego, and social dynamics (cf. Dunbar, Weiss); how the interest in cultural and social factors tends to make the importance of the others secondary at best (Fromm, Adler, etc.). In Schilder's world, all these aspects of behavior-study seem to be gathered. True, the information available to him at the time was often inadequate; the connections he conjectured often appear as far-fetched speculations. Yet the sense of unity of all aspects which he conveys makes up for his handicaps in available information, for his impatience, for the looseness of his criteria of inference.

* * *

The present-day reader may be bothered by Schilder's preoccupation with the mind-body problem and his insistence that the physiological phenomena and the psychological phenomena form two different causal series. There is indeed much justified objection to be made against this kind of formulation. But impatience with Schilder's formulation may make the reader overlook two facts: (a) It does not imply that there are *any* psychological processes without a neural substratum; indeed, he insists that every psychological phenomenon involves both a drive-intention and an apparatus. (b) It is an attempt to express a real problem: which somatic (including neural) processes have correlates amenable to investigation by psychological methods—whether the somatic process is viewed as an expression of, or the substratum of, psychologically encompassable processes—and which do not?

* * *

At this point a brief discussion of some of Schilder's leading ideas may be in place. It is hard to pick a few from the armamentarium of so rich and speculative a thinker as Schilder. One cannot help doing him injustice; many of his ideas were never implemented by him, and others he brought to bear on phenomena which appear relatively peripheral to his ideas.

Yet I venture to suggest that one of the conceptions of first order of importance to Schilder was that the human organism is by its nature geared to, directed toward, an existing real world of objects. That is, every behavior of the organism implies a drivenness toward, an intending—in Brentano's sense—of real objects. This conception also implied for him a specific gearing of the human organism to other human organisms—a constitutionally social character, or socialization potential, of the human being. This general conception was Schilder's synthesis of Brentano's act-psychology (intentionalism) and Freud's drive-psychology.

A second conception of the same order of importance to him was that these drive-intendings arise from somatic apparatuses and structuralize into psychological apparatuses. Function creates emergent structure, which in turn implies new intendings and further structuralization. What was amenable to study before it became structuralized, may no longer be afterwards. The Vogts's automatism concept, Kretschmer's "formular abbreviation," Bleuler's "occasional apparatuses," and Freud's concept of the "secondary process" meet in this Schilder conception; Lewin's ossification concept, Piaget's views of the development of schemata and "transformation groups," and Hartmann's automatization and autonomy concepts, are anticipated by it.

A third conception seems to be Schilder's "principle of the double path": that is, any behavior phenomenon may come about either by a "physiological" or a "psychological" process. This is a principle which does not imply lack of recognition of the "physiological" aspect of so-called "psychological" processes. A concrete example: a parapraxis which occurs in a neurosis due to the familiar dynamics traceable by psychological methods, may instead come about as a result of extreme fatigue or brain injury, both of which are more readily amenable to observation by physiological than by psychological methods. Observation of affects and parapraxes in normal and brain-injured persons, hypnotic findings, and early psychoanalytic studies of organ-neuroses, converged for Schilder in this conception.

A fourth conception seems to be that of the *sphere*, which for

Schilder replaces the concept of unconscious. In Schilder's view, a piece of behavior is either (a) automatized (structured), when it is performed by apparatuses and has nothing essentially "psychological" about it, that is, nothing amenable to study by psychological methods; or (b) it has a long preparatory process of evolution from vague impulse into thought or action, when it is either fully conscious or forms the background of consciousness. All of these processes of development constitute Schilder's sphere, which is the unformed background of experience (thought and behavior) and has no scope for the concept of the unconscious. In the sphere the mechanisms of condensation, displacement, etc.—formulated by Freud as the mechanisms of the primary process—hold sway. In some respects this concept of the sphere had advantages over Freud's unconscious-conscious dichotomy, even with the preconscious included, because it took broader cognizance of the many phenomena in which primary-process mechanisms manifested themselves in conscious thought. Only after the introduction of the structural point of view (id-ego-superego) did Freud take more general cognizance of these phenomena; and only Kris's work began to account specifically for them. It is in the sphere that, according to Schilder, functions structuralize, and structures become dissolved back into functions and recombine into new structures; here impulses check and delay each other, giving rise to impulse representations; here impulse-representations compete with each other, and are selected by object-directed intentions to give rise to reality-relevant thought and adaptive action. Indeed, Schilder explained pathological forms of thinking by their premature arising from the sphere or unbalanced development in it.

A fifth conception was labeled by Schilder "the undisruptibility of the psychological causal chain." By this Schilder meant partly what Freud had formulated in 1900: that nothing is unmotivated and arbitrary in psychic life, even after brain injury or in toxic hallucinosis. But partly Schilder meant that not only motivations, synthetic functions of the psyche also are always at work. Freud's formulation, Bleuler's studies of autism, H. Jackson's and Von Monakow's conceptions of levels of integration, converged in this conception. Freud came to the second aspect of it only in 1927; Nunberg (582) made it familiar later to psychoanalytic thinking; and only Hartmann (1937, 1951) assigned its systematic place in psychoanalytic theory. I have written about this conception of synthetic functions in the paper reprinted as the Appendix. Here I want to add only that, from the observed ubiquitous presence of synthetic functions, Schilder went so far as to draw the inference that the ego and the self never change; only their effectiveness may be curtailed or suppressed, by brain injury, functional disorder, etc. Quite possibly such a concept of ego and/or self can be consistently developed without getting into internal conceptual contradictions; but it is not the usual psychoanalytic conception of the ego.

For the psychoanalyst, the study of Schilder's concepts of sphere and synthetic functions cannot fail to be stimulating, and lift the blinders of his usual assumptions. To wear these, one need not be a zealot of psychoanalysis, but only normally trapped—as we all are—by the conceptual system he is familiar with; and to lift such blinders, Schilder's concepts need be no better than the usual psychoanalytic ones. Concepts are fashioned by man for nature, and even the ablest of men are far from perfect in this tailoring. The remarkable thing about Schilder is that while other men either rejected Freud's conceptions, or omitted to steep themselves in them, or having steeped themselves made blinders of them, Schilder steeped himself in them and remained free enough to question and seek weaknesses in them.

A sixth conception is that of the "body image." It is anchored partly to Freud's formulation that "the ego is primarily a body ego," and partly to observations on cases of apraxia and agnosia; it is elaborated here in relation to action, motility, apraxia and last but not least, the "appersonation" concept which was the root of what Schilder developed later into the conception of "the body image." It had a varied and far-reaching—though still not sufficiently deep—influence on many fields of psychiatric and psychological study.

A seventh conception is that of the indestructibility of the memory-traces of any experience. It is rooted partly in the concept of the continuity of the psychological chain; partly in the successful recovery of memories from epileptic twilight states and from amnesias due to brain injury, alcohol, Korsakow syndrome, etc.; partly in hypnotic and psychoanalytic recovery of memories. Combined with the conception of the "double path," this led him to postulate that there is no destruction of memory-traces in organic cases; he brought evidence that in such cases also the memories are "repressed" and manifest themselves symbolically, and that the patterns of repression, symbolization, etc., are fundamentally identical in functional disorders and disorders connected with gross brain pathology.

An eighth conception, which may give many readers pause, is that of irreducibility; that is, Schilder tends to consider the self, empathic knowledge of other people's feelings, and many other experiences, as psychological facts which are not further reducible. It is probably correct, however, to consider this conception of "irreducibility" in the context of the autonomy of emergent products (implied in the second conception above), and to regard it as an instance of such autonomization.

This enumeration is but a sample of Schilder's outstanding conceptions. Here is not the place to attempt a systematic presentation of all of them. Those presented are given to facilitate the reader's entering into Schilder's world and appraising the stature of his thought.

*　　*　　*

More personally, I undertook the translation and annotation of this unique volume with the feeling of paying a debt to Schilder —a man whom I never worked with and scarcely saw—for the wealth of stimulation I have found in studying his work for more than twenty years. It is my impression that we are all indebted to this rich unsystematic genius.

Looking over the footnotes, I notice how often I have referred to my own writing, and feel that an explanation is in place: my own studies have followed some of the pathways Schilder walked first, and these references are meant both as acknowledgments and as clarification and extension of Schilder's points.

I feel a particularly warm gratitude to those who have aided this work, which for me was characterized by this sense of tradition and affection. My first indebtedness is to Dr. Lauretta Bender, Paul Schilder's widow, for her understanding of my approach to it and for her generous allotment of time to both the translation and the annotations. My second indebtedness is to my friend, Will Gibson, who shaped the English of this volume with the same understanding and care as he has done that of my own writings. To my friends, Dr. Robert R. Holt and Dr. George S. Klein, I am indebted for their many criticisms and suggestions. The work on the manuscript and bibliography done by Mrs. Ruth Shippey and Miss Suzette Annin, secretaries of the Austen Riggs Center, exceeded by far that of routine secretarial help. Acknowledgment is also due to the Librarians of the Austen Riggs Center, Miss Sarah C. Austin and Miss Claude Picard.

Stockbridge, Mass., 1952   DAVID RAPAPORT

PREFACE

This book is meant primarily for medical men. But the aspect which psychology acquires from the vantage-point of medicine should be of interest to the psychologist too; therefore, I should like to see this book in the hands of psychologists as well. It is the problems of *practical* psychology which are urgent for the physician. He has an immediate and continuous relation to his fellowmen, deeper and more serious than that which the psychologist can establish with his experimental subjects; thus, he is in need of a live psychology, which he luckily need not draw entirely from books, but rather can gain intuitively as he adapts to his role in society. However, an attempt to formulate these matters theoretically may be of advantage for practical application too. A greater advantage is that which psychology stands to gain from the contact with real life, which earlier it had totally shunned. By this I do not mean to champion popular psychology, though it must not be overlooked that the works of great poets are replete with psychological insights. Unlike the poet, we cannot be content with the contemplation of the riches of psychological phenomena as they arise in front of us: we must approach them scientifically. This may first take the form of a scrutiny of the phenomena, to discover their phenomenological essence. But phenomenological psychology, which leans on the discoveries and formulations of Husserl (362, 363, 364) and Scheler (688), by-passes many formations, the nature of which is not revealed by phenomenological observation and/or by pure intuiting of essences.[1] These are the formations studied by psychoanalysis, the phenomena of the so-called unconscious. Moreover, psychoanalysis fosters the understanding of psychic processes, fits them into the processes of na-

[1] "Intuiting of essences" translates *Wesensschau;* this term implies the existence of a species of experience—distinct from observation and experiment—pertaining to "reason." See Scheler (689, pp. 229 and 239–240), also M. Farber (171).

ture, teaches us their causal understanding, and unlike mosaic-psychology[2] does not thereby renounce the psychology of real life. Psychoanalysis has been far too long regarded as a congeries of arbitrary constructions, a view which overlooks the factual material of its penetrating observations. Of course, one must not blind oneself deliberately and then declare that one can see no factual material; rather, the same effort and conscientiousness must be brought to bear in exploring this realm, as that which is considered a natural obligation in the exploration of other realms of science. This book refers continuously to the results of psycho-analysis, and does so in an elementary fashion, since ignorance of the fundamentals of psychoanalysis is extreme . . .

Though the considerations I present rest on the pillars of psychoanalytic views, they nevertheless take into consideration the cardinal relationships between mind and body. Cerebral pathology is used as the avenue to these problems. The novelty of this undertaking[3] should excuse its imperfections: I thought this to be the best way to present the theory of sensations, and to adduce most broadly the facts which experimental psychology has brought to daylight. Thanks to the efforts of Kuelpe's[4] school, we are now beginning to approach the central problems of psychology from the experimental side also.[5]

[2] In present-day terminology: "atomistic" (in contrast to "holistic").

[3] Schilder's pioneering attempt remains unique to this day. Although present-day "neuropsychology" has made some attempts in the same direction, it did not try to integrate psychoanalytic observations and theories. See particularly Hebb (328), also Kluever (428), to whom Schilder (see e.g. 750) frequently referred in his later writings, Teuber and Morris Bender (828), Penfield (599, 601). Other fragmentary attempts are those of McCulloch (528) from the neurophysiological-cybernetic side [see also Brazier (100)]; Koehler (434, 436), Krech (448, 449), and Klein and Krech (413) from the experimental psychological side.

[4] Kuelpe's (469) school or the Wuerzburg school pioneered in the exploration of thought and in systematic self-observation. See e.g. Ach (9).

[5] In his later writings Schilder referred to Lewin's (493) school also. Since that time experimental psychology has advanced considerably. Some of these advances relevant to medical psychology are reflected in J. McV. Hunt (361). It is, however, a question whether Schilder would have included among the advances at spanning the gap between experimental psychology and psychoanalysis, the work of what may be grossly labeled as learning theory [Sears's summary (769), Mowrer and Kluckhohn in (567), Massermann (540), Mowrer (568), Dollard and Miller (149)]. But it is probable that he would have included Allport's (26) intentionalism and the recent work on personality and perception (118, 80).

The disparate parts of this book are held together by a basic biological orientation which considers the psychological to be a biological agent. The heuristic justification of this point of view is unquestionable; I need neither describe its particulars, nor proffer detailed arguments in its favor. I have attempted this partially in another place (721), and hope to do it systematically sometime in the future. I have avoided philosophical considerations as much as possible, but could not entirely. I hope to be forgiven, and excuse it on the grounds that it is better to admit metaphysical postulates openly than to smuggle them in under the guise of empirical findings.

My attempt then is to unify in one framework, phenomenology, psychoanalysis, experimental psychology, and brain pathology. This may be called eclecticism. Yet each of these points of view and approaches has brought forth factual knowledge; and factual knowledge of different fields must, in its deepest fundaments, hang together and somehow be amenable to unification. Naturally, the outline I give here cannot replace the thorough study of these separate fields. To those interested in experimental psychology, the textbook of Froebes (258) is available as a reliable guide, in addition to the rightly valued texts of Wundt (895, 897) and Ebbinghaus (153).[6] Freud's (231) introductory lectures into psychoanalysis give a first view of that sphere of problems, though a deeper understanding of it can be obtained only through the psychoanalytic method of investigation of patients, for which a careful study of Freud's writings is an indispensable prerequisite.[7] A thorough understanding of phenomenology requires going to Husserl's[8] investigations of logic, and to his ideas concerning a pure phenomenology; though the medical man will find what is important for him in the volumes of Binswanger[9] and Kronfeld (464). Scheler's *Formalism in Ethics* (688) also is easier than Husserl's works. There is extant no comprehensive volume concerning the psychological problems of brain pathology. Monakow's (563) *Localization in the Cerebrum* offers an enor-

[6] The present-day equivalents are: Woodworth (893), Underwood (842), Stevens (808), and the Gestalt-psychologically slanted Koffka (439).

[7] See also Fenichel (180).

[8] Schilder refers to (362, 363, 364); see M. Farber (171) for a brief English rendering.

[9] Schilder refers to (75); see also Binswanger's (76) recent writing.

mous material collection, but is by no means oriented toward psychological understanding.

The goals of a medical psychology differ from those of a psychopathology; accordingly much that would have its place in a psychopathology will not be found in this volume. Jaspers's (382) excellent psychopathology is recommended as a complementary volume, though on many fundamental questions Jaspers takes views which I do not share.

The goals of my book are the same as those of Kretschmer's *Medical Psychology* (455), whose basic biological orientation I share. However, I strive for a closer relation between experimental psychology and brain pathology. Furthermore, while Kretschmer's volume is meant as an introduction, I attempt to stress more the scientific problems. Therefore, I am not addressing students, except those who already have some preparation. I have first of all presupposed a certain measure of psychiatric knowledge. Those who wish to refresh theirs are referred to Kraepelin's (446) or Bleuler's (86) shorter textbook.[10]

No individual can be expected to have complete command of the enormous material of facts available in this field. The reading of any work which covers a broader field gives investigators of special fields the opportunity to criticize shortcomings. What can be expected of the individual is that he should have come thoroughly to grips with the fundamental problems; on these I have labored for many years. I should like to hope that this attempt at integration will do justice in some measure to the issue.

PAUL SCHILDER

Vienna, February 1924.

10 Our present-day psychiatric texts are generally narrower in scope than those of Jaspers and Kretchmer. Those of pioneering scope are less comprehensive in coverage than Kraepelin and Bleuler. Noteworthy are E. Cameron (131), N. Cameron (132), Fenichel (180); and in abnormal psychology, R. White (881), Yacorzynski (899), Maslow and Mittelmann (539).

I

INTRODUCTION

The goals of general and of medical psychology. Psychology presupposes the ego concept. Psychological experience is not random. The psychological object-world. Psychological experience is a specific kind of experience. Outline of act-psychology. The ego originates acts. Quality and contents of the act must be distinguished. The object is not the result of psychic activity. The object is not a sum of sensations. Objects appear, acts are experienced. The difficulty of perceiving acts. Changes in the content of the act parallel the act itself. Feelings are reflections of attitudes. The principles of association-psychology: the psyche is built of sensations, feelings and their associations. Supplement: perseveration, assimilation; Wundt's concept of apperception. Temporal sequences and their explanation by association-psychology. The stream of experience. The growth of experiences from previous ones. The meaning-relations. The real relations of experiences are uncovered by psychoanalysis. The psychological causal-series and its relation to the somato-psychic. The physicist's concept of the world. Disorders of the mind are disorders of the brain. The untearable chain of psychic causality as argument against psychophysical parallelism. The effect-value of experiences.

Medical psychology is that aspect of psychology which has significance for the medical man; it is a segment of psychology which serves a definite practical purpose. We may expect of a psychology that it explain to us the nature of our fellow men, that it give us insight into what goes on in them, that it clarify the motives of their actions. This is the everyday meaning of the word psychology; yet experimental psychology neglected this goal. Until recently it was interested only in the structure of perception and in the simplest psychological experiences. It was a psychology of artificially isolated elements. The medical man cannot renounce the need for an experimental psychology, since it is his hope that through it he may more closely approach the relations between body and mind, and obtain information concerning the influences of the psyche upon the soma. He hopes that from experimental psychology, and from the agnosic and aphasic disorders, he will be able to encompass the formal structure of the psyche, since his intuition tells him that the forms encountered in experiment and in these disorders lead to the rich variability of the underlying psychic structure. Nor will he renounce observing the live personality and its strivings, but will rather attempt to penetrate into its nature by trenchant pure description. He will take into consideration not only the influence of affects on the body, but also the psychological changes in neuroses and psychoses which are closely related to somatic processes. To this end, and for the discovery of the causal relations in psychological processes, he will have to make use of psychoanalysis.

Let us attempt to outline more sharply the subject-matter of psychology. L. Binswanger's (75) introduction to general psychology gives a clear historical discussion of this much-debated question. To me it seems that any psychology presupposes an ego.[1] The subject-matter of psychology is the experiences of persons and egos, since when I study perceptions and sensations, they interest me as a psychologist only in so far as they are made alive, as it were, ennobled, by an ego. The subject-matter of physics and biology consists of objects conceived as independent units having no relation to the ego. In psychology my interest is directed toward my own experiences[2] and toward the experiences of others, in so far as the latter can be understood as those of foreign egos. . . . Phenomenology[3]* has taught us that there are also lawful structures outside the realm of that which is perceived. Thus, for example, a concept has many definitely describable characteristics: concept-basis, act-of-meaning, concept-sign, which stand in well-defined relationship to each other (more about this later).[4] We also recognize values, which are organized into a richly articulated world of values. The concept of the psychological cannot, therefore, be linked with that of the lawless and the arbitrary. Haas (311) put it thus: there is a psychological object-

---

[1] Cf. Claparède (135), W. Stern (807) and most recently G. Allport (26) who are the most vigorous propounders of this view. But it is also one of the implications of psychoanalytic ego-psychology; see particularly A. Freud (200, Chapters I–II), also Hartmann (318, 320) and Rapaport (656, 658).

[2] Compare, however, Pratt's (636) contrary views.

[3]* Concerning phenomenology, see the last paragraph of this chapter. [Also footnote 5.]

[4] See Chapter III, 2a, below; also Schilder (707), and Schilder (752, pp. 524–525).

world, the objects of which are not hazy but rather sharply contoured. Strictly speaking, however, not all these psychic objects belong to the narrower realm of psychology, but only those which occur in specific experiences. The study of the structure of objects is the business of phenomenology, ontology, logic, and ethics. Naturally, the psychological objects must be grasped, indeed created, by a live, real personality, and it is the job of psychology to study how that happens.

Yet there are separate physical and psychological phases. The concept of the psychological cannot be further reduced; it is, as Scheler (688) justly emphasizes, not an abstraction from individual psychological facts. Rather, it is a special form of perception, a specific act-modification[5] in which we experience the psychological, one different from that in which we experience the physical. The specific direction of the act is determined by the specific

[5] Brentano's (107) act-psychology and Husserl's (364) phenomenology shade into each other in Schilder's thinking. On act-psychology see Boring (96, Chapter 19), also Sartre (684). On Husserl, see Farber (171), where Gurwitsch writes: "The intentionality of consciousness may be defined as a relation which all, or at least certain, acts bear to an object. In this manner, Brentano introduced the notion into contemporary philosophy. Seeking to account for the difference between what he calls 'physical phenomena' and what he calls 'psychical phenomena,' Brentano found, among other characteristics, that the latter are distinguished by a relation to, or a direction toward, an object. This directedness of psychical phenomena is interpreted by Brentano as their containing within themselves an 'immanent' object-like entity. Although Husserl takes over Brentano's notion of intentionality, he raises some objections against this interpretation. His examination of Brentano's conception of intentionality finally leads him to abandon it completely; but he agrees with Brentano in acknowledging the existence of a highly important class of mental factors—for which Husserl reserves the title of acts—which have the peculiarity of presenting the subject with an object. Experiencing an act, the subject is aware of an object, so that the act may be characterized . . . as a *consciousness* of an object whether real or ideal, whether existent or imaginary," (p. 65). The act then is the psychological "turning toward," "orientation toward," or "intending of" an object. The act results in the consciousness of the object as a content. The act itself is usually not noticed, though it *can* be made the object of introspective reflection. There are many varieties of acts: perceptual, memorial, imaginal, thought, and other varieties. These may have the same object, e.g., an inkwell; yet depending on the variety of act taking place, an inkwell *seen*, an inkwell *remembered*, an inkwell *imagined*, or an inkwell *thought of* will be the resulting experience. Acts have modifications also. Here Schilder speaks about a modification of the thought-act, which brings "the psychological" as a content into consciousness; in our everyday language we would refer to this act-modification as a form of reflective introspection. Compare also Schilder's (738a) later discussion.

object, which here is the ego. The refutation of Wundt's (895, 897) and Ebbinghaus's (153) contrary points of view may be found in Scheler (688) and Binswanger (75).

I have before me a patient. She believes herself influenced by a machine, and has a clear bodily experience of this influence. She has surmised that she is influenced by means of electricity. This patient can make her feelings and sensations the subject-matter of psychological observation, but not the machine or the electricity produced by it. These are for her physical objects: she means them in the same sense as we mean[6] really existing objects. But for us, when we inquire into the origin of the girl's delusions, these objects conceived by her are psychological objects. We bring this machine into relation with the experience of the patient, and do not grant it any independence. Thus everything psychological presupposes an ego and a personality.

In the preceding we spoke of objects and of ego- and act-orientations. These expressions are not those of everyday language, they originate in a specific psychological view called act-psychology, a rough synopsis of which is: acts, the intending of[7] objects, emanate from the ego. But what are objects? We must free ourselves from the fetters of sensualist views which compound perceptions from sensations. To begin with, no sensations are demonstrable in a percept of mine. I simply see the inkwell, it is an object. I turn toward it, I intend it.[8] I do not intend the sensation, nor the visual content, nor the experience of the tactile impression which is not contained directly in the visual percept, nor the after-image; I intend simply the object which stands before me.

Now it could be argued that there is something which from the sensations, conceived as substances, build this object. It must, however, be stressed that no trace of this is contained in the experience. The experience contains only the direction, the intention toward the object, and not even these imply any activity. The object is not created by psychic activity from sensations; there is in experiences nothing initially to indicate that I arrive at the

6 "Mean" translates *meinen.* Schilder uses the term here to designate the intending of the object by a thought-act.

7 "Intending" translates *Zuwendung,* literally "turning toward." It is one of the terms used to indicate the essential ingredient of all acts.

8 "I intend it" translates *ich meine ihn.*

object by way of sensations: the object is simply given. It is only by simple experiments that we become aware that besides the object, which is before me, there occurs something in my body too: sensation is but an experience on one's own body. To see an object is entirely different from arriving—by means of experiments and considerations—at the view that certain changes have taken place in my body.

Epicurus's view, according to which pictures emanate from objects and enter the eye, in its naive way represents correctly the psychological state of affairs. First I perceive something, then it affects me: we distinguish the act of perceiving from that which is perceived. But many disclaim that the intending, the perceiving, is experienced as such, and maintain with Aristotle that the perceived and perceiving are identical. Association-psychology recognizes no acts, nor does Natorp (576), who is otherwise so far from association-psychology. I, however, believe that it is inherent to experience that the object meets an experiencing ego, and that the intending, the act, is present in the experience. In turn, the object's arising from the intending, my seeing the inkwell, is not an experienced activity, but a process that takes place outside of consciousness.

The sensations, which constitute the object, are in a *continuous flux*; they are altered by contrast, fatigue, irradiation, ocular movements, and objective changes of illumination. Even my turning the inkwell brings about essential changes in sensations, but the object remains the same. We thus differentiate the sensations, the contents, from the object. The object builds itself from sensations. Now Husserl (364) has demonstrated that I intend the same object in perception and in imagination.[9] Here the image-elements must not be mistaken for the object. Even if we intend the object in imagination, there still appears an abundance of details—spots, word-images—but all very changeable. Through all the changing visual, kinesthetic, tactile, acoustic image-elements, I intend the unchanging self-contained object which coincides with the object of perception. This very intending is the act of perceiving and the act of imaging.

I can, however, intend concepts and thoughts also; moreover, I can become absorbed, to various degrees, in the percept, in the

9 Cf. Sartre (684) and a review of this book (653).

image, and in the concept. Acts show extraordinarily rich qualitative gradations, which we designate as the quality of the act. This qualitative series, as will become clear later, shows yet another series of gradations. The changing forms of the elements must not be mistaken for what Husserl has called the matter of the act. Thus, for example, I can grasp the same object now as an equilateral, now as an equiangular, triangle; or I can intend Napoleon as a person, as a war-lord, as an emperor, or as a total personality. Husserl's "matter of acts" refers to these various aspects of the object.

Acts are thus qualitatively graduated. There are perceiving-, imaging-, and thinking-acts, all of which arrange themselves in varying degrees of certainty from assumptions which guarantee nothing, to full evidence.[10] But besides these, there are acts of wishing, willing, which to be sure, according to Husserl, must rest on acts of imaging, thinking, and perceiving. The intention of these acts presupposes another intention, according to Husserl's theory. Like wishing and willing, activity, the grasping of the object, the intending of the object in action, also presupposes its imaging or perceiving. But is there no direct wishing, willing, act which is not based on an act of imaging?

These considerations do not imply the metaphysical reality of things, though they definitely assume, by-passing epistemology, that things appear as objects. I can get various impressions of the thing. I can turn it all around, touch it, palpate it, smell it, try to taste it. Through all this abundance of experiences I will still have it before me as an object. It can, to use Husserl's expression, take on the most varied aspects; indeed, taking on aspects may be regarded as characteristic for the various objects of the external world, while throughout the object proper remains intended. The object is met by the ego.

Again: we distinguish in the act the ego-factor; the object onto which it is directed; the specific elaboration of the object—the matter of the act; the quality of the act (whether of imaging, perceiving, willing, doing, etc.); and finally, sensations, image-elements, thoughts, feelings—that is, the contents of acts.

How can we doubt that there are acts? To be sure, they are not contained in the psychic process in the same way as are objects

10 Cf. Rapaport (659, 661).

and contents which present themselves; they are experienced rather in an immediate manner, and it takes a certain effort to perceive them, to have them before us as objects; yet they are inherent to experience. There adheres to every act something which makes it "mine," and it is always the same ego that is experienced within every act. The ego is something steady and constant, unchanging through life. The contrast of ego and object is incomplete if we do not represent with it a mid-region, referred to as "my body."[11] This is the whole of all sensations, and on the one hand appears as object-like as anything else, and on the other hand is ego-closer. It can be said that every intention expresses itself also in sensations. The grasping of every object implies sensations, and at the same time the never absent coenesthetic sensations[12] characterize the body as "my body." This gives a crude description of what happens psychologically in perceiving, and raises the further problem: what happens in the psyche in internal experiences? This is easily answered for images, feelings, sensations, thoughts: these appear when certain attitudes[13] are present.

Acts, or we might say intentions, turnings toward, orientations, are experienced. But how are they grasped? Brentano (107) thought that linked to each act was the perception of the act as such. Against this, it should be stated, as was stressed by Husserl, that there are basic differences between, on the one hand, the appearance of objects, percepts, images, thoughts, feelings, and on the other, the experience of the act. Naturally, we can put an act before us, but then we no longer experience it—it becomes an object. If we want to know something about the act too, we must consider it separately. Perhaps only in passing need it be mentioned that the physical concept of time must not be applied to experiences. Experience unfolds on many levels. It is probable that it is experienced on one level, and simultaneously perceived

11 By "ego" Schilder seems to refer here to the "self" [for current concepts cf. Hartmann (320) and also Sullivan (825)], rather than strictly to the psychoanalytic concept of the ego which is defined as "a cohesive organization of mental processes" (Freud, 239). Cf. also Claparède (135) on "me-ness" and Koffka on "ego" (439, pp. 323 ff.).

12 "Coenesthetic sensations" translates *Gemeinempfindungen.*

13 "Attitude" translates *Einstellung;* the more common term "set" used in translations is too narrow and specific for Schilder's use of the term. Cf. Rapaport (658, pp. 28–29, 660–661).

from another. It is thus that we can base our knowledge of acts on direct self-observation.

But we are faced here with an important generalization of the concept of object. An object no longer is what is perceived or imaged, but simply what is intended, that is, anything I bring before myself. Anything which I bring before myself as a whole by means of its particulars of image, sensation and thought, is an object.

An additional difficulty in the way of recognizing the actual nature of acts is that in turning toward the object, the matter of the acts is altered. When I turn toward an object in the act of wishing, the object is penetrated and transfigured by the wish. According to Husserl, there corresponds to the form of the act (also called noesis), a certain molding of the matter of the act, that is, of the noematic correlate. When I turn toward an object attentively, it becomes attention-charged. Thus, every change on the act side is accompanied by another on the object side.[14]

Here we have approached the problem of feelings. We speak of a feeling-tone of sensations (Ziehen, 904). Others, for example Wundt (897), consider feelings as independent, and indeed, will and intending are for him only particular feeling-processes. For many other authors, feelings are nothing but particular kinds of proprioception (James and Lange, 375). Though I cannot agree with these views, I must admit that coenesthesia is somehow related to feelings. I have already mentioned that correlated with perceptions is a change in the sensations of the body. Feelings too correlate with intending, so that acts of perception are reflected not only in coenesthesia but also in feeling, and this reflection comprises not only the specific act, but also the general attitude and orientation of the individual and his body. Yet I cannot ascribe to feelings the over-riding significance attributed to them by Wundt (897) and Lipps (512). The change of the object resulting from the change of noesis[15] is not exhausted by the addition of feelings and coenesthesias. Beyond doubt, the act of

14 For instance, the psychological event of the perception of a pencil is analyzed here into its content (pencil) which is the *noema* and into the experiencing of this content (the perceptual act) which is the *noesis*. The pencil (as a part of perceived reality) is the matter of the act, it is the noematic correlate.

15 Husserl's distinction **noesis** vs. **noema** roughly parallels Brentano's distinction of act vs. content.

attention alters the setting of the motor apparatus (eye-movements, accommodation) and with it even the gross perceptual content.[16]

We distinguish thus in perception: the contents, the act of perceiving, and that which is perceived. This theory does not consider the percept as the simple sum of sensations and reproduced elements. It stands thus in stark opposition to the theory of association-psychology which has long ruled scientific thinking.[17] That theory may be summarized: the psychological consists only of sensation elements, such as red, pointed, odorous, high-C, and of the image-elements which are replicas of and are closely related to them. Sensation and what is sensed are not distinguished, neither is the perceived from perception. The act as such is thus not recognized, nor, naturally, are the modifications of it; for this point of view, there are neither will-acts nor strivings. One variant of this theory recognizes feelings also, besides sensations, as independent units of psychic life, though some consider these feelings as organ-sensations. Another variant speaks only of the feeling-tone of sensations, ascribing it to them as a third attribute besides quality and intensity. Sensations and images (and feelings) are thus considered by this psychology as elements, out of which it is to build up the entire psychic life. For this purpose, association-psychology makes use of the conception that the connection of sensations and images is regulated by certain laws called the association laws. These laws assert that simultaneously with the appearance of a sensation, all other sensations which were spatially or temporally contiguous with it, or are similar to it, are reproduced.

We speak of associations by contiguity and by similarity, but there have been attempts to derive the latter from the former, conceiving of similarity as partial identity. Naturally, the repro-

[16] Cf. Heinz Werner's (871, 873) recent work, and other recent studies in perception (118, 80), particularly Bruner (114). T. Burrow's (129, 128) studies in "attention" and "cotention" are also pertinent, but have not as yet been checked or disentangled from the diffuse theoretical network in which they were presented. Note also Hebb's (328) pertinent, though divergent, view.

[17] The descendants of association psychology are the "conditioning theories" of various vintages (see Hilgard and Marquis, 347, Hilgard, 348). What Schilder asserts here for association psychology seems to hold more or less for most of these "conditioning theories," but this has so far not been systematically demonstrated.

duction does not occur in the form of sensation-elements, but rather in the form of image-elements. Association-psychology deems these to be sufficient basic assumptions, though a few amendments have already proven necessary. Thus, Mueller and Pilzecker (571) have added the perseverative factor to the associative and reproductive ones: it was demonstrated that an element once arrived tends to persist in consciousness. More important is that, according to association-psychology, impressions of any complexity would have to be reduced into an inconceivable sequence of elements—an assumption starkly countermanded by experience. Therefore, the process must be described so that what is associatively related may be already involved in the process of sensation. Wundt (897) earlier used the term assimilation. According to this theory, the orderedness of our experiences and experience in general originates from the emergence, out of the infinite abundance of possible associations (and assimilations), of only those which are brought together by the general conditions of the individual and of the perceiving.

Thus, all of psychic life dissolves into simple elements. To be sure, this leaves it entirely in the dark how the combination of sensations and images ever brings about anything new. It takes nothing but an unprejudiced view to see that we experience concepts, propositions and judgments, and that such a judgment as, "This linen is white," cannot be dissolved into the juxtaposition of linen and white, or into any association or assimilation. One must resort to psychological chemistry, by means of which something new, unforeseen, a new compound, arises from the elements.

Necessity has induced Wundt to add two supplements to the association theory. One is the creative resultant: two simultaneous experiences are not simply additive, something new appears, which has nothing in common with what was originally given. The other is the recognition of a central psychological function, which Wundt calls apperception. This Wundtian concept is in essence an approach to the act concept. It is a central orientation, which underlies attending, willing, comparing. To be sure, Wundt definitely tends to reduce apperception to a particular feeling- and sensation-process. It is beyond doubt that not even this extension of the theory can account for the actually existing experience-structures. The association theory is thus in essence a genetic theory, which attempts to set forth how psychic life arises from its elements. These elements have a close relation to the world of matter, and indeed materialism and association-psychology are historically closely linked. Association-psychology meets the demands of materialism by the formula that what is psychological arises from these or those sensations and from images which can be considered reflections of sensations. It attempts to explain psychic processes on these same grounds, and meets no difficulties in this respect either, since it is in time that associations run their course.

Act-psychology takes an entirely different view of psychic processes; it deals first of all with the actual experience-material, analyzes and represents it, and asks not whence it comes. Having been born in the struggle against the genetic association-psychology, it is in danger of altogether disregarding genetic connections. Neither Scheler nor Husserl shows any deep concern for psychological time-sequences. But since the will-act is recognized by act-psychology as a particular experience, we sense that it should be possible for act-psychology—just as it was for association-psychology—to describe time sequences in a way that does justice to the facts.

Now we must turn from static experiences to those which change in time. Kant has actually considered time to be a form of apperception[18] of the internal sense, and Bergson (61) considered pure duration, *la durée vécue,* as the essential sign of life. James (373) speaks of a stream of consciousness, and indeed unprejudiced observation of psychic life will always find it a process of change, a flow, a life in time. Psychic life cannot be correctly comprehended if this vital aspect of it is disregarded. Percepts, images, and concepts appear in this context as mere passing formations, as fixation-points, as relatively lifeless. For James too, the relation of the structured parts of experience to the unstructured ones is a most salient problem. Act-psychology is familiar with acts and their manifold varieties of perceiving, imaging, wishing, willing. These acts are not static because they can be conceived only in time. Yet the formulations of act-psychology make these live acts appear static; it is not concerned with the

---

[18] **"Form of apperception"** translates *Anschauungsform*—often translated as "form of (sensuous) intuition." See Kant (401, Part One—"Transcendental Aesthetic").

relation of an act to the preceding and following acts, but isolates
it.

This makes it comprehensible that Husserl—to whom act-
psychology owes much of its depth—developed a science of essences,[19] phenomenology, which according to him has no relation
to psychology. In it, the intuiting consciousness abstracts from all
actualities, and investigates the intuiting, the act, the noesis, and
the corresponding noematic correlates. Husserl's phenomenology
is a theory of essences, which does not depend upon whether that
which it comprehends was, is, or ever will be, real.

The problem arises continuously: how are the single pieces
of the psyche fitted together, what joins them into a cohesive,
psychic life? Neither the close interweaving of single experiences
nor the experiencing of them in time can explain that all experiences are those of an ego, of a personality; therefore, we must
assume that it is a particular kind of experience in time. Concerning this particular kind of temporal experience, act-psychology so far has had little to say. Jaspers (382), who is close to this
school, speaks, partly in the sense of Dilthey (148), in terms of
rational connections.[20] A child who reaches for an apple has the
experience that the action originated in the wish aroused by the
tempting apple. In general, we know from experience how new
impressions, perceptions, images, thoughts, attitudes, arise from
old ones. This arising we do not experience as something different
from the attitude, nor is it a point-by-point progression; it is
rather that whole groups of attitudes find fixation-points in imaginal, perceptual, and conceptual objects, which in turn become
fixation-points only in relation to these attitudes. The attitudes
in question do not run parallel to each other, but rather criss-
cross like the rays of different cones of light-beams. But this simile
fails to express that each attitude attains its meaning and coloring
only from those adjacent, preceding and subsequent.

This process is not chaotic, but rather so integrated and ar-

19 "Science of essences" translates *Wesenswissenschaft*, i.e., concerned not
with appearances which are relative, but with absolutes.

20 "Rational connection" translates *verstaendliche Zusammenhaenge*; Dilthey's use of this term, however, implies the doubt that historical and psychological events can be encompassed by causal connections (nomothetic laws) and
the assumption that they can be described only in terms of connections that
impress us as rationally understandable, though not causal. Cf. Jaspers (380).

ticulated that it expresses at any given time the total orientation
of the individual—even though in ever-new aspects.[21] Psychoanalysis has demonstrated this in detail by means of rich factual
material. Thus, every love-relationship expresses the totality of
previous love-attitudes; it arises from these, though naturally
enriched by new acquisitions. In every anxiety there is a resonance
of all previously experienced anxieties, including the anxiety of
birth.[22] This appearance of ever-new attitudes has a character
of both will and drive. In experiencing, I turn toward new impressions because they interest me, and this interest-charged intending is a will-, or drive-action.[23]

Wundt's apperception-psychology accounts for this state of
affairs, in so far as it considers attention to be closely related to
will, though it fails to recognize the specificity of willing and reduces it to a particular arrangement of sensations and feelings.
Besides these psychological processes, Wundt recognizes associations also. B follows A, because A and B have been previously experienced simultaneously, or because B is similar to A. There is
nothing else that ties A and B together; B follows A mechanically.
I do not believe that there are such associations in psychic life:
when B follows A, it does so because, to begin with, the intending
pertained to both parts of the experience. If A is a percept which
arouses a memory of the percept B once connected with A, then
A has given rise to an attitude directed toward B.[24] Nevertheless,
association-psychology gives us a framework for psychological
processes.

It must also be stressed that so far association-psychology has
been more interested in psychological development and genetic
relationships than has act-psychology. This is, to my mind, not
due to the nature of their points of view, but rather to a historical
accident. Act-psychology devoted its primary attention to psychic

[21] For a more detailed discussion of this point see Schilder (695) and Schilder (750, Chapters 18, 19).

[22] Cf. Rank (648) and Freud's (244) *The Problem of Anxiety.*

[23] Here—as in all of Schilder's writings—"attitude," "orientation," "interest," and "will" are presented as partaking in drive-character. It seems implied, but is never explicitly stated, that Schilder conceived of them as hierarchically organized drive-derivatives. Cf. Appendix, pp. 345 ff., infra.

[24] Lewin (490, 492) offered experimental proof for this assumption, which
is one of the basic implications of the psychoanalytic theory of thinking. Cf.
also Bartlett (46).

structures because it struggled against those points of view which considered these structures as mechanical couplings of primitive elements. The mosaic-psychologies[25] in turn built a genetic view, without paying due regard to the multifariousness of psychological experience.

Now we may turn to a question which is particularly important in the introduction of a medical psychology: can psychology be considered a natural science, or can there be a psychology which is not a natural science? Husserl had strictly isolated his phenomenology from natural sciences, making it independent of any real existence. To be sure, he did not label it psychology. Natural science is a theory of the actually existing, of the laws which obtain in nature as reality, the knowledge of which permits prediction. This implies the possibility of altering the actual course of events in keeping with desired goals. The point of view of natural science is mathematical and physical. Science's picture of the world is meager in qualities; it is concerned only with prediction and attains this best by disregarding qualities, by reducing the world to matter and energy. The physical view is one in terms of processes. The physical formulas would not change were all men color-blind, nor would the physicist's world change were ultraviolet wave-lengths seen as colors.

But there is a manifold of psychic structures which cannot be encompassed by a physicalistic view. The ego is a supra-physical entity; the world of the physicist is independent of the existence of personalities and reduces them to chemical and physical formulas. For the physicist a world without conscious processes is quite comprehensible, and he does not know what to do with consciousness.[26] One must not assume that the qualitative multifariousness of psychological phenomena can somehow be accounted for physically. Husserl's distinction between the meaning of concepts, and their communication and content (see Chapter III, 2, on language), makes no sense in terms of natural science. Similarly,

25 Cf. Preface, footnote 2, supra.

26 Schilder's psychological stand here grossly parallels that of Gestalt-psychology (see Koffka, 439), and that of the organismic biologists (see Bertalanffy, 66; Woodger, 892). Indeed, even modern physics seems to refrain from that sort of intransigeant reductionism which is opposed here by Schilder (see Delbrueck, 143). Yet Schilder's phrase "supra-physical" appears to overshoot the mark, giving the impression that metaphysical entities, rather than non-reducible emergents, are being assumed. For a view contrary to Schilder's, see Pratt (636).

the arising of psychological experiences from each other eludes natural science.

Finally, intending cannot possibly become the object of natural science, as it is actually its prerequisite. Thus, what is vital in psychology could not be encompassed by natural science—a conclusion which would both aggrieve the medical man and be out of keeping with his experience. The older materialists pointed out continuously that a drop of water in the brain would destroy psychic processes. Everyday experience shows that poisons alter psychological processes. After all, Meynert (555) was able to formulate: mental disorders are brain-disorders, and we are actually in a position to explain a part of mental disorders by organic changes in the brain, to refer another part to more or less known toxic effects on the brain, and to assume for the rest some alteration of somatic brain function.

There must be essential connections between somatic and psychological sequences. These may be conceived as follows. Though the course of the psychological series is particular in its kind, it may nevertheless be considered a causal series—but only at the price of abstracting from its qualities. For instance, the acceptance of a command determines causally its execution; or the arising of an overpowering drive-like wish is the cause of the drive-action. Into this chain of psychological causations the somatic continuously intervenes: it may take alcohol for a decision to become an action; or a thought-process may be aborted by toxic influence. In other words, there is a psychological causal series which is continuously altered by a somatic causal series, and which in turn influences the somatic causal series. For example, every will-action implies changes in the somatic series, and every psychic process is accompanied by somatic changes, such as the change of muscle-tension in fright.

It could be said that the influences of the somatic causal series on the psychological, and those of the psychological on the somatic, constitute the main subject-matter of medical psychology.[27] In saying so, we disregard the epistemological problem of

[27] This view seems antiquated; recently the tendency is to consider the "psychological" and the "somatic" simply as aspects of the organismic unity, and to use for exploration and therapy that method of approach (psychological or physiological) to which the prevalent aspect of the phenomenon lends itself more readily. For the standard psychoanalytic view, see Bibring (71). Cf. also Angyal (31a).

whether there are brain changes corresponding to the psychological causal series—as psychophysical parallelism would have it.[28] According to our assumption, what we label as the psychological causal series is only one of the causal series which take their course within the brain structure.

I must stress, however, that we may not consider the psychological causal series to be merely of the same order as the other causal series, since, and this sets the stage for later considerations, it has the characteristic that, though it can be altered, so long as life persists it cannot be severed.[29] For instance, his individual prehistory and ego express themselves in the activities of the drunkard, and not even general paresis can prevent a patient's premorbid personality from influencing his present behavior. The psychological causal series differs from all others in that it cannot be severed. To my mind, this fact cannot be explained by the assumption of psychophysical parallelism. Thus, it is demonstrated that the viewpoint of natural science can and must be brought to bear upon parts of the field of psychology. The influence of somatic illness on the psychological causal chain, and the manner in which the ego and the personality function in spite of these causal influences, are main subject-matters of medical psychology.

In viewing experience phenomenologically, we describe psychic processes in such a way that one experience arises from another. The loss of a relative fills me with pain and mourning; the mourning eliminates other things from my ken, and makes me immobile and limp; I experience my condition as arising from a certain experience. It can be assumed that in an active person the "same" mourning would have less effect. On the other hand, the degree and kind of mourning depend not only upon my attachment to this relative, but also upon what I have experienced and am experiencing otherwise. Finally, it may be assumed that the mourning would take a different form if a physical illness, say an

28 This is not only the philosophical view of psychophysical parallelism; some empirical psychologists also share it. See Koehler (434), Hebb (328), Krech (448), Klein and Krech (416).

29 Schilder gave a striking empirical demonstration of this point in his *Studies in General Paresis* (752). Psychoanalytic ego-psychology would treat this point in terms of the concept of "the synthetic function of the ego." See Nunberg (582), Hartmann (321).

attack of jaundice, were to come between the mourning and its effects. Or one can drown one's mourning in the cup. It is obvious that somatic factors cogwheel here into the psychological process. The course of the process must be connected somehow with physical causality. I can consider the sorrowful event as a causal factor, saying that factor A induces a change in the psychological economy; for example, it diminishes the driving-forces of action. We could say factor A has an effect-value, and could speak in general about the effect-values of psychological experience. In the present example, the effect-value would be dependent partly on the degree of my attachment to my relative, and partly on my present somatic situation, which is determined both by my past experiences and by my constitution.

The effect-value so accrued varies in its effect, however, according to what happens afterwards psychologically or somatically. A decision may remain ineffective until alcohol eliminates the inhibitions. The attitude assumed toward the hypnotist may, under certain circumstances, bring about sleep only if it is given somatic support by means of sedatives. Purely deductively, it may be worth while to distinguish between the effect-value and its alterations, and the apparatus on which it acts. Thus it is conceivable that identical effect-values of mourning will have different results dependent upon the condition of the motor apparatus. But then mourning moves from the sphere of experience into that of psychophysical processes, of somatic causes and effects, because effect-value is a quantity amenable to physical measurement. The best illustration of what I mean is that the hypnotized person needs less chloroform for deep narcosis than the not-hypnotized[30]; so it can be said that the effect of the psychological attitude called hypnosis may be equated with the effect of the chloroform saved.

Conversely, it is well known that extremely intoxicated people can be sobered up by rousing accidents. Here the effect of the alcohol is canceled through a psychological avenue. These relationships are of decisive significance for the medical point of view. In epidemic encephalitis, parts of the brain which have to do with the motor impulses are destroyed by an organic lesion.

---

[30] See Friedlaender (250); cf. also Horsley (357), and Brenman and Gill (102).

The patients do not produce motor driving-forces unless an affect supersedes the organically determined defect.

Thus, the somatic and the psychological continuously interact. The description of experience as such cannot teach us anything about these relationships, even though a somatic happening can reflect itself in the psychological; the intending certainly will be altered, and the arising of one experience from another will be differently colored according to the effect-value of the experience. However, the concept of effect-value, which is defined entirely in somatic terms, must not be equated with this coloring. We speak of effect-value only in the context of natural science.

The discussions of this section are based on phenomenology.[31] The term phenomenology is often used for the pure, careful, unbiased description of givens; it is in this sense of descriptive psychology that Jaspers uses it too. Husserl, though in the beginning he did not differentiate sharply the phenomenological point of view from the psychological, later gave the term new meaning. His phenomenology is a contemplation of essences,[32] demonstrating the structures of comprehension independent of whether they appear in real individual experiences. It wants to establish the essence independent of experience, that is, it aims—to use an analogy—to do for psychology what mathematics and geometry do for natural sciences. In order to penetrate further into these problems, the study of Husserl's work is indispensable. Husserl's phenomenology claims validity independent of all experience, and is in its nature not a psychology. The same holds for Meinong's (547) object-theory. This claim has been—to my mind—correctly contested, and the close relationship of phenomenology and psychology has been repeatedly stressed (e.g., Messer, 550).

Yet it is beyond doubt that a theory of essences can be developed, and with it a system to which specific psychological discoveries can be related. Here I pursue deliberately a "psychological phenomenology," certainly with an eye to a surmised theory of essences. The best survey of these problems will be found in Kronfeld (464) and Binswanger (75), and I want to refer to Jasper's (382) general psychopathology, from whose basic tenets mine differ in many ways. My own viewpoint I have expressed in *Selbtbewusstsein und Persoenlichkeitsbewusstsein* (690) and in *Seele und Leben* (707). Concerning the concepts of effect-value and psychological energy, see my paper "Ueber den Wirkungswert psychischer Erlebnisse, etc." (709).

31 Cf. footnote 5, supra.
32 Cf. Preface, footnote 1; and footnote 19, supra.

II

THE THEORY OF PERCEPTION

1. PERCEPTIONS AND IMAGES

Perceptions are self-contained. Images point beyond themselves. Fantasy-images and memory-images. The transitions between images and percepts. Acts of imaging and acts of perceiving. Image- and sensation-elements, and their merger under the influence of intentions. Eidetic images as transitions between images and percepts. The law of identical layering in eidetic images and percepts. Space is common to both images and percepts. Hypnagogic hallucinations. Hallucinations cannot be sharply distinguished from pseudo-hallucinations.

In the act of perceiving I direct myself[1] toward an object. I can direct myself toward the same object in an act of imaging. In perceiving, the object is self-contained, it has a corporeal presence; in imaging, however, I relate myself to it in a less direct way. Images derive from perceptions, and could be subdivided into true memories and fantasy images in the broadest sense, meaning those which create out of the memory material something which is new for the experiencing individual. But both kinds of images point beyond themselves to a "real world," whether one of fantasy or story, or one of scientific hypothesis. The act of imaging thus always points beyond itself to a related percept, which may belong either to the past or to the future.

To a certain degree, however, the image may remain corporeal. When I have a patient before me, and I close my eyes and

[1] This phrase is frequently used by Schilder to express the intentionality of the act. [Cf. Allport (26, p. 187 ff.), and Introduction, footnote 5, supra, on intention.] The following is a discussion of the varieties of acts, i.e., of intendings. From the point of view of dynamic psychology, the intending implicit to the act seems to take the form of attitudes, interests (cf. Bartlett, 46; Rapaport, 655; also Appendix, pp. 347 ff., infra), or generally motivations. Yet such a reduction of intentionality to motivations has so far failed to account for the varieties of acts (cf. Rapaport, 659).

try immediately to image him, then my act of imaging is closer to perceiving than that by which I image either a patient I saw a year ago or a golden mountain. In the first act I refer to something which exists here and now. Walking up and down in a room I do not perceive the objects which are at any given time behind me, yet I do not apprehend them very differently from those which I do perceive. Thus, it is always important whether an image refers to something fantasied or really extant, or whether the really extant is past or present, and the fantasied is possible or impossible. Conversely, there are percepts which do not refer to anything real—or at least real in the external world. Though I perceive an optical after-image, I do not refer this percept to the external world, but rather to my body. To the mirror picture too I attribute a lesser reality.

Thus, both percepts and images are always connected with acts which relate to the reality or unreality of the perceived objects. But in simple perception, the act of perceiving in itself so implies the act of considering-it-real that the latter can be called an attribute of the act of perceiving; in imaging, the act of considering-it-real and the act of imaging are separated; and in perception of the after-image, an act of not-considering-it-real enters. Thus, we must distinguish on the one hand the self-containedness and corporealness of the percept, in contrast to the image, which points beyond itself; and on the other, the acts of considering-it-real and of not-considering-it-real. In general, corporealness and considering-it-real go together. The act of considering-it-real was called by Goldstein (286) reality-judgment; yet it is questionable whether we are actually dealing here with a predicative relationship—the only kind which can be termed judgment. I would prefer to speak of an act of realization, though I must admit that the act of perceiving the after-image changes the act of realization into a judgment.[2] Thus, there are many qualitatively different acts in imaging and perceiving.

There are, furthermore, differences in contents. The image-element is different from the sensation-element, though in actual perceptions image- and sensation-elements shade into each other. In the visual percept of a chair, there appear tactile qualities (occasionally also acoustic, and other) which have not been directly

2 Cf. Freud (216) and (232).

experienced, as well as many reproduced—that is, image-like—visual elements. To be sure, under the influence of the act of perceiving, the image elements merge with the sensation-elements. Conversely, some images contain sensation-components, and it may be asked whether or not all images contain sensations: but here too we deal with merger processes. For example, when I instruct a visually well-endowed subject to close his eyes and image his hand triply enlarged, then in the imaged hand there very frequently arise sensations.[3] Synesthesias in general have a great influence: we itch when we hear about lice, and this synesthesia no doubt does not remain central, but extends to the periphery of the body and is accompanied by vasomotor phenomena. Whether or not the

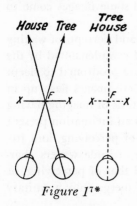

Figure 1[7*]

participation of the periphery in synesthesias follows strict laws is an open question.[4] However, there is no question but that there are transitions between image- and sensation-elements; to these belong the eidetic images described by Urbantschitsch (843) and systematically investigated by Jaensch.[5] These are particularly lively and true images, and—as Jaensch demonstrated—they follow the same laws as perceptions.[6] Thus, Hering's law of the identical visual direction holds for eidetic images also.

Thus eidetic images like other images, lie in the same space as percepts (Jaensch, 371; Martin, 536). The space in which objects are perceived, and the space in which they are imaged, are one and the same. The phenomena of sensory-memory have an intermedi-

[3] Cf. Schilder (692).
[4] Cf. H. Werner (870).
[5] See Jaensch (371), also (372).
[6] On eidetic imagery see also Allport (21, 22) and Kluever (427).
[7*] The basic experiment is this: the subject fixates on a nearby point, for example, on an inkspot (F) [fixation point] on a window-pane, so that the line of vision of one eye points to a distant and distinct object, for example, a tree (T), and the line of vision of the other eye to another object, for example, a house (H), quite to the side of (T). These are found by closing first one eye, then the other eye, and bringing the spot and the object in line. Now if the subject fixates on F with both eyes, he will see F, T, and H in the same line of direction behind each other. This naturally holds for all other objects lying on either fixation-line this side of them.

ary position between eidetic images and percepts. For example, Henle relates that in the evening, after having worked for hours at the microscope, when he rubbed his eyes or coughed he suddenly saw luminous pictures of the slides in all their details. On the other hand, the eidetic images shade imperceptibly into common images. Thus, all the customarily stated distinctions between the contents of images and percepts are relative.[8] Images are considered less intense, weaker, less penetrating, pale, bodiless, gappy, unsteady, and fleeting in time. One could say that images and percepts have different past histories. Percepts enter consciousness without preparation, we are passive toward them; we are active in creating images. But this contrast is not generally valid either: some percepts we acquire with effort, and some images come to consciousness without being called for.

The observations made on the images and percepts of waking normal people are richly corroborated and complemented by the study of the pictures which arise in the state prodromal to sleep: the so-called hypnagogic hallucinations. Here images flash up in colors of sensory-vividness, without the attitude of imaging having to change toward them; to be sure, there is an inclination present to take toward such contents an attitude of perceiving, and frequently one gets the impression that the attitude wavers characteristically between that of imaging and that of perceiving, or that the acts of imaging and perceiving merge into a unitary intermediate form.

Then again there are those percepts, the perceiving of which we do not link with an acknowledgment of reality. In psychoses and in abnormal experiences also we encounter similar attitudes and contents.[9] False percepts may appear as percepts proper, or as percepts proper but of decreased reality-value (illusions), but they may even be recognized as false percepts and still remain vivid. Thus, one of my patients, speaking about a colored vision of his which he had captured in a drawing (*Wahn und Erkenntnis*, 692, Case 4), said he would have considered it a percept had he not known that other people did not see it. Phenomena of sensory vividness, experienced as images, can be very stable and are then

<hr/>

8 Cf. Kluever (427).

9 Concerning this question of reality vs. irreality, compare Rapaport (658, 659).

labeled as pseudo-hallucinations (Kandinski, 400; Jaspers, 379); they too may oscillate between imagery and perception. There is no sharp demarcation here, any more than there is between image and percept. The relationships here described hold not only for visual phenomena, where it is easiest to demonstrate them, but for all senses.

The renewed interest in these problems is due to Jaspers's (379) studies on false percepts, and his survey gives an excellent total view of the problems involved. Yet the factual conclusion of his study, that image and percept are fundamentally different, cannot be accepted. Lindworsky (506), Stumpf (824), and the present author (particularly in *Wahn und Erkenntnis*, 692) have come to a diametrically opposite conclusion.

A remarkable clue to the nature of object-character,[10] and to the relation of imaging and perceiving, is the synesthesias. Lehmann and Bleuler (479) have given detailed descriptions of these. In some people, certain sensory impressions (for example, tones) elicit simultaneously other impressions (for example, colors—and under certain circumstances, olfactory and other impressions also). In the first case we speak of visual synesthesias, or of secondary visual sensations. But a visual impression too can arouse a simultaneous acoustic one. A red color may arouse a trumpet-tone (acoustic synesthesia). According to Bleuler, synesthesias are perceived. A blue spot connected with an acoustic impression is seen and is localized where the tone is heard. Obviously we are dealing here with a reproduction. Even though the role of previous experiences in the formation of synesthesia has not been clarified, it should be stressed that they do crucially influence synesthesia, and Bleuler's view that we have here a structurally determined connection of perceptions is questionable.[11] It is rather that obviously reproduced material, presenting itself in the form of imagery, attains the character of perception as a consequence of the presence of a true percept. This would then demonstrate anew the close connection of images and percepts. On the other hand, synesthesia is an expression of the object's tendency to express itself through various sensory avenues. Thus, synesthesia would have a special relation to, and be a special expression of, the

[10] "Object-character" translates *Gegenstaendlichkeit*, in other words, that which makes a percept appear as an object. The term *object* is used here not in the psychoanalytic but in the broadest sense.
[11] Cf. H. Werner (870), particularly pp. 92 ff.

object-function[12] which we regard as a physiological factor. In this respect Bleuler would be right, but the specific form of the synesthesia would be determined by specific experiences.

2. Visual Perception

a) *Elementary visual sensations*

Quality, intensity, saturation, contrast, after-image, impressiveness. Preliminaries concerning attention. The role of attention in impressiveness. The Koster and the Aubert-Foerster phenomenon.

This presentation is not intended to give details of sensory-physiology. These can be found in Wundt's (895) text of physiological psychology, as well as in the texts of Froebes (258) and Ebbinghaus-Buehler (155). Here basic information will be repeated only in so far as it will be required for our discussion of the principles of perception.[13] Visual perception best lends itself to such discussion, since it is not only by its nature richly differentiated, but has also been studied with particular care.

Visual sensations can be divided into those of brightness and color; in these, in turn, we can distinguish hue (that is, red, blue, green, black), intensity, and saturation. It may be assumed as known that these qualitative varieties of color and brightness can be arranged into a color-octahedron or color-sphere. The description of this, as well as of the mixing of colors, may be found elsewhere. The wave-length of the stimulus determines hue; the intensity of the stimulus determines brightness and saturation. Let us note also that the form of appearance of colors is dependent upon the intensity of the stimuli: with its increase, the saturation decreases, the colors shift toward white, and the green and blue spread at the expense of the neighboring colors. When the objective intensity is significantly decreased, red, green and blue-violet stand out at the expense of the neighboring colors, while all colors become dark and lose their saturation. While in a spectrum of intermediate intensity the point of maximal brightness lies in the yellow, with decreasing intensity it shifts toward the green. Further decrease of intensity makes all the colors disap-

[12] "Object-function" translates *Gegenstandsfunktion,* and refers presumably to the processes that produce the object-character.

[13] For more recent sources see Koffka (439), Woodworth (893), Boring (95), Kluever (428), S. S. Stevens (808).

pear; the maximal brightness is where otherwise the green is, and the spectrum appears as it would to the totally color-blind at usual light intensities. This, the so-called Purkinje phenomenon, does not obtain for those parts of the retina which are directly adjacent to the fovea.

More important for the problems which are of interest to us here are the phenomena of contrast. A gray piece of paper put on various colored objects appears in colors complementary to those of the objects; if instead of gray, colored paper is used, a mixing of its color with one complementary to the background occurs. This is not only an influence of the background on the foreground, but is mutual. Basically, the composition of any part of the visual field is never entirely irrelevant for the color-impressions that come about in any other part of the field. The phenomena of contrast become more striking when seen through a transparent paper. Helmholtz (333) assumes that color-contrast comes about by means of unconscious inferences: we expect the background to be a continuous plane of color, and when we see an interrupting gray we perceive in its place a color which is complementary to the color of the background, and which mixed with it would form a gray. Helmholtz brings still other arguments to prove that higher-order psychological factors (judgments) are at work in this. But all his arguments notwithstanding, since Hering (341) we know that here we are dealing with interactions of physiological excitations, though, as Wundt (895) stresses, it is undeniable that psychological factors alter these physiologically-rooted contrast-phenomena and determine their extent and impressiveness.

The temporal relations of the excitation, as well as the spatial, are important. Every light-stimulation requires a certain latency to reach its brightness and saturation. Light and dark adaptations of the eye cause the same light-stimulus to be experienced as sometimes lighter, sometimes darker. The positive and negative after-images are local adaptations; in the negative after-image a reversal in brightness values occurs, and colors are changed into their complementaries; but sensations have positive after-effects also. Thus, immediately after the stimulation ceases, the excitation persists, as in the positive after-image, so that an apparently even spread of light over a whole disk is observed when a disk of white and black sectors is rotated at sufficient speed, and this spread of light conforms to the laws of color-mixture.

Helmholtz's theory of color vision, according to which there are red-, green- and blue- (violet-) excitations which merge in the fashion of spectral color-mixture, has proven untenable. At present Hering's (341) theory offers the best interpretation of the known facts.[14] Hering assumes six qualitatively different processes, having their site somewhere in the neural substance of the visual system. These are white, black, yellow, blue, red, and green. Each pair of these has a single substratum. To be sure, Hering's theory must be supplemented by the duplicity-theory of Kries (459), according to which we must distinguish in the eye photopic and scotopic apparatuses. The work of night-vision is performed by the rods and that of daylight-vision by the cones. The phenomena of dark-adaptation—the specific distribution of brightness in the spectrum—coincide with those observed in total color-blindness. It must be admitted that so far not all phenomena can be fully explained by Hering's theory: this is particularly true of the various forms of color-blindness.[15]

This elementary presentation does not exhaust what is to be said about the simple sensory qualities of the eye. Besides hue, brightness, and saturation, there is a further elementary quality: the impressiveness of the color's appearance. The Koster-phenomenon is that colors of identical saturation and brightness appear more impressive when seen on small and near objects than on big and far-away ones. Koster (442) himself thought this a matter of saturation, and only Jaensch (370) recognized the actual state of affairs. But if I look at the world with my head upside down between my knees, then too colors appear more luminous, more impressive. There can be no doubt that here the setting of attention is altered: one views the world with greater curiosity. To explain the Koster-phenomenon too, the influence of attention must be taken into account, because the physical conditions are identical for both sets of objects. But does one remain in the frame of reference of sensations when discussing impressiveness? This has in fact been questioned (Goldstein and Gelb, 287). What then is sensation, and what factors play a role

14 Cf. footnote 15, infra.
15 For surveys of recent investigations see H. Hartridge (322) and S. S. Stevens (808, Chapter 22).

here? Altogether, what is the justification of the concept of sensation?

Before discussing these problems, let us note that the Koster-phenomenon is not an isolated curiosity. There is the related Aubert-Foerster phenomenon, also more thoroughly investigated by Jaensch (369). The Aubert (36) phenomenon is that small close-by visual objects are recognized in a greater part of the visual field than are large far-off ones, when both appear under a visual angle of the same magnitude. Jaensch was able to demonstrate that this phenomenon cannot be explained by peripheral conditions, but only by attention orientations.

Thus, it is clear that "psychological" factors must be of importance even in simple percepts. Naturally, this process of attention-distribution is not identical with the voluntary turning of attention which takes place when we insist on following a boring lecture: it is something more instinctive, more involuntary, and—as it were—more impersonal.[16] But the "impressiveness" of a color is as direct an experience as any, and it appears to be raw "sensation" material; so the problem, "What actually is sensation?" becomes increasingly urgent. I will discuss this now, though I must invoke data which will be presented in detail only later on.

b) Generalities concerning sensations

The relation of sensation to the "physical stimulus." Color contrast is of central origin. The periphery and the central nervous systems play an equal role in determining sensations. The differential threshold of visual impressions is largely independent of central influence, color-constancy, contrast, and anticipation-influences. But contrast has sensation character. It is impossible to separate central factors from "pure sensation." The act-attitude and its noematic correlate in relation to the central factors. The apparent role of unconscious inferences (Helmholtz). More about attention-sets. The self-regulation of attention. The relation of attention to the motor apparatus. The relation of central physical factors to intentionality. Sensations do not fully correspond to the physical stimuli. Are there isolated sensations? Sensations are not the real elements of which psychic life is built. The syncretism of primitive experience. The psychology of sensation. Coenesthesia.

The color of light depends directly on the wave length, and changes in the intensity of the light-stimulus also parallel certain changes of sensation; the pitch of the sound depends on the wavelength, its intensity on the amplitude. Now one could designate

16 Compare Schilder (695, particularly p. 500), where attention-set is subsumed under "affect-influence." For the distinction of the two kinds of attention, cf. Rapaport (650, Volume I, 658 and 659).

as sensation everything that has a constant relation to the stimulus, and connect this with a conception according to which the excitation would pass without essential alterations from the peripheral receptor to the center. As simple as such a conception would be, even a superficial consideration reveals that it cannot be carried through.[17] In addition to its pitch and intensity, a sound certainly has other characteristics, whether they are called color or vocality, and to these there does not correspond any characteristic of the physical form of the sound-wave.[18] Nevertheless, one can maintain that by-and-large there is a close relation between the physical processes of the external world and what we call sensations. Indeed, it might even seem that the psychologist calls sensations those units found by abstraction, which have a simple relation to changes in the external world.

The next best view would be to assume that the processes in the peripheral sense-organ are crucial for sensations. Yet color-contrast, the directly sensory character of which cannot be denied, is a centrally determined phenomenon. Wundt had contrast experiences in a retinal scotoma, and these must have been of central origin, since the peripheral receptor was destroyed. Brueckner (113) was able to demonstrate contrast phenomena in the anoptic half of the visual field in hemianopsia of central origin. But it does not make a difference in the reception of new stimulations whether or not there is a contrasting background, since the contrast-color mixes with the new color-stimulus, and what comes about by the contrast may be carried over into the after-image. Thus, it may be generally asserted that the "tuning" of the central apparatus is of importance, and Helmholtz notwithstanding, the form of appearance of colors depends not on unconscious inferences, but rather on both peripheral and central physiological processes (which cannot be encompassed psychologically), in such fashion that the same peripheral excitation may arouse different sensations dependent upon the "tuning" of the central apparatus.[19] But can this central factor then be considered entirely independent from the psychological? Is it not amenable to influence by experience and attitude? Actually, the

17 Cf. Schilder's (750, Chapter 1) later treatment of this problem.
18 This assertion appears to be questionable.
19 Cf. Gelb (268) on color-constancy.

same increase in brightness of a gray may be due to memory-colors,[20]* to the contrast effect of a neighboring black, or to the fact that before the onset of the stimulation, the observer expected a darker gray than the one presented.

Katz (405) has experimentally demonstrated that colors whose brightness was increased or decreased by the influence of experience, behave like other colors with respect to differential sensitivity. The subtlety of differential sensitivity depends essentially on retinal factors. At identical retinal excitation due to (shadowed or unshadowed) surface colors,[21]* it always takes identical peripheral increases in light for the difference to become noticeable, no matter what alterations by central factors the retinal excitations may undergo. Thus, though the central factors alter the form of appearance of colors, the orientation depends on the physically measurable stimulus, on the immediate retinal impression. It is known that to obtain a noticeable increase of brightness, it takes a greater increase of light for a lighter than for a darker surface (compare p. 50, below). The differential threshold would then be independent of central influence, and what the latter adds could be separable from the sensation proper. Thus the retinal excitation would attain a special position. Jaensch (370), however, was able to demonstrate that the rules found by Katz hold not only for memory-colors and for the influences of anticipation, but—at least within broad limits—for brightness- and color-contrast also, the sensation character of which cannot be denied. So neither is this a way to arrive at "pure sensation." Every sensation is determined not only by the peripheral conditions, but also by the central ones, which in turn are closely dependent upon the prior experiences of the person, on his past and present attitudes.[22] In other words, we are back

[20]* Memory-colors are those which we attribute to things as constant characteristics and see on them regardless of the conditions of lighting [object color].

[21]* Surface-colors are those color impressions which we obtain from the surfaces of objects.

[22] Recently Klein (415), Holzmann (355), Gardner (261) have demonstrated experimentally the role in perception of several central factors of great generality; they have termed these cognitive styles. The role of specific motivational factors in perception was demonstrated by Murphy and his pupils (574), by Bruner and collaborators (116), and others (118, 80). All these studies seem to have derived some of their impetus from the spread of psychoanalytic thought and "projective techniques," one of the major implications of which is the role of central factors in perception.

where we started: every act-orientation brings with it an altered noematic correlate, and these noematic correlates must be considered closely related to processes which can be encompassed by pure sensory-physiology.

Contrast- and memory-colors follow very similar laws, but in the latter it is very tempting to assume that processes of inference, or of something comparable, play a role. The inferences would be of this sort: in daylight this object is red; the illumination is now poorer, but the object has not changed; in order to see the true color of the object I must take the darker illumination into account; thus, I see the object again in the same color. Here we encounter for the first time the surmise that purely physical processes may take a course as though they were psychological. There is no doubt that the memory-colors do not come about by means of such inferences, but the somatic process underlying them takes such a course that one is led to surmise that such deductions have taken place. Therein lies the correct core of Helmholtz's view.

Now it becomes obvious that the phenomena here described shade imperceptibly into those sensory phenomena in which attention-setting brings about essential alterations. I refer to the Koster and the Aubert-Foerster phenomena. The impressiveness of the color, even the visual size of objects, and, according to Jaensch's investigations, the depth-impression too, are dependent on attention. Attended objects appear closer; the localization of attention determines the depth-impression and gives it sensory vividness.

Let us add that such fluctuations of attention are accompanied by incipient eye-movements. These are convergence-impulses when we attend to an object particularly; but these in turn are followed by divergence-impulses: attention which just now was focussed closely, disperses over broader vistas. Thus, we have here a tendency toward self-regulation which finds expression, on the one hand, in the psychological behavior of attention-orientation, and on the other, in certain motor mechanisms. In the motor system, the physiological and psychological aspects seem to be particularly closely linked with each other. Thus, acts cogwheel, in an undetermined fashion, into somatic events, both on the sensory and on the motor end. When I turn my attention, simultaneously a psychophysical apparatus begins to function, which alters the form of appearance of things. Thus, even if we must differentiate between those central factors which are not dependent on intentionality (i.e., on the psychological), and those which are, there can be no doubt as to the deep and intrinsic relatedness of the two.

For the problem of sensation, the consequences are the following: the "stimulus-close"[23] experience can in no way be separated from the rest. In every sensation there is a central factor, and this in turn implies something psychological. If one means by the term sensation a psychological experience which is directly related to the stimulus, then there is no such thing as sensation. If, however, one means by the term sensation a simple psychic experience, as is useful to define it, which we relate to our body, then it must be stated that sensations and stimuli do not correspond to each other.

Now we may raise the question whether such structures can exist in isolation. Baade's (40) answer is that they can. He obtained sensations by prematurely interrupting the process of perception.[24] As yet, however, we lack sufficiently detailed reports of these experiments. Should sensations thus obtained not be considered still as belonging to the body? Be this as it may, neither Poppelreuter (632, 635) nor Pick (625) recognize simple sensations.

In any case, sensations cannot be considered the building-stones of which psychic life is put together, because—taking it even purely physiologically—sensations represent total reactions of the organism. Periphery, center, and the—psychologically conceived—personality, all interact in them. Koffka, in harmony with Koehler,[25] rejects a fixed stimulus-sensation relationship, and replaces it by the organism-environment relationship; he considers the typical form of the brain-process correlated to experience (sensation- and Gestalt-experience) not as an isolated

23 "Stimulus-close" translates *reiznahe;* the term implies that the experience in question sticks close to the "photographic recording" of the stimulus with minimal central elaboration of it. The form of experiencing in question is akin to what Goldstein (291) labeled "concrete."

24 While Baade's conclusions did not hold up (cf. Schilder 750, Chapter 1, also Hebb 328), his method strongly influenced Schilder's thinking (cf. 695). For similar experimental orientation, see the work of Krueger's Leipzig school on *Aktualgenese,* e.g., Sander (683).

25 Schilder refers to Koffka (437) and Koehler (432, 433); cf. the more recent Koehler (435) and Koffka (439).

excitation in the brain plus associations, but rather as whole-processes and their whole-qualities. Besides, we do not have evidence to show that isolated sensations genetically precede the more complex structures.

What little we know of these matters seems rather to indicate that the primitive percept is unarticulated, very complex, and much more unitary than the articulated, fully developed percept.[26] If in the latter we do not find isolated perceptions, except perhaps under specially created conditions, even less can we expect to find them in the experiences of the child or the preliterate. On the contrary, we have reason to assume that an experience of the preliterate is much more intimately interwoven with his total experience than is that of the adult man of our civilization. Thus, sensations cannot be considered the elements, the building-stones, of perception.

It seems rather that the heuristic value of the theory of sensations, and its significance in the history of psychology, is that the assumption of sensations helps in making certain relations between stimulus and percept understandable.[27] The concept of sensation can further psychology only if sensations, and images which are conceived as their copies, are not regarded as the real elements out of which psychological life is built.

The quest after the sensation as a psychological element must be separated from the theory of sensations as somatic experiences. The latter puts the concept of sensations in its proper place, and explains why coenesthesia may indeed be considered the prototype of all sensations, and why coenesthesia cannot be brought into relation with the external world. We always experience the body more or less as a whole, and this too is a reason why we cannot assume isolated sensations.

c) Empty space: space- and color-perception

Empty intermediary space may be experienced as a specific sensation. The role of horizontal disparity in space-perception. Horizontal disparity does not lead to a direct perception of depth. Attention fluctuations co-determine depth-

26 See Schilder's similar point concerning action in Chapter III, 1, a, infra; cf. also Werner's (870), Hebb's (328) and Piaget's (613, 617) corroborating evidence.
27 Cf. Schilder (750, Chapter I). For a recent view of the relation of sensation and perception, see Gibson (273, particularly Chapter I), and Hebb (328).

perception. The vision of individuals who were born blind and have been operated on. Space-colors, film-colors, and surface-colors. Color constancy and memory-colors. Objects are seen in definite colors relatively independent of illumination. The role of peripheral and central factors in this phenomenon. The ability to see surface-colors may be disturbed by occipital lesions. Colors are attached to objects as surface-colors by phylogenetic and ontogenetic experience. There are no unconscious inferences involved in color constancy, but the central functions guaranteeing it have a psychological past. The synthetic function creating surface-colors and color-constancy is of a somatic character, but has a psychological prehistory.

No doubt we do not have direct access to all sensory qualities, and more thorough observation might yet reveal new sensations. This assertion is limited by our refusal to consider sensations as elements. Schumann (765), for example, has recently asserted that there is a sensory perception of the empty intermediary space.

Can this perception be considered an elementary sensation, or is it something more complex? The perception of the transparent medium presupposes the perception of contours, of space. Can we conceive of space-perception as a simple given?

Under Hering's (341) influence, a nativistic conception of space has begun to gain ground. According to him, horizontal disparity leads to a direct perception of depth.[28*] Karpinska's (402) experiments have shown, however, that horizontal disparity does not result directly in space perception, but only through several intermediary steps. Thus, horizontal disparity appears as one experiential factor among others which play a role in depth-perception.[29] Jaensch (369) has shown that fluctuation of attention and eye-movements are also involved. Thereby the dominant role of horizontal disparity for space-perception and depth-vision was called into question, and the view developed that there are a number of experiential factors involved, such as sensations of eye-movement, sensations of touch, fluctuations of attention. In any case, some phylogenetically given mechanisms must also come

[28*] Corresponding retinal points of the two eyes are those which coincide in the common field of vision. If we imagine the two retinas placed so that the foveas and the horizontal axes cover each other, then the corresponding points too will grossly coincide. The non-corresponding retinal points are referred to as disparate, and the images formed on these result in double vision, particularly when the disparate points are not close to the corresponding ones. When two retinal points lie on disparate vertical, but corresponding horizontal sections, then they are horizontally disparate.

[29] For recent views see Koffka (439), Brunswik (119), Gibson (273) and S. S. Stevens (808, Chapter 23). Cf. also Ames's (410a) work.

into play, to bring about something so entirely new and sensation-like. Psychologically, the immediate sensation-character of depth-perception cannot be doubted, and this again should remind us that "sensation" is a very complex experience. At any rate, depth-perception is not determined unequivocally by the physical conditions—but for us this is no argument against its "sensation" character. Persons who were born blind and have been operated on undoubtedly do see some spatial relations, though what they see is an unformed chaos of single impressions which do not merge into each other; and though the blind-born individual cannot immediately bring them into relation with his touch-experiences, they nevertheless have a definite location, and probably also a certain depth dimension. The objects they see seem to reach the eye and to touch it; they are more like "genuine sensations" which have not yet detached themselves from the body.[30] Yet their world has a depth dimension, though unsharp and indefinite.[31]

The form of appearance of colors is dependent on spatial values. Katz[32] distinguished between film-, surface-, and three-dimensional colors. The surface-colors appear only on objects; most common objects give rise to them in diffuse daylight. Surface-colors adhere to the object, giving the impression of impenetrability and tight-fittingness. The film colors are looser and do not seem to offer such resistance: they give the impression that one could penetrate into them. The unaccommodated eye is prone to give film-color impressions. While surface-colors conform to the object, film-colors are essentially flat, like the blue of the sky. Tridimensional colors fill a space. If there is no object behind them, they approximate the film-colors. Looking at a somewhat dark corner, one has the impression of a space-filling gray; the case is similar when air veils the objects, or when one is in a cloud and some objects emerge dimly from it.

30 Schilder regards sensations as the experiencing of the somatic impact of stimuli, which become percepts only through the synthetic functions of the neural-psychological apparatus. (See Schilder 752, pp. 578–80, also Appendix, pp. 350 ff., infra.) Only when "detached from the body" by these synthetic processes are sensations changed into perceptions of objects in the external world.

31 For a survey of pertinent studies see Senden (774); cf. also Hebb (328, Chapter 2).

32 Schilder refers to Katz (405); see also Katz's (408) later study.

According to Katz, the phenomena of color-constancy hold in essence only for surface-colors. The concept of color-constancy originated with Hering, who called attention to the fact that, though the illumination changes, we see objects in the colors and brightnesses which are proper to them. While Helmholtz spoke in this connection of judgments, Hering explained color-constancy by the physiological adaptation-processes of the eye (changes of pupillary aperture, interaction of the visual fields of the two eyes, and adaptation). He assumed the working of yet another factor, a psychological one—the so-called memory-colors: "The color in which we have mostly seen an external object impresses itself indelibly in our memory and becomes a fixed attribute of the memory-image. What the layman calls the real color of a thing is that color which is fixed in his memory: I propose to call it the memory-color of the thing." Katz ascribes crucial influence to neither the physiological regulations nor the memory-colors, and assumes that the prevailing illumination is taken into account, resulting in an extensive central modification of the retinal color quality.[33]

A real psychological understanding of all these phenomena was initiated only by pathology. Gelb (267) observed two cases who lost their ability to see surface-colors and saw instead only loose, penetrable film-colors which they could not localize in spatial distance with the same certainty as normals. The color expanded into space, and when the patient brought his finger close to the colored object, his finger seemed to dip into the color. Let us note that in both of Gelb's cases, this disturbance arose from extensive disorder of color-vision, and that besides this there existed further disturbances of visual perception. This disorder then belongs to the agnosias, and will permit a glance into the nature of visual perception in general. To be sure, we must assume that the formation of surface-colors (and of color-constancy) is not represented by psychological experiences,[34] and it is certainly not a matter of unconscious inferences as Helmholtz assumed. On the other hand, Hering too had to speak of an after-

[33] Cf. also Gelb (268), and Stevens (808, Chapter 22).

[34] Schilder means that the processes in question are physiological and have no psychological representation except in their end-product; i.e., in the experience of surface-color.

effect of memory-colors, and Katz of the account taken of illumination. Katz also stressed that color-constancy changes the retinal
colors so that they become more like the "proper" colors of the
objects. Apparently here too the essential factor is the intention
directed toward the object. It is noteworthy that Gelb observed
color-constancy even in his patients' film-colors when they perceived them on objects, but not when they perceived shadows.
Here too we see then the role of the object-function, of the directedness toward objects. Somatic apparatuses enter into the service
of this object-function.[35] Even if Helmholtz's view is not literally
correct, it is noteworthy that persons who are born blind, after
operation experience a color-chaos which reaches to their body,
and consists presumably only of film- and tri-dimensional-colors;
only under the influence of experience are these film- and tri-
dimensional-colors brought into fixed relationship to objects and
made surface-colors. We have good reason to assume that this
change in sensations is brought about by the directedness toward
objects.

Experience then would be directed and determined by the
directedness toward objects; and the act of perception, which we
conceive as somatically determined, would have at its disposal
apparatuses which are nothing but structuralized forms of such
directedness toward objects.[36] Here we come to an understanding
of what Katz terms the central modification of sensations. Let us
stress that phylogenetic components play a considerable role here,
and that a goodly part of our experience is simply a form of appearance of old phylogenetic acquisitions. Accordingly, such organic forms would be sediments of past psychological attitudes,
though we have no right to look for a psychological attitude in
them now.[37] In color-constancy and in surface-colors then, we
would be dealing with phenomena which lie on the borderline of
the psychological and the somatic. We have no reason to assume

35 The term object-function—as the context indicates—implies here that
it is the intentional act which forms objects out of sensations. Concerning the
somatic apparatuses, see Schilder (752, pp. 577 ff.).

36 The implied assumption is that the "neural apparatuses" in question
develop from acts of intending, are structures created by this function. Cf.
Hartmann's (321) concepts of "automatization" and "secondary autonomy,"
also Hebb's (328) "assemblies."

37 Cf. footnote 34, supra.

that the binding of tri-dimensional-colors to objects occurs in the present by way of a psychological avenue. Yet this binding does have a partly ontogenetic, partly phylogenetic, psychological history. In each of Gelb's pathological cases there was an occipital lesion, though its exact localization was unclear. (But since central vision was intact in both cases, and the narrowing of the visual field was concentric, extending only over the periphery, it must be assumed that the calcarine fissure around the pole of the occiput was unaffected.)

Thus, the organic lesion alters a function which mediates object-perception. This function is not the same as that which unites into one whole the partial aspects of a book which is revolved in front of us. I will term the former the synthetic function, and the latter the object-function. The two are closely related. The synthetic function has many components, and even though it must be considered somatic and not psychological, its close relation to the former is patent. Though here these considerations refer only to an important specific instance, they are paradigmatic for a broad group of phenomena.[38]

The study of pathological cases reinforces this view. There are hallucinated film-colors. These are quite primitive hallucinations (compare Pick, 629; and H. Hartmann, 316). It is noteworthy that they are often associated with primitive movement-hallucinations, and appear outright as hallucinated sensations. In some cases we can trace the way in which these hallucinated film-colors and movements become linked to objects: the film-color then becomes a surface-color (H. Hartmann).[39]

d) Depth-perception and attention as somatic functions

Alterations of depth-perception by attention-orientations. Attention has somatic foundations. The disturbance of depth-perception by cerebral lesion. Sensory clarity and attention-clarity. The relation of the fovea to attention. Active and passive attention. The disturbance of attention by brain lesion. Attention is one of the central factors which determine sensations.

[38] These synthetic functions are more akin to Gestalt-forming processes (Koehler, 435) than to the psychoanalytic concept of the synthetic function of the ego (Freud, 239, 244; Nunberg, 582). Yet it is possible that when explored their relation will prove closer than meets the eye. Cf. Appendix, pp. 340 ff., infra.

[39] Cf. Schilder (750, Chapter 2).

The pathology of depth-perception requires the same kind of consideration as the problem of surface- and film-colors. We know that depth-perception too has a long prehistory, and it is this which supplies the basis for the empiricist conception of space. Yet no reference to previous experience is to be found later in depth-perception, except that attention-influences and interest-orientations co-determine depth-localization in much the same way as they do color-constancy.

But the concept of attention as used here does not simply coincide with the usual concept of it. What point our interest will get anchored on is not always up to us; therefore, the concepts of attention and voluntariness must not be merged.[40] The fovea is that point of the eye to which the greatest attention-charge attaches—or more correctly, the objects that are represented on the fovea (a physiological process) necessarily are seen with greater attention than those on the periphery of the visual field. On the other hand, there are somatic mechanisms which take care that whatever is represented on the fovea shall not retain its attention-charge too long: objects on the periphery command attention, particularly if they are in motion, and somatic mechanisms then adjust the eye to them. Thus it is a contradiction to say that depth-perception is dependent partly on psychological factors, and partly on relatively stable somatic structures, which in some measure can be conceived of as brain structures. Pick (618) traces disorders of depth-localization to lesions of the angular gyrus. Poppelreuter (632) has pointed to disturbances of depth-localization in lesions of the occiput. A case of Wilbrand and Saenger (886, 887) lost his ability to estimate distance: he mistook distant for near objects. To a case of Csapody (137), objects did not seem to be in the right place.

40 The problem of attention has been quite neglected in recent decades; cf., however, Freud (204), Titchener (835), Bleuler (86), and, for a survey, Rapaport (658). Schilder's persistent emphasis on the concept points to many problems which require further exploration of the phenomena which are the referents of the concept of attention, to lead either to a firm definition of the concept or to new explanatory concepts to replace it. Recently H. Teuber and Morris Bender (51, 52, p. 29) have called into question attention as a concept; cf. also Hebb (328, pp. 4, 87, 102). For recent literature pertaining to the distinction of voluntary (concentration) and involuntary attention, see Rapaport, Schafer and Gill (650), Halstead (314), Diethelm and Jones (147), and Rapaport (658). See also Gibbs and Gibbs (271, pp. 46–50) for the literature on electroencephalographic changes accompanying attending.

Though the nature of attention cannot be fully understood before the dynamics of psychological life have been discussed, the problem is so often encountered in the theory of perception that we must consider it here.

We may conceive of attention as that act of intending which effects the changes termed attention-experience. But attentive comprehension is itself an act-experience. The dynamic processes which lead to attentive comprehension must in any case be distinguished from the static experience of attentive comprehension, which can be encompassed descriptively. What is attentively comprehended appears with particular clarity, and this is not referable to any direct alteration of perception. The object attentively comprehended in semidarkness is in this same sense clearer than the object unattentively comprehended in full light. The clarity of attention is thus a particular act in its own right, and simultaneously I, when attending, am in a particular condition. Furthermore, this particular act has a definite somatic resonance. The tense posture of the attentive person is in contrast to the relaxed posture of the non-attentive. Attention is the same, whether it is active attention, having come about as a sequel of a specific decision and persistence, or passive attention, having forced itself on me without my contribution, or even against my will. My present existence reaches its pinnacle in that which I attentively comprehend: I live fully in it. It is the forground of experience; the rest recedes into the background. The attention-experience is complete when the foreground-experience has absorbed the background-experience, and thus is not in danger of being abandoned for the sake of another experience.[41] In superficial attention-experiences, the background-experience does not cease to command attention. In full attention-experience, attention changes in directions set by the object; in superficial attention-experiences, it turns to irrelevancies.

Somatic apparatuses prevent a fettering of attention: thus, in vision, the eye muscles and the retinal attention-apparatus abet the demands for attention to objects in the lateral field of vision. As already mentioned, every convergence-impulse of the eye creates a readiness for a divergence-impulse.[42] The distribu-

[41] Cf. Freud (204. p. 529, also pp. 515–516, 535–536, 546).
[42] Cf. Halstead (314) on the dynamic visual field, also Hebb (328, pp. 33–37).

tion and constancy of attention is thus preformed by somatic apparatuses, among which the brain is the most important. There are impairments of visual attention due to occipital lesions (F. Hartmann, 315; Oppenheim, 592; Poppelreuter, 632). In a case of Balint, a parieto-occipital lesion prevented the turning of attention to certain parts of the visual field. Pick (618, 621) described a particular visual disorder in senile dementia, with an isolated disorder of visual attention connected with an occipital lesion. In Balint's (44) case, visual attention was limited to the momentarily fixated object; the patient was able to comprehend only one object at a time, whether small or large.

All in all, it seems that clarity of attention is related to grosser changes in perception, and that it may rest upon a particular mode of utilizing the auxiliary apparatuses of perception. In vision, for instance, this would mean a more appropriate accommodation, or a particular sequence of fixations, as well as certain changes in the central nervous system. We have shown that every experience is co-determined by conditions in the central nervous system. In attentive comprehension, the availability of past experience is altered, and accordingly altered conditions in the central nervous system influence the resulting sensation. This would establish a relation between the clarity due to better illumination and that due to heightened attention.

e) On the pathology of two-dimensional visual perception and the problem of Gestalt. The visual perception of motion. The so-called perceptual agnosia

Lesions of the occipital lobe effect disturbances of two-dimensional perception. Cerebral metamorphopsia and cerebral disturbances of size-estimation. Occipital lobe lesions may make impossible the apprehension of even simplest Gestalten. Linearity as a Gestalt. A melody (i.e., a sequence of tones) is more than the sum of the single tones. Gestalt is additional to the perceptual elements. Does this additional arise as a creative emergent (Meinong, 547; Witasek, 889), or is it a physiologically determined transverse process (Wertheimer, 876)? Image-production is certainly involved in Gestalt-formation. The perception of motion as a specific experience. Exner's (169) concept of motion-sensation. In addition to central factors, peripheral ones also partake in the visual perception of motion. More about centrally determined disorders of Gestalt-perception. Alexia (pure word-blindness) as a disorder of Gestalt-apprehension. Agnosia of geometrical forms.

Spatial perception is not only the perception of depth, but also that of two dimensions. Jaensch (368, 369) has demonstrated that attention influences size-perception also. Occipital-lobe lesions alter matters here too. Nothnagel's (579) patient lost his ability to image the size of objects, Badal's his ability to estimate it.[43*] In Lenz's (484, 485) case, all horizontal surfaces sloped off sharply to the right side of the visual field. To Henschen's (340) patient, people appeared bent. Cerebral metamorphopsia was observed by Lenz (484, 485) and Oppenheim (592): in their case, objects were distorted now concavely, now convexly. In a case of Poetzl's (630, 631), parts of percepts appeared as their own mirror-image: upper and lower were exchanged, and previous impressions were fused with new ones, in disregard of the spatial factor. This reminds one of Stern's (805) observation that children are insensitive to "spatial displacements of forms," so that they recognize and draw objects even when rotated from their natural position at any angle.

The disorders in Goldstein and Gelb's (287, 288) case exceed any of these: in spite of good acuity, he could not perceive even the most primitive Gestalten, nor maintain an impression of linearity or curvature, nor recognize even a quadrangle.

Here we encounter for the first time the important problem of Gestalt.[44] Ehrenfels (157) put it thus: when several stimuli reach a sense-organ, we have in our consciousness something besides the sensations. Thus, a series of tones is apprehended as a melody, as more than the sum of the tones contained in it. In a wallpaper pattern we can perceive now this, now another, Gestalt. Figure 2 can be apprehended in the most varied ways: as a square filled with dots, as a cross, etc. It is inconceivable that these Gestalt-qualities should arise from peripheral processes; it seems that central factors must be invoked to explain them.

Figure 2

But the nature of these central factors is a disputed matter.[45]

[43*] In atropin delirium there frequently appear microptic, but occasionally also megaloptic or dysmegaloptic, hallucinations. Besides the peripheral paralysis of accommodation, central influences are also doubtless involved in these conditions—certainly in dysmegalopsia, studied particularly by Fischer (187, 188). [For the psychogenesis of related phenomena, see Bartemeier (45).]

[44] For Schilder's views on Gestalt, see his introduction to L. Bender (50).

[45] Cf. on the one hand the isomorphism theory of Gestalt-psychology: Koehler (434, 436), Koffka (439); and on the other Lashley et al. (477) and Hebb (328, Chapters 3, 4, 5).

According to Linke (508), we are dealing here with processes connected with perception as such: every perception is also a perception of a Gestalt. But the case of Gelb and Goldstein (287, 288) perceived without perceiving a Gestalt. It is possible that what pathology reflects is not the psychological structure of Gestalt, but its physiological aspect. Even if one assumes that there *are* Gestalt processes in sensation, however, it would seem to me certain that, in the progression from sensation and perception to Gestalt, a further psychological elaboration takes place.[46*] In the abstraction experiments of Seifert (770) too, perceptions which are not fully Gestalted appear in the first phase.[47] Accordingly, it is justified to assume that Gestalt apprehension adds something to perception. Wertheimer (876) assumes that we are dealing here with a brain process—he terms it a transverse process —conceived as an overflow of excitation processes in the central nervous system. Gestalt perception then would come about much like perception in general: it would enter consciousness as a whole,[48*] and would be based simply on a physiological plus added to perception. Meinong's pupils, particularly Witasek (889), speak of image-creation, and imply that this is an active psychological process of Gestaltung. [Meinong (547) says that the constituents persist in the complex.] According to Froebes (258), Gestalt adds a unification to the complex of sensations, which is perceptual and must not be mistaken for an abstract understanding of relations. This perceptual apprehension is co-determined by sequence, emphasis, and grouping. Schumann (763) stressed similar ideas. The point of departure in Gestalt-formation is without doubt understandable psychologically, even though some aspects of it belong to that realm where the psychological shades imperceptibly into the organic.[49] Thus in Gestalt-formation we encounter problems very similar to those of color-perception. In Gelb and Goldstein's case,

[46*] At any rate, Goldstein and Gelb's interpretation of their case has recently been sharply criticized by Poppelreuter (635), who demonstrated that the case was not a disorder of apprehension but rather one of perception—one of an incomplete scotoma.

[47] But compare Sander (683) to the contrary.

[48*] Wertheimer had developed this view first for the visual perception of motion, and found supporters for it in Koffka and his students, Gelb (267) and Fuchs (259). The theory was then enlarged to Gestalten proper.

[49] Cf. translator's Foreword.

the perceptual psychic-blindness means that both the structuralized Gestalt-apperception[50] and those live processes which lead to Gestalten are disturbed. One cannot disregard the "creative" aspect of Gestalt-formation.

Poppelreuter (635) proposes the following schema of visual perception and Gestalt-apperception. There is a series of part-systems: a) dark-light system; b) color system; c) space (form) system; d) motion; e) direction (so far unexplored). Each of these systems can be disordered in relative isolation. There is also a topographical principle (the cortical projection). Achievements are not simply lost, they become less differentiated. According to Poppelreuter, there is no total hemianopia: vague sensations always exist. There are gradual transitions from these rudimentary residual functions to normal form-perception, so that paradoxically we regard hemianoptic defects as a particular kind of geometric coordination. "Vision has a lowest level, in which color-, size-, form-, motion-, and space-perceptions are lost and only brightnesses are registered. On the next level there are size- and localization-perceptions, but no form-perception proper; on the following level there is perception of size, but none of numerousness; on the next, no motion-sensation as yet; and finally, the level of higher Gestalt-perceptions." Each segment of the visual field contains several of these levels.

The rudimentary visual system of the first level is capable only of amorphous sensations of brightness, but not of differentiation of location, direction, size, numerousness, form, and motion. On the second level amorphous size-perceptions come about, which depend upon the visual angle, and the depth of which is indeterminate; gross directions are distinguishable, but not simultaneously given impressions: they fuse with each other. On the third level rudimentary form-perceptions appear, but as yet no perception of a manifold of distinct points, though the Gestalt, to which the multitude of the single points would add up, can be perceived. Thus a Gestalt appears at first as a gross global form, and the differentiation of its elements is the product only of further development. On the fourth level distinct perception of

---

[50] "Structuralized Gestalt-apperception" translates *Form gewordene Gestaltauffassung;* Schilder seems to imply that he considers these processes to be represented by "neural structure."

numerousness is achieved: the patients can perceive two images simultaneously and yet separately. There is a fifth level of mild amblyopia, of decreased acuity, in which—according to Poppelreuter—the central visual field takes on attributes which are more typical of the extreme periphery.

Poppelreuter rejects the assumption that straight and curved are the most primitive Gestalten, and distinguishes the following Gestalten: *First level:* the visual field is simply visual expanse without form. *Second level:* the visual field differentiates qualitatively into diffuse illumination, left and right, etc. *Third level:* size appears. *Fourth level:* awareness of direction. *Fifth level:* form differentiation. *Sixth level:* several images are seen simultaneously and discretely. *Seventh level:* precise differentiation of straight, curved, etc. There is a line of development from uncertain to certain form.[51]

It is conceivable that the Gestalt-principle is purely physiological. Poppelreuter conceives of it in terms of a dual structure: on the one hand, the physiological variations in the stimulus-Gestalt; on the other, and partly independent of the first, the variations in the actual Gestalt-experience. Poppelreuter does not consider it proven that there exists a psychic blindness due solely to a disturbance of Gestalt-apprehension.

Gelb and Goldstein's patient lost his ability to see motion also. We know since Exner (169) that perception of motion is not identical with seeing an object now in one place, now in an adjacent one. Rather, there is a specific impression of motion, which Exner conceives as a sensation, and Wertheimer as a transversal function, an exchange of excitations between neighboring points of the brain. Wertheimer's view rests on variations of Schumann's basic experiment, in which a vertical line is quickly followed by a horizontal one of equal length, in tachistoscopic exposure, so that they halve each other, and a shift of the vertical into the horizontal line, that is, a motion, is seen. I consider Exner's view to be the factually more correct: first, because of the phenomena of motion-after-images; second, because after-images of briefly exposed bright objects include motion-phenomena, which take the form of waves and must be related to the original retinal excita-

---

[51] For recent literature see Woodworth (893), Kluever (428), Morris Bender and Teuber (52, 53).

tion. In other words, to my mind, retinal factors are directly involved in the impression of motion, though naturally, just as in any other sensation, central excitation processes are also involved. The absence of motion-perception in the case of Goldstein and Gelb is thus, in my opinion, due to a central disturbance of sensation. To be sure, Poppelreuter was right—we cannot definitely decide whether or not there are purely central disturbances of sensation. Yet the possibility of invoking central attention-disturbances for explanation always remains open. Poetzl and Redlich's (630) patient lost her motion-perception following a central lesion, and apprehended moving objects as a multitude of objects; while Goldstein and Gelb's patient saw the moving object now here, now there, without gaining an impression of motion.

In any case, there is Gestalt-formation even in sensation, but it is overlaid by ever-new Gestalt-forming processes. Actually, we speak of Gestalt only when the perception has initiated new processes. We have reason to distinguish these from perception as such.[52]

f) The so-called associative psychic blindness

The apprehension of visual impressions is delayed. First the general categories arise to which the object belongs. Within the categories there arise concepts and percepts related to the one sought, and occasionally the one sought, which then may even be rejected. The delayed impressions fuse with irrelevant ones, and their coordination within the spatial continuum is thereby impaired. Attention disturbs apprehension. Agnosic and neurotic parapraxes are analogous. The relation of compulsion-neurotic manifestations and symbolism to agnosia. More on the disrupting effect of goal-consciousness. Integration disturbances in atrophies of the occipital lobe. Analogous disturbances in the congenitally blind after operation. The failure to perceive one's own defects.

From the perceptual forms of psychic blindness thus far discussed, we turn to those called by Lissauer (514) "associative forms." In these cases Gestalten are perceived as such, but the patients cannot make use of their visual impressions, even though their visual acuity and visual field are adequate. Stauffenberg's

---

[52] For Schilder's views on Gestalt, cf. his (750, Chapter 9), and his Introduction to L. Bender (50). See also my note concerning Baade, footnote 24, supra. Schilder's views on Gestalten are not easy to follow, because he regards them as products of synthetic (integrating) functions of various levels (cf. Appendix, pp. 351 ff., infra), an approach alien to the Gestalt literature proper, but not to the Leipzig school of Krueger.

(789) case, which we will use as a paradigm, indicates how enormously varied are the achievements. Though simple, commonplace, familiar objects are as a rule cognized, this patient fails on most other objects. Spontaneously well-cognized objects and pictures are not cognized on testing—that is, when the subject's voluntary attention is directed to them.[53] Objects correctly apprehended on first glance are misrecognized on prolonged contemplation, although occasionally this may lead to a hesitant cognition too. Conceptual contents aroused by previous naming, suggestive questions, or some roundabout train of thought, influence perception with astounding ease: while contemplating an object, the patient is able to produce the image of a false suggestion in an outright hallucinatory fashion. Perseverations also play a role. Even details of concepts become supplements of these creations of fantasy: the patient considers a celluloid toothbrush to be a bottle and adds, "A stopper belongs here." Such hallucinatory transformations take place even in spontaneous perceiving. The correct label, the cognition, is often found only in stages and after delay. Frequently the correct designation is found, only to be negated: of the picture of a hen, the patient said, "It ain't no chicken." According to Stauffenberg, these concepts arise without a feeling of familiarity, and these utterances convey the lack of it. But to some extent, they all represent the first—infinitely drawn out—phase of the normal cognition-process: there too a first rapidly progressing and unnoticed process, in which preliminary concepts appear, prepares for the further analysis of the object. When pathological, the reaction often ends merely in arousing a conceptually related idea, and thus frequently a gross similarity in form determines the reaction: a violin may be described as "similar to an umbrella." Occasionally one gets the impression that, though the correct concept arises, there is insufficient energy to find the correct name for it (optic aphasia).[54]

If the patient is asked to describe the details of a visual complex which she has recognized as a whole, she never succeeds in naming the single parts or in relating them to the whole.[55] Thus,

---

[53] Cf. Buerger-Prinz and Kaila (123, pp. 677–678, 680–681).

[54] Cf. the observations and experiments in Schilder (752), and Buerger-Prinz and Kaila (123); see also Schilder (751).

[55] Cf. Appendix, p. 341, infra.

as in Lissauer's case, the eye of a portrait is called a man; the horns of an ox are pointed out in the wrong place. In prolonged observation the patient loses perspective, and repeated presentation of an object does not improve the achievement, though visual imagery is intact.

Stauffenberg (789) writes, "If we want to analyze the normally very fast and subliminal course of the process, we may assume that the first overview, a sketchy outline, as it were, is obtained at diffuse attention, which integrates only the outstanding characteristics, such as form, size, color, spatial position, into an unclear picture; this occasions the arousal of general concepts, leading to further analysis by attention under the direction of general categorical images. The process is completed in the interaction of the two active spheres—the images prompting to further articulation of percepts, and percepts arousing new images and rejecting others; this interaction leads gradually to a completed cognition, and to the relaxing feeling of knowing." In the case cited this process is disturbed, but if premature focusing of attention does not interfere, the initial orienting schema is occasionally apprehended, and under particularly favorable circumstances even the pertinent concept may be aroused by it.

Usually, however, various circumstances disrupt this process. First of all, the visual impression itself, the technical aspect of vision, as it were, is particularly pale and incomplete. (Regrettably, we know little about these elusive details, since most patients' communications are unclear.) The insecurity attending this paleness and incompleteness results in a premature focusing of active attention.[56] This occurs before a preparatory, general cognition can develop far enough; that is, before a framework has been erected which can then be filled in by further action. That which is prematurely attended to perseverates, disrupting the subsequent process. The second stage interferes with the not yet completed first one; the perseveration disturbs and makes impossible the necessary freedom and speed of the interaction between concept and object, percept and image. When preserved

[56] Cf. footnote 40, supra. Even if this explanation by attention-dynamics should have to be supplanted by one of the sort Morris Bender and Teuber (52) suggest, it will retain importance because it is applicable to the phenomenology of functional thought-disorders, of normal and neurotic obsessional as well as schizophrenic thinking.

imagery is once stimulated, it gains the upper hand; it exerts a disturbing influence on the perception process. That which in any case was seen with little clarity is either misinterpreted, due to the projection of the images excited, which in turn make for contradictions, unclarity, and confusion; or the projection completely veils the visual impressions, and complete falsifications, illusions, arise. This is the more possible since, presumably, undisturbed cognition requires a correct balance of these two functions.

If the whole is occasionally apprehended—which, as we saw, happens only accidentally, and without the contribution of attention—it cannot be sustained once attention is brought to bear on it. It is as though the visual field were broad enough in relaxed passive vision to encompass a broad whole, but narrows maximally as soon as the will to see[57] makes its appearance. This is, however, but a comparison: the actual visual field does not change, only the field of consciousness does.[58] The primary impression of the whole is entirely too brief for even a most approximate cognition to occur; therefore the whole immediately dissolves into details, to sustain which requires all available attention, and so no integration with the preceding steps can take place; thus everything onto which attention falls is completely torn out of its relationships, loses the meaning it gains from the whole, and thereby becomes difficult to comprehend. The visual images further interfere with this conceptual process: it has insufficient perceptual guidance, and is therefore easily misled by the vagueness of that which is available. The normal tendency also is for this centrifugal [conceptual] process to become particularly vivid when perception is incomplete, as for instance at dusk when confused impressions arouse all sorts of fantasies. But there we know about it; here the usual situation is disordered by causes unknown to us, and thus the conditions favor producing true illusions. So particularly in those cases of psychic blindness in whom visual imagery is well retained, we see the predominance of such parapraxes as against a simple loss of meanings; and this is the more apparent the less the patient comprehends the contrast between seeing per se and the ability to conceptualize what is seen.

[57] I.e., voluntary attention.   [58] Cf. Fuchs (259).

This role of attention seems to have a particular significance for the symptomatology of psychic blindness. Apparently this function, mediating between the external and the internal, achieves the necessary free play only when visual impressions are sufficiently clear, sharp, and persistent—that is, when the "peripheral" elementary phases of the cerebral visual function are to some extent intact. When this is not the case, a more intensive attention-activity will try to make up for the insufficiency, and will either by interference disrupt the normal process, or by narrowing sever the relationships. A similar situation may obtain for other higher senses; for example, the word-deaf too as a rule correctly apprehend single sounds, and even words, but no broader connections—though at relaxed attention even these are at times correctly understood. In cases of a tactile anesthesia, the process is arrested at the level of elementary sensations. In all these cases, the patient's easy fatiguability and relatively great effort are striking; these probably indicate the fitful straining of attention with which such patients try to increase the usefulness of the insufficient projection material—an insufficiency resulting from the sharper focusing, which in turn is achieved always at the price of narrowed consciousness.

Poetzl (631) had previously observed something essentially similar in the remission of a case of cortical blindness. He presented to this patient a decoration, a golden cross in a white field, on a dark background. The patient saw at first only the white area, then made some forced adaptive movements to bring the object into his residual peripheral field, and finally identified it as "a cross, yellow." In addition, he pantomimed the form. Now the patient was shown a bouquet of flowers from which a strikingly long asparagus stem stood out. He apprehended only the red rose, in keeping with his predilection for red. Now the bouquet was removed, and the patient was asked to establish the color of the facings of the officers present. By forced adaptive movements, he brought the collar of one of them into his residual field and said, "A green necktie-pin." This is a correct delayed-delivery of a form-impression, but without reference to its context. Such a belatedly developed image is, like dream-images, capable of all kinds of condensations, and gives the impression that at this stage the patient captures only successively, and in a piecemeal fashion, those form-perceptions of indirect vision which in remission he subsequently proved able to weld simultaneously into a unitary complex, as normal indirect vision can. One observes similar fragmentation in the tachistoscopic vision of normals, but there it is successfully welded together afterwards. It is noteworthy that in agnosias, particularly in the more severe cases, only a minority manifests such a subsequent welding together.

These reactions in the cases cited resulted from a central scotoma in which a peripheral vision developed, following initial blindness. But they are also seen in visual agnosias with preserved central vision. Summing up:

A. Apperception is delayed.
B. The belated apperception provides at first only an outline, the general category (we will label this, in the following, *the sphere;* more about this concept later).
C. Within this category related concepts (or percepts) emerge, and among them occasionally also the one sought; but it does not prevail, and indeed may be rejected outright.
D. The images delivered after a delay are merged with other, not factually pertinent, impressions.
E. The integration into the spatial continuum is faulty.
F. Training conceals the disorder. The patients fail more readily when faced with a task than when left to their own spontaneity.

Each of these points is of importance. Later on it will be shown that images, thoughts, and percepts behave very similarly under the influence of drive-impulses.[59] Poetzl (631) has already called attention to the significant similarity between agnosic parapraxes and dream-images; the latter are completely explicable by the purely psychological considerations of psychoanalysis. I refer here to the theory of drives, where it becomes clear that parts of the perceptual and imaginal material are suppressed, and emerge therefore after a delay—at times only in the course of psychoanalysis. Freud gives the following example: the patient has the obsessional idea that if he permits himself to have intercourse a fatal mishap will befall Ella, his sister's child. The completed wording reads: if I permit myself to have intercourse I will be reminded that my girl-friend, who has been operated on,

[59] Cf. footnote 54, supra.

cannot have a child; enviously I will wish Ella dead, and the wish will take effect. It is clear how much of the text of the obsessional idea is suppressed, and may appear when the inhibition vanishes.

The psychoanalytic theory of symbols shows that, instead of what was really meant, another image belonging to the same conceptual realm may arise. Thus, in place of female genitals a jewel-box may appear, or in place of water, fire. Everything we know about dreams constitutes one great example showing that the belatedly delivered perceptual material merges with other percepts. These relationships will be pursued later on.

Let us mention again that, in the tachistoscopic perception of normals, the same defects appear as in agnosias.[60]

The disturbing effect of task-consciousness is due to an inappropriate distribution of attention. The inability to direct the distribution of attention is an important and frequent sequel of brain-lesions.[61] All the particulars are there, but they are not at the patient's disposal; and they are more readily at his disposal under an immediate need than on a command, the import of which the patient cannot estimate. Moreover, it is a general rule that an achievement can be hampered by the awareness that one must accomplish it.

The credit for having paved the way toward psychological considerations of this sort belongs to Pick (621). He observed, in a case of occipital-lobe atrophy, a disorder of the function which integrates visual impressions into a unity. The patient was unable to survey with one act of consciousness the individual parts of a whole in their spatial relationships; he absolutely could not put together large colored pictures, of simple objects, divided into four parts, even though he recognized the separate parts; the non-fixated parts, particularly those in the peripheral field of vision, appear to be of little effect.[62]

It is very significant that, according to Raehlmann (643), the congenitally blind, after operation, easily lose sight of fixated ob-

60 Compare Bruner (115, 116, 117).

61 Cf. the psychoanalytic theory of attention (footnotes 40 and 41, supra) which makes it plausible that brain lesions should result in an inability to direct attention.

62 Cf. footnotes 30 and 38, supra, on synthetic functions, also Halstead (314) and Buerger-Prinz (123).

jects as soon as these are moved, and seem to have only central vision. Another patient of Raehlmann, though he saw the individual parts of a dog, could not form an image of these parts joined together. Nor could Raehlmann's patients apprehend many points simultaneously.[63]

A few comments on lack of awareness of their own defects in brain-injured patients may be in place here. Anton (33) has demonstrated that there are patients who show psychic blindness for their own (central) blindness, or psychic deafness for their own deafness. They do not perceive their own defects, and the root of the psychological attitudes underlying this perceptual failure is organic. Psychologically this manifests itself as a repression tendency.[64] Redlich and Bonvicini (662) had observed general psychological changes, which likewise resulted in an attitude of disregard toward the patient's own defects. But no doubt there are cases of the Anton type: Albrecht (13) also has called attention to them. In sensory aphasia too, a focally caused psychological mechanism determines the overlooking of the defect (to be discussed later).[65]

g) More about psychic blindness, agnosia, and attention

Images are not destroyed in psychic blindness. Is Charcot's case a neurosis, or an instance of depersonalization? The probability that depersonalization and psychic blindness are related, and that affects in the former, and organic brain-damage in the latter, elicit the disorder. Geometric visual amnesia. Pure word-blindness. The word-Gestalt is of psychological origin. Psychic experiences can become incorporated into organic structure. Color-agnosia as a disturbance of memory-color formation. Orientation disturbances in cases of occipital-lobe lesion.

The original conception of psychic blindness was that while perception is maintained in it, imagery is lost: the center of imagery is destroyed. Charcot's (133) view of his case, which is clinically and psychologically unsatisfactory, furthered this mis-

[63] Cf. Senden (774), Schilder (750, Chapter 4), also Hebb (328) on Senden's data.

[64] On the relation of organic and psychological mechanisms see Betlheim and Hartmann (69), Schilder (752), Buerger-Prinz and Kaila (123).

[65] On anosognosia (lack of awareness of illness) cf. Schilder (740, p. 29 ff.); see also for a survey of the literature, Redlich and Dorsey (663), Stengel and Steele (797), and Weinstein and Kahn (863).

conception. I will present here an excerpt of this famous and instructive case.

Mr. X., who had an excellent visual but poor auditory memory, encountered upsetting business adversities, and began to eat and sleep poorly. One day he became confused, and since everything in his environment appeared so new and strange, he became frightened that this signalled a nervous breakdown. He had become nervous and irritable, and though he could see everything clearly, he had lost his visual memory for forms and colors. Still, he could carry on his business tolerably well, using his memory in other ways. On his way home from work he looked at the statues, buildings, and streets with as much surprise as if seeing them for the first time. Nevertheless he could find his way. He could no longer sketch the main square of a familiar city. His drawing of a minaret was primitive. He described an arcade quite well, but complained that he had no visual image of it. When he drew a tree poorly he said, "I don't know, I don't know at all how this came about." The features of his relatives appeared unfamiliar to him. His own image in the mirror was so strange to him that he turned and asked the observer to get out of his way. "I know perfectly well that my wife's hair is black, but I can no more find these colors in my memory than I can imagine her person."[66] Nor could he image the distant past. Since this had begun Mr. X. had called on his acoustic and movement images for help. He reports that he slowly developed an inner hearing. He no longer dreams in pictures. He does not recognize the Greek letters as he used to. Examination showed a myopia of seven dioptries and a mild, evenly distributed impairment of color-sensation. The notes the patient made are particularly important. He stresses that his impressions have changed radically, though he is still in possession of his abstract thinking. Daily he is surprised by things which should be familiar to him. "The root of the complete change in my existence, and the notable change of my nature, seems to lie in that undefinable strangeness of my sensations, or rather impressions. I used to be sensitive to impressions, was easily enthused and had a rich fantasy;—now I am quiet, cold, and my fantasy cannot carry my thoughts further . . . I am much less subject to anger or mental anguish. I have told you that I have recently lost my mother, whom I dearly loved. I experienced much less pain than if I had still been able to image her face, the phases of her illness, and the effect of her premature death on the members of my family."[67]

Close study of cases like this readily shows that here one must speak not of a loss of images, but rather of a particular conflict over, and inhibition of, imaging. Obviously, the absence of objective methods for testing the capacity for imagery creates some difficulty here; but many cases of associative psychic blindness give exact reports which do not differ from those of normals.[68] Among recent authors only Gelb and Goldstein (288) report, in their

66 Cf. this case with those of Buerger-Prinz and Kaila (123), and this point particularly with their observation, p. 656.

67 Cf. Buerger-Prinz and Kaila (123, pp. 651–652).

68 Objective methods have been developed by Goldstein and Scheerer (292), Scheerer (687), Kluever (428), and Teuber and Morris Bender (829, 830).

already mentioned case of perceptual psychic blindness, that they observed a loss of images—to me, a rather improbable finding. It may be assumed that in such severe disturbances of Gestalt-apprehension, image-content also will show changes, which may limit the usefulness of the imagery. But I do not believe that an actual *loss* of visual images is involved.[69] The limitation of images in Charcot's (133) and Wilbrand's (886, 887) cases is so much like that seen in depersonalization that Janet (526) could suppose Charcot's case was a *scrupuleux*, a pathological doubter. Nevertheless, Wilbrand's case with a well-established occipital lesion makes it probable that what in depersonalization is due to the well-known dynamic-affective conditions,[70] may be brought about also by an organic lesion—a fact to which our discussion will return later. Psychic blindness is an extraordinarily rare phenomenon; more frequently the agnosias do not extend to all of visual apprehension, and involve only portions of the sphere of visual experience. Thus, there are forms of agnosia in which it is primarily the geometric figures which are not apprehended and, simultaneously, spatial orientation is disturbed.

In another group of cases, the disorder of visual apprehension pertains to letters. These are the cases of the so-called pure word-blindness, in which the Gestalt of letters, in milder cases, of words, cannot be apprehended, while other visual-agnosic disturbances are present only in very small degree.[71]

One may stop and consider here. The cognition of letters—reading—is a result of a laborious process of teaching and learning. We may surmise that this teaching and learning process has structuralized,[72] and is not revived in every act of reading—that, rather, only the completed Gestalts as such come to consciousness. From this vantage-point one may attempt to bridge the gap between the

---

[69] Schilder expresses here a principle to demonstrate the validity of which he undertook a great variety of studies in the recovery of memories of organic amnesias; see e.g. (710, 711). The specific point in question here is borne out by Buerger-Prinz and Kaila's (123) observations and is in agreement with Goldstein's (293) later views.

[70] Cf. Schilder (690) and more recently Oberndorf (583, 584, 585, 586).

[71] See Goldstein (293), Weisenburg and McBride (864); cf. also Hebb (328; pp. 285 ff.).

[72] Cf. this concept of "structuralization" with Hartmann's (32) concept of automatization; for other views on automatization see Rapaport (658), and Hebb (328) on "assembly" formation.

views of Wertheimer (876) and Koffka (439) on the one hand, and Meinong (547), Witasek (889) and Benussi (56) on the other. As mentioned, the former do not consider Gestalten to be a product of psychological activity, but see in it only a correlate of transverse functions which take their course in the brain without psychological equivalents. The Graz-school,[73] however, speaks of image-creation, and means thereby that in Gestalt-perception there is an active psychological process. If one assumes that the active Gestalt-formation may, but need not, structuralize, one has attained a mediating position.

Besides the partial agnosias mentioned so far, the disturbances of color-perception, or color-amnesias, deserve special attention. These must not be mistaken for central disorders of color-perception, which according to Wilbrand and Saenger (887) arise from mild lesions in the visual irradiation-area causing— according to Lenz (484, 485)—secondary damages in the deeper layers of the cortex and in the superficial layers of the calcarine fissure. These color-amnesias[74] are forms of total color-blindness which correspond, sometimes more, sometimes less, to congenital total color-blindness. In color agnosia it is not color-perception, but color-apperception,[75] which is impaired; and there are partial disorders of the color-sense also, in some of which the apprehension of blue and green, in others that of yellow and red, is impaired. We have seen that in psychic blindness the concept of the object is occasionally aroused without the capacity for reaching it, via the corresponding word; so in color agnosias too the colors may be cognized without its being possible to find the corresponding color-name. As Peters (602) has demonstrated, in cases of highgrade feeble-minded children, inability to find color-names may secondarily impair color-apprehension. Pick (626) relates these phenomena to Hering's (341) memory-colors, and speaks in these cases of a loss of memory-colors. Thus there seem to be noteworthy analogies between perceptual stages in disturbances which arise from brain-lesions, and the stages discovered through psychological analysis. Disturbances both of surface-colors and memory-colors, due to brain-lesions, are demonstrable. What we

---

73 Cf. Boring (95, 96).
74 Cf. Goldstein and Gelb (290).
75 I.e., the process impaired is primarily a central one.

have described as disturbances of visual attention are fundamentally closely related to agnosic disorders. We have conceived
of these attention-disturbances as disturbances in the sequence
of acts of intending. The various degrees of attention also appear to be the outcome of such intendings. When we use the term
attention, the experience of intending must be separated from
the "image-experience" if confusion is to be avoided (cf. p. 59
above).

Disturbances of orientation have been observed repeatedly
in lesions of the occipital lobe. In the well-known case of Foerster
(193), only an extraordinarily small portion of the central visual
field was retained. But the patient's orientation was much worse
than that in simple blindness. For instance, he was much bothered
that after three weeks he was unable to find, without being led,
the lavatory, which was six steps from his hospital room and used
by him many times daily. If his eyes were covered, he could not
get from one piece of furniture in his room to another, but stood
totally helpless, not knowing which way to turn; when forced to
a decision he almost always failed. We find orientation-disturb-
ances in the most varied lesions of the occipital lobes: apparently
here we have to do with a disturbance of evolving spatial-visual
images and percepts. It is probable that the agnosic disorders in
question can be relatively well delineated.

Poetzl (630, 631) has pointed out that in gunshot-wounds of
the occipital region and in mild lesions of the occipital lobe,
those double pictures which arise either physiologically or by
mild disturbances of muscle equilibrium, and which in normals
are suppressed by a process of abstraction, stand out with disturbing effect. After-images also persist painfully. In general it might
be said that abstraction requires an intact brain.[76]

It seems that processes of visual perception and apprehension
have many part-apparatuses, which play into forming the final
Gestalt. Furthermore, each of these part-apparatuses consists of
hierarchically arranged part-functions. Intendings of attention and interest continuously cogwheel into the working of these
part-apparatuses, and even more so into the coordination of the
part-functions. The higher the level of the act of visual appre-

---

[76] Cf. Goldstein (291, 293) on abstract attitudes; and Hebb (328) on abstraction, schemata and assemblies.

hension, the more decisive is the role attained by attention and interest.[77]

h) The problem of localization

The subdivision of the cortex into areas. Cytoarchitectonics. Myeloarchitectonics. The calcarine fissure as the projection of the retina. The rigorous relation of retinal points to those of the calcarine fissure. Macular and perimacular scotomata. The relativity of scotomata. Sensations cannot be localized. Specific parts of the brain as necessary apparatuses for specific achievements. Impairments due to cortical lesions. Motor and sensory areas. Perception must pass through these loci as demonstrated by stimulation experiments. The spastic phenomena following lesions of pyramidal pathways are expressions of primitive functions. There is no destruction of images by brain-lesion. Disorders of cognition are inhibitions of hierarchically layered processes. Preliminary phases of the cognition-process come to the fore. Certain parts of the brain are necessary to develop a process and bring it to a closure. Neurotic inhibitory mechanisms are related to disorders which follow brain-lesions. Functions are facilitated and further developed by cortical loci. Rejection of the view that psychological elements are conducted by long association-pathways. Disturbance of association-pathways, if it causes any agnosic disorder, makes for emergence of more primitive functions; thus the association-pathways guarantee only the furtherance of function. The act is unlocalizable, but the intending occurs through brain-apparatuses (frontal-lobe, striate body). The brain-apparatuses have circumscribed functions, and the course of psychological functions is bound to these auxiliary apparatuses.

We come now to the important problem of brain localization, and will discuss it with particular reference to vision. Anatomically the structure of the cortex is quite varied, though a basic six-layer structure may be assumed. Yet a great number of well-circumscribed and anatomically well-characterized areas may be distinguished. Brodmann (110) distinguishes more than fifty areas on the basis of their cell-arrangements. (Compare Figures 3 and 3a.) These areas coincide essentially with those demonstrable by the anatomical arrangement of fibers (Vogt, 850), except that the myeloarchitecture permits a greater articulation into areas than does the cytoarchitecture. To be sure, C. and O. Vogt distinguish at present 200 sharply demarcated cytoarchitectonic areas. It is demonstrable with certitude that those areas which are particularly distinguished by their cyto- and myeloarchitec-

[77] Even if Schilder's conception should prove to be a purely phenomenological description, his stress on attention, interest, apparatuses and their hierarchies, focuses on those characteristics of mental functioning which have been least explored and most deserve it. Schilder's emphasis is justified by recent systematizing surveys of the literature: Hebb (328), Rapaport (658).

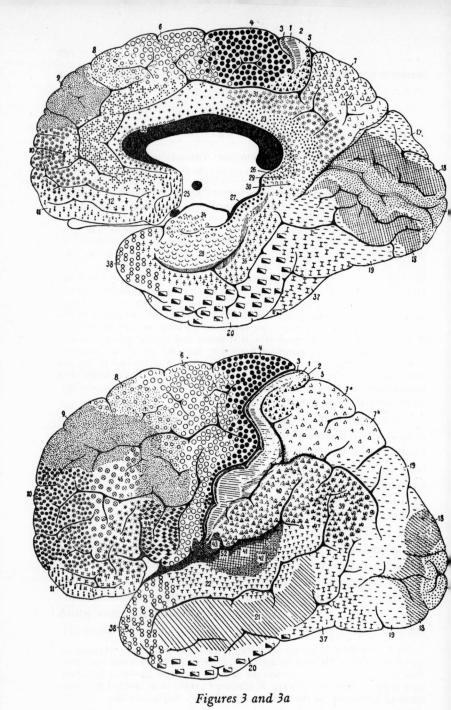

Figures 3 and 3a

The cytoarchitectonic fields of the cortex according to Brodmann

tonics are related to definite functions.[78] For instance, the area
which interests us first of all, the calcinary fissure, shows a quite
definite architectonic type, and is most closely related to the possibility of seeing. It may be said that the retina is projected into
the cortex (Henschen, 340; Wilbrand and Saenger, 887).

Since in lesions of the occipital lobe the points of clearest
vision are strikingly often preserved (as, for example, in the case
of Foerster above), Monakow assumed that the macula is diffusely
localized in the entire occiput. Yet war-cases in which only the
point of sharpest vision was involved, or scotomata existed at
least in the immediate vicinity of the macula, speak against this
assumption. It has been shown also, particularly by the war-obser-
vations, that the horizontal and the vertical meridians have specific
representations in the calcarine fissure; that the lesions in the
lower lip of the fissure correspond to defects in the upper, and
those in the upper lip to defects in the lower half of the visual
field; and that the frontal part of the fissure corresponds to the
periphery, its occipital pole to the macula. The macula is so often
preserved, not because of a diffuse representation in the occipital
cortex, but because of the particular vascular supply of this point.
In this sense there seems to be an absolute projection, but it must
be stressed that the scotomata due to occipital-lobe lesions are
characteristically not absolute (cf. Poetzl, 630; and Poppelreuter,
634, 635). Working in a dark-room with sufficiently strong lights
and large surfaces, one often obtains perceptions of light in the
scotoma which cannot be explained by the anatomical findings as
such. Functional factors also must be at play here. But the possibility of localization is not limited to the sensations. To begin
with, the following crude localizations may be listed: alexia (pure
word-blindness), in the lingual gyrus; visual-geometric agnosia,
in the lateral surface of the cuneus; and the centers of eye-accom-
modation movements, also in that region.[79]

What then is localized? Many authors, with Monakow in the
fore, stress that localization is a misleading term. From the locus in
question only the function in question can be disturbed—but that

---

[78] Cf. Fulton (260), Penfield and Rasmussen (599), and Hebb (328, particularly pp. 282 ff.).

[79] Note Schilder's reservations below and compare the evidence Hebb (328,
pp. 285 ff.) marshaled against such a conception of localization.

is no proof that the function has its site there. In fact, the localization concept makes sense for perception only if one agrees in this with Monakow. Visual perception is a process which presupposes many part-apparatuses—the eye itself, the optic nerve, etc. The cortex is, after all, but one of these stations. Perception cannot have its site there because it presupposes the total person, and this cannot be localized in any single point of the brain. The localization of sensations in the cortex means merely that for a certain perception to come about, a specific part of the brain is necessary —since the perception is somehow mediated through it. But in this sense there is a strict localization. That Cushing (138) and Valckenburg (844) have succeeded in obtaining tactile sensations by stimulating the central posterior gyrus is significant, in that it indicates this gyrus functions in such sensations. Not only sight and touch, but also smell, taste, and hearing, have an exact cortical localization.[80] Like the sensory functions, the motor ones also have a circumscribed localization. I insert here a schema showing the distribution of the motor functions in the central anterior gyrus. C. and O. Vogt (850) have demonstrated, by exact stimulation-experiments, that sharply delimited functions correspond to sharp anatomical boundaries of cortical fields; by means of electric stimulation, even outside the strictly motor region, they obtained circumscribed physiological effects from a surprisingly large number of areas. Pick (624, 628) has recently called attention to the probability that a great many combinations of movements have representations. Not only does motor localization manifest itself by defects due to lesions, but is clearly demonstrated by electric stimulation. This was used in Fritsch and Hitzig's (257) experiments, which rearoused interest in brain localization. Thus, the innervation, the intention to move, must pass through the loci in question. Figure 4 presents the schema of the excitable foci, after Krause.

Lesions of the cortical motor region, and of the pyramidal tract issuing from it, result not only in paralyses, but also in the much more significant spastic phenomena and movement combinations which—according to Gierlich's (274, 275) and Foerster's

---

[80] Cf. Penfield and Rasmussen (599, particularly p. 24), and Hebb (328) for evidence both supporting and limiting this view.

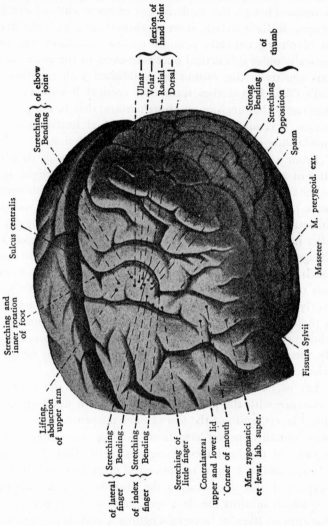

Figure 4

The left cortical hemisphere of man, with F. Krause's results obtained by faradic stimulation in twelve operations. All foci lie in the central anterior gyrus. (After F. Krause.)

(192, 193) assumption—are returns of phylogenetically ancient functions. Though the explanations of these authors are badly divergent in their details, it seems assured that, with the destruction of phylogenetically younger cortical functions, the phylogenetically older subcortical ones take over. In the realm of cutaneous sensitivity this cannot be established with certitude; but Head's (323, 324) studies show that cortical lesions apparently disturb only the precision of apprehension, that is, a higher level function. I remind the reader that residual functions are still demonstrable in scotomata following cortical lesions.

From a logical point of view, one could speak with more justice of a localization of images. At any rate, we might assume that the images were deposited in the brain, and are destroyed by a brain-lesion. This is the logically watertight view of the classic localization theory; the only trouble is that the facts rigidly contradict it.[81] There are no diseases of the brain which lead to loss of images, so we cannot explain disorders following brain-diseases by such loss. We have seen that psychic blindness is not based on a loss of visual images. Goldstein and Gelb (288) have spoken recently of a loss of visual images in the patient mentioned, but their view in this respect is not incontestable, nor do they explain psychic blindness by the loss of images they assume. Naturally, the evolving of images, just as of percepts, may be affected by circumscribed brain-lesions.

Let us be reminded that in optic agnosias the issue is an interference with the process of cognition as it develops in hierarchical layers, and not the loss of some elements. The cognition-process remains incomplete; from this we may infer that the guarantee of the final Gestaltung lies in the damaged parts of the brain, and so it must be conceived of as localized. This may be expressed also thus: due to the brain-lesion there appears a factor which inhibits the development of visual cognition. This factor appears likewise in certain neuroses, and there we can characterize it psychologically as a psychic denial, as repression.[82] The remaining parts of the brain permit only a more primitive mode

81 Cf. Penfield and Rasmussen (599), and Penfield (600, 601), whose facts seem, on the contrary, to support a version of the idea Schilder opposes.

82 Cf. on the one hand Hartmann (316 a) and Betlheim and Hartmann (69), on the other Morris Bender and Teuber (52, 53).

of function, which gives rise merely to the preliminary phases of the visual cognition process; these phases in turn strongly resemble phylogenetic and ontogenetic pre-stages of vision. Here we find a connection to the observations concerning lesions of the motor region; and we come to the general view that, as a consequence of cortical lesions, there emerge more primitive forms of function.[83] As yet we have no proof for anything analogous in the acoustic and tactile realm.

In the older localization theory, an important role was played by the view that lesions of the long association-pathways disrupt the coordination of parts of the brain. Alexia, for instance, was explained as a disruption of the connection between the letter-locus and the word-sound-locus. According to Liepmann (499, 501, 503), apraxia—the inability to act—is a severance of the connections between the sensory-motor centers on the one hand, and the acoustic, optic, and tactile centers on the other. But, as already mentioned, we see in alexia a gnostic disorder, a disorder of integration; and in general all disorders of cognition appear to us as disturbances in the layering of the various functions.[84] To be sure, here there is involved a severance of connections also; for example, in optic agnosia the harmony of the purely sensory- and motor-apparatuses of the eye is impaired. No doubt functional relations exist between the speech centers and the visual centers related to the act of reading. But we have no reason to assume that these relations exist by virtue of long association-fibers, and we have even less reason to assume that these long fibers conduct what is referred to ordinarily as visual impressions.

We know only one certain instance where the lesion of long fibers brings about a disturbance of higher functions, and this is the case of the sympathetic apraxia which comes about when the connection between the right and left motor-regions is disturbed. This disorder may then be expected to occur with lesions of the anterior part of the corpus callosum. It consists of a certain characteristic awkwardness of the left hand which will be discussed later. But it should be stressed that here also we are dealing not with the elimination of certain psychic elements from the action, but rather with the arousal of a more primitive mode of function-

[83] But cf. Werner (870, pp. 31–35).
[84] Cf. Hebb (328, pp. 285 ff.).

ing due to the lesion of the long pathways. The act involved does
not reach completion.

Thus, cortical lesions do not simply cause a deficit of certain
elementary functions;[85]* they also disrupt the layering of complex ones, and bring to the fore more primitive modes of functioning. Images prove unlocalizable; and this is no wonder, if it
is realized that their development involves a series of complicated
processes. To localize the act, the intending itself, would obviously
be senseless, since in it the total personality, the active brain, the
whole man, is involved.[86]

But a discussion of the localization problem must not fail
to indicate that the function of intending also, the impulse itself,
may be disordered by a circumscribed brain-lesion. Such disorders
of impulse are seen in lesions of the frontal lobes, and particularly in lesions of the striate body. There are two kinds of such
disorders, either an excess or deficit in impulse, and correspondingly an excess or deficit in the effectiveness of intending. Here too
the question may be raised whether the impulse originates at the
point where its disruption is possible. The answer is, no: in the
locus we have merely *one* of the conditions for the impulse; it is
only conducted and distributed from that point. These points
can only aid the persistence of the impulse and its effectiveness
in certain experiences. The act as such is not localized. This implies also a stringent argument against localization of images,
which are developing, crystallizing formations built up from a
manifold of partial strivings.

In this sense Jaspers (382) is right in saying that there is no
known single brain-process which directly parallels a psychological process. But such generalizations must not make us forget the
relation between sharply bounded parts of the brain and certain
psychological processes. Specific brain-apparatuses are necessary
for specific functions. We assume with Monakow (563) that psychological processes are functions of the brain as a whole, yet we
must persist in the conception that specific parts of the brain
partake in this whole-function in an exactly defined fashion. Berze
(68) maintains that the more one approximates what is the psyche
proper, the less is localization possible. At the same time, we must

85* Perhaps even these elementary deficits involve functional changes.
86 Cf. Allport (26, pp. 187 ff.).

insist that circumscribed brain-disorders result in circumscribed disorders of psychic functions.

A survey of the ramified and hotly-debated problem of cerebral localization was given by Goldstein and Foerster at the 1922 Convention of the Gesellschaft Deutscher Nervenärzte. For advances in the psychology of visual apprehension-processes, see Poppelreuter's (635) volume.

3. ACOUSTIC PERCEPTION[87]

Sounds and noises. The characteristics of sounds. Intensity, pitch, timbre (bright, dark, vocal character). People who differentiate vocality but not pitch can follow a conversation, but have no musical experiences. Various explanations of tone-deafness due to brain-lesion. Vocality (sound-color) cannot be brought into relation with specific characteristics of the physical acoustic waves. The nature of consonance and dissonance. Stumpf's (820, 823), Wundt's (895, 896), Helmholtz's, and Krueger's theories. The acoustic character of speech-sounds. The perception of noise. Psychic deafness. The central auditory region lies in the transverse gyrus (Flechsig, 191; Henschen, 340). Flechsig's myelo-genetic method and the objections to it. Preliminary comments on language-comprehension, melody-comprehension, and paraphasia. Attention-disturbances are associated with word-deafness.

The world of acoustic perceptions may be divided into sounds and noises. Koehler (433) has rightly stressed that biologically noises play a more important role in our lives than sounds, which are more easily studied and have attracted the attention of investigators ever since Helmholtz. Helmholtz (332) distinguished pitch, intensity and timbre. By timbre he understood on the one hand the bright-dark quality, on the other the vocal character. According to Koehler, some sounds have a vocal character which has nothing to do with the pitch. Thus, at heights where the pitch can no longer be distinguished, there are still clear differences in vocal character.

There are people who do not enjoy musical Gestalten: they hear music only as noise. Koehler was able to demonstrate that such a person was unable to distinguish pitch, though he distinguished vocal quality in individual sounds; and it was this that gave him his excellent ability to follow conversations. Koehler considers that the cases of tone-deafness following brain-diseases which have been reported in the medical literature [Alt (30) has surveyed these] are insufficiently described; he therefore finds it

[87] For recent surveys see Woodworth (893); cf. Schilder (750, Chapter VII), Schilder (739), Boring (95) and Stevens (808).

an open question whether these impairments are like that of his subject. Stumpf (823) explained a case of tone-deafness by the lack of feeling-sensations; Pfeifer (604) seems inclined to assume that the cause of tone-deafness following cerebral lesion is that the fibers subserving the projection of the deepest tones are most easily affected, and that the sensory agnosia of cortical origin is therefore due to loss of sensation of deep tones. However, in considering a pertinent case, he also assumes with Quensel (605) that an oversensitivity to acoustic stimulations may also play a role in it. The autopsy findings in a case of Edgreen suggest that damage to the anterior third of the temporal lobe causes a disturbance of melody-apprehension, but this was questioned by Pfeifer.

Stumpf (820) agrees now with Brentano (107) in assuming specificity of tone-color (identical tones of different octaves are similar to each other—all C-s, D-s, etc., have something in common); he does not recognize Koehler's vocal qualities, but explains their return in each octave by the characteristics of tone-color, and asserts that there is no constant vocal quality there. Koehler in turn explains tone-colors by vocal qualities.

Be that as it may, Koehler's view is significant because the vocality of tones which he stresses is a characteristic not correlated with the physical characteristics of the acoustic wave. The amplitude of the wave corresponds to intensity, the frequency to pitch; timbre, however, cannot be brought into relation to the physical characteristics of acoustic waves.[88]

The problem of the nature of consonance and dissonance has held the center of interest in the psychology of sounds; at present we have two opposing theories. According to Stumpf, consonance is based on fusion of tones, in which two tones are merged into one. In dissonance, component tones diverge. This explanation goes back to the characteristics of tones themselves. Helmholtz thought that consonance is based on the relatedness of tones—that is, on common overtones—and on the absence of beats due to the simultaneous occurrence of soundwaves of differing frequency.[89]* According to Wundt, there is another relatedness based on two tones being overtones of a common basic tone.

88 Cf. Woodworth (893, pp. 513–514).
89* The number of beats equals the difference in frequency between the two tones.

Krueger emphasizes the absence of difference-tones[90*] in consonance, which gives it the character of cleanness and smoothness, as against the presence of such middle-tones and beats in dissonance. Clash of neighboring tones and roughness is most patent in the strongest dissonances. So far, pathology has not learned from, nor contributed to, the study of consonance (compare Froebes, 258).[91]

More important is the psychology of noise, particularly when it becomes clear that speech too must be so classified, though according to Wundt the vowels approximate pure tones. According to Herschmann (342), vowels have a middle position between tones and noises. In consonants the noises predominate, though according to Koehler S and F still have a relation to certain pitches; but it must be remembered that the whole problem changes its aspect once one follows Koehler in separating the timbre of the tone from its pitch. Attention to noises can probably be disordered independently. In a case of Kehrer (410) there was a total lack of reactivity to acoustic stimuli of the most varied kinds and intensities—excepting speech; and as a word-deafness also present slowly underwent remission, deafness for everything except speech remained unchanged. There exists, apparently, an inability to direct attention to noises. But this question can be pursued further only in a broader context.

Just as in the visual realm so in the acoustic there is a projection onto a certain part of the brain (cf. Henschen, 340). Flechsig (191) had established the central auditory area by means of the myelogenetic method. Maturation of nervous tissue takes place at various times of embryonic and post-fetal life, and in the course of this, according to Flechsig, the functionally related parts are myelinized more or less simultaneously. The pathways subserving the immediate projection of sensory impressions onto the brain, and those subserving motor discharges from the brain, are myelinized earlier; thus, the sensory-centers can thereby be separated from the association centers. Flechsig developed a myelogenetic brain-chart on the basis of these assumptions. But according to

90* When two tones sound simultaneously, often others are also heard, particularly the first difference tone, the frequency of which is the difference of the frequencies of the original tones. . .

91 This discussion of dissonance disregards the role the historical-cultural framework plays in determining what is experienced as a dissonance.

C. and O. Vogt (850), this method does not study the cortex but rather the subcortical tissue; and myelogenesis itself is subject to changes and uncertainties, so that it is not possible to derive definite laws from it. Furthermore, there are projection fibers in all parts of the brain. In spite of these justified reservations, it must be stressed that Flechsig did discover with his method a series of important fiber-connections. Indeed, even the general conception of the articulation of the brain into parts related to primitive sensory, motor and integrative functions seems to be correct in its broad outlines.

In Henschen's (340) case, both temporal lobes were extensively destroyed, and only the left transverse gyrus was retained; nevertheless, the patient did hear. Apparently a primitive, purely sensory hearing exists, even though different in kind from what we know as hearing proper. I have already indicated in the discussion of visual perception that perception may have a preliminary sensory phase. In this case of bilateral destruction of the temporal lobes, there was a pure word-deafness also. Here we first come to the disorders of speech-comprehension, with which later we shall be concerned in detail. Only a gross sketch follows here.[92] The posterior third of the first temporal gyrus, and perhaps also the neighboring parts of the second, contains, according to Wernicke's (874) discovery, apparatuses which are indispensable for speech-comprehension. Lesions in these parts lead to word-deafness. Patients with unimpaired hearing are unable to comprehend words. Simultaneously there appear distortions (paraphasia) of spontaneous speech. The transverse gyrus, subserving the perception of tone, is anterior to this area. Adjacent, in the anterior parts of the first temporal lobe, are centers of music-comprehension. It is possible that the second and third temporal gyri partake in the perception of noise.

Bilateral lesion of these areas, which if damaged on the left give rise to word-deafness and paraphasia (sensory aphasia), brings pure word-deafness. This again shows that reception and elaboration of the sensory world must take place in different parts of the brain, and once more prompts us to maintain a theory of strict localization. It also calls to our attention the interaction of the

---

[92] Cf. Fulton (260, pp. 395–397); Weisenburg and McBride (864); and Goldstein (293).

two hemispheres of the brain. The destruction of the right hemisphere decreases, so to speak, the disturbances following the destruction of the left: though speech-comprehension is extinguished, patients are able to speak without distorting words or sentences. Therefore the distortion of speech in sensory aphasia is apparently referable to the function of the right hemisphere; but these matters should be detailed only later.

Thus, there seems to be a far-reaching parallel between the brain-organization of visual and of acoustic perception. We stress again that disorders of attention accompany disorders of apprehension. Particularly characteristic is the inattention to noise present in a relatively great number of cases of pure word-deafness, and the inattention to speech-sounds in sensory aphasia. It seems that these gross brain-lesions determine disturbances of attention in specific directions.[93]

It must be stressed that, in this area too, much is in flux. Koehler's theory of vocal-qualities is contested. Bonhoeffer (94) denies that paraphasia results from lesions of the right hemisphere, and his observations pose difficulties for the Flechsig-Henschen view of localization of the auditory area. A noteworthy observation concerning central deafness was reported recently by Balassa (43).

4. TACTILE PERCEPTION AND KINESTHESIA[94]

a) Touch-agnosia[95]

Touch-agnosias. Their associative and perceptive forms. The role of the visual factor in the absence of displacements and condensations in tactile agnosia. Agnosia-like phenomena in peripheral lesions. Percept-development is disrupted by absence of sensations. The generalization of this principle. Phenomena due to decreased acuity of vision, resembling psychic blindness.

Just as in the visual realm, so in tactile perception also there are central disturbances which prevent cognizing of objects, even though sensations are well preserved . . . Here also, two basic forms can be distinguished. In the first form, even the primitive Gestalt-perceptions are absent (perceptual touch agnosia); in the other form, though primitive Gestalten come about—round, cor-

---

[93] Cf. footnote 61, supra, on "attention."
[94] For more recent surveys cf. Katz (407), Woodworth (893), Boring (95, pp. 566–568), S. S. Stevens (808); see also Schilder (740, Part I, 1 and 6), Schilder (750, Chapter VI), and Schilder (730).
[95] Cf. Weisenburg and McBride (864), Schilder (740).

nered, and the like— no cognition is achieved (associative touch agnosia). Under certain circumstances, these agnosias can be limited to a few fingers.[96] For a long time it was contested that there are touch-agnosias; they were explained as disturbances of sensation—which, though minor, were usually present. Meanwhile, however, a sufficient number of cases accumulated in which the usual clinical methods of investigation could demonstrate no sensation-disturbances. But clinical investigations of tactile-sensations are as yet very imperfect (cf. Weizsäcker, 868), and the last word on this matter has not been said. It is noteworthy that the striking displacements within the sphere, so characteristic for the visual disturbances, have never been observed in tactile-blindness.[97] This may be because the tactile agnosias observed so far involve only circumscribed parts of the body. But it is also probable that processes of visual imagery exert a corrective influence, since conversely in the case of Goldstein and Gelb (288), where the sense of touch was intact, a severe disorder of tactile cognition corresponded to the disorder of visual apprehension. This will be discussed further below. Considering its pre-eminent role, visual cognition should be able to prevent, in tactile agnosia, displacements within the sphere. But there exist noteworthy observations of minute sensation-disturbances of peripheral origin, which include disorders very similar to optic agnosia. For instance, Niessl v. Mayendorf (578a) described tactile-blindness in a case of lesion of the posterior radix.

I myself observed a case in which, despite unimpaired tactile, temperature, and pain sensitivity, and retained localization-ability, there was a most severe disturbance of tactile cognition. It is true, though, that sensations of position were seriously impaired, and the two-point discrimination-thresholds were increased (two needles on the fingertips could be distinguished only when 11 mm. apart). This patient would lose objects out of her hands; she could not be sure whether or not she held them. Though she could describe details correctly, she was unable to unite them into a total picture.

[96] Cf. Schilder (740, particularly pp. 40–43), and Strauss and Werner (817); also Fulton (260, pp. 396–397).

[97] See II, 2 e, supra; concerning the concept of the sphere see III, 2 c, d, supra, and V, 10 and 12, supra; also Schilder (751).

In general, we know little of how the loss of single qualities affects total apprehension. We must assume that the total material is elaborated centrally, and that even minor changes of the total material will disturb its central elaboration; so the resulting disorders not only mirror the loss directly, but also reflect a disturbance of the central elaboration. This explains the similarity of sensation-disorders and disorders of central character pointed up by Siemerling (780), who had produced effects similar to psychic blindness through the use of very dark monochromatic glasses. It is most remarkable that not only disorders of cognition can be thus produced, but also those of the third type of psychic blindness—that is, disorders of empathy.[98] It seems to be a basic proposition that minor disturbances in sensory raw material may give rise to severe disorders of apprehension.

b) Elementary qualities. Non-visual perception of motion. Vertigo

Superficial and deep sensitivity. The sense of force. Motion perception through the skin, and the perception of one's own motion. Motion experience of one's own body as the core of vertigo-experience.

What are the elementary qualities in the realm of touch? Besides contact-, pain-, and cold-perceptions as such, there is the discrimination of two simultaneously touched points—that is, the location sense of the skin, the touch-circles of Weber. That this function is quite independent of simple contact-sensitivity is demonstrated by its frequent disorder in pathological cases where contact-sensitivity remains intact. The stimuli which impinge on the skin are also localized, and we must ask whether or not this localization is contained in the sensation. The answer to this question presupposes a discussion of deep sensitivity, which is related to surface-sensitivity. Struempell (819) and Head[99] speak of a pressure sensitivity in deeper tissues, but their view is contested by Frey[100]; he explains so-called deep-pressure-sensitivity by mechanical conduction of the pressure to more sensitive skin-regions. According to more recent studies of Goldscheider (284),

[98] "Empathy" translates *Sichhineinversetzen*.
[99] Schilder refers to Head (324); see also Head (327).
[100] Schilder refers to Frey (249); cf. Boring (95, pp. 469–475 and pp. 514–515).

though deep-pressure-sensitivity exists, it plays an insignificant role in perception of pressure-stimuli. The problem of kinesthetic sensations is particularly important. According to Frey's (249) investigations, there can be no question that there are finely graded sensations which orient us as to the state of contraction of muscles and the tension of sinews. Frey speaks of a sense of force, and doubts the justification of Goldscheider's theory which attributes particular sensitivity to joints. He explains the perception of passive movements of joints by tactile surface-sensations elicited by such movements. Frey was able to demonstrate that perception of passive movements is not disrupted by destruction of the joint. The estimation of weights is undisturbed in amputees (Katz, 406; Allers and Borak, 17).

The problem of motion perception, encountered in discussing visual perception, arises in the tactile realm as well. Motions are chiefly perceived through surface-sensibility. Benussi (56) repeated Schumann's experiment (p. 64, supra) in the tactile realm, and obtained apparent movement by successive stimulation of two neighboring points on the skin. Benussi held that this is not a sensation, but a central act of apprehension. We encounter the same problem in deep-sensibility also. Is there motion-sensation mediated by sensibility of joints or muscles? Since we agree with Frey in not recognizing a sensibility of joints, we must ask: Do the sense of force and the conducted pressure-sensations give rise to motion-sensation? Or, as Oehrwall (587) assumes, do more complicated acts of apprehension also play a role here? There is, however, a very important sensory area, the vestibular one, which does supply motion-sensations.[101] In an astute study, Leidler (483) has come to the conclusion that it is by the qualities of the sensations released from the vestibular apparatus that we perceive locomotions of our head and of our body as a whole. One must agree with Leidler that the core of vertigo-experience is a motion-sensation, though many other sensations and feelings—such as nausea, dizziness, particular visual perceptions, feelings of tension and release—as well as disturbances of higher functions, are associated with this core. At any rate, the relation to each other of various kinds of motion perceptions has not been clarified, and

[101] Cf. Witkin (890), H. Werner (870), Stevens (808, Chapters 5, 30, 31), also Schilder (740) and Schilder (750, Chapter 8).

it seems at least probable, particularly in view of the vestibular motion-sensations, that there *are* elementary motion-sensations.

c) Localization of skin stimulations and tactile space[102]

Organization of tactile experiences into the body-image, with the aid of vision. The phantom limb of amputees as an obvious manifestation of the body-image. Movements of the phantom limb. Dependence of the phantom on central factors. Automatic localization. Disturbance of localization by interference with the visual aspect of the body-image. Substitution of the visual image by touch-tremors. Role of the visual aspect of the body-image in space-perception. Tactile-kinesthetic constituents of the body-image. Agnosia of the body-image. The Autotopagnosia (Pick, 620, 375, 628). Relation of clothing to the body-image. Tactile-kinesthetic apprehension of space is rudimentary.

The foregoing remarks are prerequisite to a factual consideration of the localization problem. We must assume that single sensations do not stand helter-skelter side by side in memory, but are ordered into a total image of the body—or, to use Head's expression, into a schema. Every new stimulus is met by previously fixed structures,[103] by a body-image, in the building of which visual impressions also partake. These schemata make their most striking appearance in amputees, who continue to experience their amputated limb for long periods of time. Mitchell, James (373, II), Pick (620, 628), and Katz (406) have given particular attention to this phenomenon. In the amputated limb these patients experience pins and needles, tickle, cold, warmth, movement, muscle-tension. Often the distal parts are more vividly experienced than those lying between them and the stump. The certainty of the phantom experience is so great that the patient, believing he still possesses the limb, actually falls: one of my patients, both of whose legs were amputated, once jumped off a high chest; a horseman fell because he experienced holding the reins with his amputated hand. There are many other similar examples. The phantom is often represented visually also, strongly suggesting that there exists a visual as well as a tactile body-schema. Amputees often have the impression of carrying out movements with their amputated leg. Simultaneously, as a rule, there are movements on the stump, but these do not elicit the

[102] Cf. Schilder (740) and (750, Chapters 6, 8, 12); also Katz (407).
[103] "Structure" here translates *Form;* cf. footnote 36, supra. Concerning schemata, see also MacCurdy (525), Bartlett (46), Hebb (328), Rapaport (658).

movement-impressions: on the one hand, they may be present without experience of movement in the phantom limb; on the other, they do not correspond to its movements. The crucial factor is rather the movement-intention which applies to the image, though the co-innervation of stump and of symmetrical muscles does enliven the experience.

In general, the amputated limb appears shrunken and closer to the body than the other. To some, the amputated hand appears as a child's hand right at the shoulder. We have no explanation of these interesting phenomena. The phantom cannot be explained by a displacement of the sensation to the terminal extension of the nerve, since some amputees specifically report that they felt their big toe being squeezed, or that they lost the phantom-limb experience bit by bit. In one of my cases, the perception of the toes was all that remained of the initial perception of the entire foot. It seems that the body-image as such, a more complex higher unit into which the raw impressions are integrated, must be at work here. Head demonstrated that an appropriate brain-lesion makes the phantom limb disappear.

Obviously, the body-image plays an essential role in the localization of tactile stimuli, though this holds only for conscious localization.[104] Following Henri (339), we may, in normals, distinguish on the one hand purely automatic localization which occurs without specific attention, and on the other deliberate localization in which the individual turns his attention to the tactile sensation. In automatic localization, the localizing movement of the touching finger, regarded as a low-level reflex-achievement, plays the main role. But it is very improbable that this would be a spinal reflex, as Henri assumed. It is an instinctive action, the psychological representation of which is as yet to be explored.

If touch occurs in the course of a localizing movement, control of hitherto inaccurate localization is achieved. In deliberate[105] localization, special attention to tactile sensations and visual images plays the critical role. Before we end the discussion of the role of visual perception and imagery in the localization of skin stimulations, Goldstein and Gelb's (288) case of psychic blindness should again be cited. The patient had a peculiar disturbance

104 Cf. Schilder (740, I, 13).
105 "Deliberate" translates *willkuerlich*.

of touch: he was incapable of cognitive achievements by touch, though he could copy objects surprisingly well. As long as a limb was motionless, he could give no information whatever regarding it. He could not distinguish his horizontal position from one at 25 degrees tilt, and considered both horizontal. He was totally unable to report, without help, on the direction and extent of passively executed movements. It was extremely difficult for him even to initiate movements with his eyes closed, and in this condition he could not carry out movement-sequences except unequivocal and well-habituated ones. He invariably obtained only one impression from two simultaneously applied pins. He could not say whether he was being touched by a finger or by a whole hand. With his body at rest and his eyes closed, he could not localize at all, and could state only that he was being touched, but never where. When he did carry out certain touch- and muscle-movements, that is, touch-tremors, he could localize to some extent, but only crudely. These touch-tremors, which are minor muscle-movements, were the mediating links to which the localizing movements attached. These touch-movements appeared first all over the body, and only by the congruence of the touch-impression with the kinesthetic sensations involved in these touch-tremors was crude localization achieved. "The patient localizes without any image of the stimulated place. He does not localize, in the proper sense of the word, but makes only reflex-like movements in the direction of the stimulated place."

In Goldstein and Gelb's case, tactile qualities per se were preserved; therefore, they concluded, there is no such thing as tactile spatial imagery. They even maintained that the sense of touch is incapable of eliciting visual images without the mediation of kinesthetic impressions or their residues. They denied that touch-sensations have spatial values. Not even the modelling products of the blind prove that they have real spatial images, though, in the light of the achievements of blind sculptors, it was customary to attribute to them an unusually well-developed spatial sense, and consequently to assume the existence of a tactile space with good location-discrimination.[106] Ziehen (905) too has stressed that the spatial qualities of tactile perception have been overestimated. Like kinesthetic sensations, these qualities are graded,

[106] Cf. V. Loewenfeld (516).

but do not imply any direct spatial experiences. We shall return to this later. At any rate it may be said that the body-image contains essential visual constituents in addition to tactile and kinesthetic components, and that for the proper localization of sensation an intact body-image is requisite.[107]*

But as Head and Holmes (323) showed, we find the most severe disorders of localization in lesions of the sensory cortex. Despite intact visual perception and image-formation, there is no correct localization. The body-image thus has also a tactile component which is indispensable for localization. In Goldstein and Gelb's case, the patient could initiate movements only with difficulty when his eyes were closed. The body-image must play an important role in initiation of movement. In the analysis of action we shall discuss this in detail.

Here we wish to make one more point. There are disturbances of the use of the body-image which amount to agnosia. Such patients, while oriented in external space, are not oriented on their body; they cannot find their mouth, nose, eyes, ear, right or left. They are agnosic in respect to their own body. Pick (620, 628) labeled this disorder autotopagnosia. There is good reason to link it with localized brain-lesions, though Pick has also found it in functional disorders. One patient could not handle those parts of his body which were removed from direct visual perception.

To repeat: an image of one's body is developed, and individual experiences are constantly integrated with this body-image. The body-image is not rigid. Pushing with a stick against a solid object, I experience the resistance at the end of the stick. Jewelry and clothing enter into a close relation with the body-image. Obviously the body-image is subject to continuous change and rebuilding. In this connection, it is particularly worth noting that in time the phantom limbs of amputees shrink. Is it possible that here previous experience-complexes, previous body-images, make their appearance?[108]

Goldstein and Gelb, as mentioned, deny that the sense of

107* These problems are entirely in flux. Goldstein and Gelb's is an isolated observation. It is probable, though not definitely demonstrable, that in their case tactile cognition was disordered by way of *visual* cognition and not independently (autotopagnosia).

108 Cf. Schilder (740).

touch implies a space-perception. But it can hardly be assumed that modeling without any spatial images is possible, and some blind have reached significant artistry in modeling. Even Goldstein and Gelb's patient could copy surprisingly well. Thus a primitive spatial apprehension must be feasible even tactile-kinesthetically. True, kinesthesia seems to play a special role, and, it must be admitted, space-perception, without the aid of vision, is rudimentary. In people of intact vision, "tactile" space-perception occurs always in conjunction with the visual.

d) Weber-Fechner law[109]

Discussion of perception in terms of individual sense-organs cannot avoid being a piecemeal theory of perception. My justification for discussing the problem of differential sensitivity in connection with the tactile and kinesthetic sense is historical: it was with weight-discriminations that Weber first established that the differential threshold steadily increases as one recedes from the absolute threshold, and that the proportion of absolute stimulus-intensity to differential threshold remains constant. Increase in stimulus-intensity results in a change of sensation only if a certain constant proportion is reached between the increment and the stimulus present. This proportion holds only within a certain range of stimulus-intensity. Furthermore, the transfer of this law to spatial and temporal relations encounters difficulties.

According to Fechner, the above facts express the law of psychophysical relation between stimulus and sensation: sensation increments are proportional to the logarithm of the stimulus. According to others, constancy of the differential threshold is based purely on physiological arrangements. According to Wundt, whom I follow here, this constancy is a law of apperceptive comparison, implying that psychological magnitudes are compared only as to their relative value; that is, the sensation is directly equivalent to the stimulus, and the Weber-Fechner law rests on judging sensations.[110]

109 Cf. Woodworth (893), Boring (95), see also Delbrueck (143).
110 Note the physicist Delbrueck's (143) considerations on the nature of the Weber-Fechner "law." Note also the complexities introduced by Koehler's (434) and Lauenstein's (478) studies of successive comparison, and the further complexities of individual differences and "perceptual styles" introduced by the studies of Klein (415) and his associates Holzmann (355) and Gardner (261).

e) Comments on organic foundations of the process of sensation

Though the organic foundations of the sensory process are not our theme proper, we must mention Head's[111] bold attempt at representing the manifold physiological bases of sensation as an ordered whole. Though his views cannot all be considered proven, I, indeed, have my doubts about them, we have no comparably inclusive attempt at a synthesis.

Head severed one of his own cutaneous nerves and observed its restitution, noting the separation of protopathic from epicritic sensibility. The former, the more primitive, recovers first; it is linked to distinct points and subserves pain- and temperature-sensations, with the exception of those between 27° and 38° C. These temperature spots conform to the all-or-none principle, and the reaction does not depend on the degree of temperature, but only on the number of temperature spots involved. Cognition and localization of touch- and pressure-stimuli is relatively good even when the skin has only protopathic sensibility, effected by deep sensibility. The glans penis even normally has only protopathic sensibility. The epicritic sensibility subserves two-point discrimination and the sensation of temperature between 27° and 38° C. It also makes possible discrimination of temperature-differences and temperature-adaptation, and is not solely dependent upon cold- and warmth-spots.

Cold spots may be stimulated by temperatures of 45° C. and below. However, this cold-sensation may be suppressed by the common warmth-sensations, and there are also combinations of heat-, cold-, and pain-sensations which occur in the spinal cord.

As long as surface-sensibility is entirely destroyed, there is an exact localization of touch by means of preserved deep-sensibility. With the return of protopathic sensibility, localization becomes severely impaired, because this primitive surface-system reacts diffusely and tends to produce sensations which are displaced to distant parts. The localization-disturbance wrought by the protopathic system can disrupt the correct localization effected through deep-sensibility. Tactile sensations can be correctly localized if the lesion in question is below the nuclei of the posterior columns. As long as tactile sensibility is intact it can be localized, regardless of whether or not the position of the limb in space is recognizable and discrimination possible. Above the nuclei of the posterior columns, impulses resulting in tactile sensation separate from those pertaining to localization. Deep-sensibility makes possible three-dimensional spatial orientation and the localization of single points. Recognition of forms, however, depends on tactile discrimination. The first sign of the recovery of epicritic sensibility is the return of the power of discrimination.

In the spinal cord there occurs a reorganization of pain- and temperature-sensations. The temperature-experience is now differentiated into the systems of warmth and cold. The tracts which mediate surface touch-sensation, deep sensibility, and with it localization ability, remain uncrossed. In certain individuals the tract mediating touch-sensation crosses over. While peripherally

111 Schilder refers to Head (324); see also Head (327). Cf. footnote 100, supra, on the relation of Head's and Frey's findings and views.

the surface- and deep-touch sensitiveness remain separated, they are united in the spinal cord.112* This reorganization is best illustrated by a case Head and Holmes (323) observed of a Brown-Sequart paralysis due to lesion of the second cervical segment. On the left side movements and reflexes were intact, but pain, warmth and cold were not perceived, while tactile sensibility, discrimination, position-sensations, and localization, were completely preserved. The right side, originally paralyzed, showed intact touch-, pain-, warmth-, and cold-sensations, but the patient was unable to recognize the position of his right arm and leg, had no discrimination, did not recognize objects, and could not estimate weights, though localization was undisturbed.

The tracts of tactile discrimination also are in the posterior columns. Above the nuclei of the posterior columns, impulses subserving cognition of position and passive movement separate from those subserving tactile discrimination. The example is a case of hypophysis-lesion in which passive movements of the hand were not cognized, while discrimination and cognition of forms in all dimensions were retained.

Besides the impulses which arouse sensations, there are those which go through the cerebellum and have nothing to do with sensations.

There are also many impulses which per se could arouse sensations, but are suppressed. Thus, temperatures between 40° and 45° C. cause agreeable sensations of warmth, but if the warmth-sensation is impaired, they cause pain. Pain-sensations are thus suppressed by simultaneous warmth-sensations. Irradiation of protopathic sensations too is suppressed by the return of epicritic sensibility, without increase of their threshold. Thus, presence of non-sensory afferent impulses plays an important role here.

A new reorganization takes place in the thalamus. This organ reacts primarily to the affective aspect of sensibility: here pleasure and pain are added to the somatic and visceral sensations. Furthermore, it is here that the sensory tracts terminate, are switched, and are channeled to the cortex.

The cortex takes care of the finer discrimination of stimuli and their quantitative gradation. Above the nuclei of the posterior columns, the spatial impressions are carried over three distinct tracts separate from those carrying touch- and pressure-impressions. These spatial elements have no relation to the thalamus, but only to the cortex. Those elements which mediate the cognition of the position and passive movement of limbs, also enable us to make weight-discriminations with the unsupported hand. In cases of cortical lesions, the patients' responses are so uncertain that it is not possible to determine an exact threshold: the patient now does, now does not recognize the identity of weights. The cortical lesion also destroys the ability to discriminate two similar impressions; thus the patient cannot distinguish which of two weights is the heavier. Finally, the cortex subserves spatial apprehension, and damage to it leaves the patient unable to determine the position of the afflicted part of the body: both discrimination and localization are poor. Responses are unreliable and hallucinations frequent. The cortex is also the locus for the storage of previous experiences. All new impressions, before they become conscious, are checked against the ones previously integrated into the schema. Cortical lesion destroys the schemata, and thus makes impossible a secure cognition of spatial relations. Cortical lesions are accompanied by hypotonia. It is not necessary to go into details here. This summarizes Head's views.

112* According to Head and Struempell (819) even light touch of a needle-point arouses deep-pressure sensation.

By way of criticism, we may repeat that, according to Frey's (249) investigations, Head overestimates the role of "deep"-sensibility.[113] Trotter and Davies (838) have also shown that the assumption of a protopathic and an epicritic sensibility leads to difficulties. Furthermore, the relation of the thalamus to feeling is by no means proven.[114] It is true that the general reaction of these patients to pain is particularly intense, but no unusual pleasantness of sensations was demonstrable on my, admittedly limited, number of cases; the literature contains no relevant reports, and Head's own records are not fully convincing.

But the conception which Head derives from his observations appears significant: the process of sensation runs its course in stages, and reorganization to a new stage takes place in every gray-matter center. The functioning of the lower stages is not amenable to introspection. He formulates this rule: the arrangements of the peripheral nervous system depend on structural and developmental factors; those of the intramedullary stage depend primarily on functional or physiological ones; and the terminal processes leading to sensation are ordered according to categories which can be explored by introspection. If the influence of the cortex is removed, the thalamus is liberated and sensibility attains a thalamic character. If the epicritic sensibility is eliminated, the protopathic system makes its appearance in its true colors. The deeper, more primitive organization is under the control of the higher system. Head stressed that suspension of the higher system does not simply bring to the fore a phylogenetically older one. A lesion which liberates the thalamus of man produces specific phenomena which are not present in phylogenesis. Since later on we shall have to speak repeatedly of a return of phylogenetically older stages, let us say here that even though any organ integrated into a broader whole thereby gains new relationships and functions, and loses old ones, its phylogenetic relationships often do emerge strikingly when an organ superordinate to it is destroyed. This holds particularly for motility. Mourgue (565, 566), whose views are in many respects close to

113 Cf. footnote 100, supra, and Boring (95a) and (95, pp. 465–475, particularly p. 474).

114 Cf. Lashley's (476a) critique and Rapaport (654, Chapter II) as well as Lindsley's (Chapter 14, in 808) surveys of the literature.

those of the English school, uses similar considerations—to my mind, unjustifiably—to deny the relation of certain disturbances of motility to phylogenetically older formations. Naturally, one must not expect exact replicas—nothing of the sort occurs in the recapitulation of phylogenesis in the embryo's development.[115] But certainly Haeckel's basic biogenetic law can lead to a better understanding of phylogenesis and ontogenesis.

According to Head, the processes of various stages must be reorganized and integrated into higher units (cf. Sherrington, 779). Stimuli which would otherwise lead to sensations may be suppressed on the physiological level; and there are also transactions which never reach consciousness: some impulses are selected, others rejected. Stimuli may have deep and far-reaching effects, particularly on the higher physiological levels, even though they do not arouse consciousness. Thus, position-impulses which spread upwards in the nuclei of the posterior columns on the one hand arouse sensation in the cortex; on the other they are transmitted to the cerebellum, making coordination possible; but the coordination may be adequate even if they do not give rise to sensations.

The activity of the central nervous system abides by three principles. Impulses of the same kind facilitate each other; conversely, of two simultaneously aroused but incompatible impulses, one passes and the other is rejected; finally, the vital processes of the nervous system effect the process of adaptation. No stimulus, however mechanically constant, elicits a constant response, since preceding stimuli effect a change in the reacting centers. Every stimulus effects a different reaction at each level of the nervous system, but these three basic principles remain in operation. If a receptive center is destroyed, the functions of this stage drop out; but the blocked impulses exert their effect on lower levels.

On the highest levels the stimulus is not referred to the body, but to an external object (projected sensation). The protopathic system shows a diffuse segmental reaction-pattern to stimuli. The sensation radiates broadly and is displaced to distant parts. An example is the oversensitivity of the skin in diseases of internal organs. With higher development of the central nervous system, segmental reactions are replaced by mass-reactions: the phenomena following total transection of the spinal cord illustrate this. Both the segmental and the mass reactions subserve the purpose of keeping away noxious influences; but normally they are controlled by higher centers.

Head defines the object as a complex of projected responses, a product of cortical activity. When the cortex is destroyed, the object disappears, though its affective and qualitative aspects continue to elicit impressions. All "projected sensations" leave physiological traces behind them. The activity of the cortex

115 Cf. Werner (870, pp. 31–35) for a recent discussion of these issues.

effects not only spatial projection, but makes possible the cognition of temporal relations. In cases of brain-lesion rhythmically repeated stimuli are experienced as though they were continuously present. Spatial and temporal connections are recognized by means of projected elements of the sensation. These depend mostly upon present physiological activity and traces of past activity. When they do reach consciousness, they appear as ordered sensations, which extend in time and are related to other phenomena of the external world.

I have reported with deliberate extensiveness the non-psychological views of Head (327). A careful comparison of his physiological constructions concerning integration and dissociation with his psychological views concerning affectivity, to be discussed later, shows far-reaching similarities. The organization of the psychological and the physiological is similar in essence. However, Head fails to recognize that the activity of the cortex is amenable to thorough psychological investigation, as I have tried to demonstrate in the preceding chapters.

III

ACTION AND LANGUAGE

1. ACTION

a) Volitional and automatic action[1]

Psychological analysis must not always begin with the elementary. Volitional action intends the object and implies the intending of its own innervation. The relation between the interest in the object and the innervation in the course of automatization. The elimination of psychological partial phases. Action takes its course on various levels of consciousness. Pressing the lever in simple reaction-experiments is neither a reflex, nor an automatism, but a volitional action. Sensory and motor sets. Rejection of Wundt's classification of actions. Action is not built up out of reflexes, but only uses them.

Usually the following schema is accepted for the psychology of action: out of primitive reflexes, more complex mechanisms are constructed.[2] Indeed, there are psychologists who assume that action that implies choice developed from the reflex in the course of phylogenesis. To my mind, here also it is not right to start with the apparently simplest case; we should rather take fully developed action, that is, volitional action, for our point of departure.[3] "I do something" means that I direct myself in action toward the object, which is usually of the external world. For instance, I grasp an object standing before me and put it on another spot. It is obvious that simultaneously something happens in the body also: the innervation of various muscles. It would be a mistake to assume that these muscle innervations are intended at the full height of consciousness; actually they take place with-

[1] Cf. Lewin (495, particularly pp. 144–150); and Hebb (328, Chapters 7 and 8).

[2] For recent versions of such theories see Hilgard and Marquis (347), Mowrer (568), Dollard and Miller (149); but cf. Hilgard (348), and Hebb (328, particularly Chapter 8) for their critique.

[3] For a similar point of view and actual analyses see Lewin (493, 495).

103

out our explicit contribution. But they must somehow be given psychologically, since when the task is difficult we begin to attend to what we are doing, until with the progress of training the object of the action again comes to the fore. For instance, the beginner on the bicycle will still attend to his movements and actions; the experienced rider will center on the road before him, not on the details of his movements. Indeed, one can agree with Pick (624) that the prerequisite of effective action is that the act as such be disregarded.

In the automatization[4] of difficult actions, one encounters two different processes. First of all, with the progress of training there occurs a purely somatic change in the musculature (and in the corresponding nervous apparatuses). Secondly, a psychological reorganization also occurs. At the outset, external world and innervation are equally willed, and the innervation may even be more attended to;[5] later, the emphasis shifts from body to external world, and the innervation of the body becomes, as it were, a secondary intention, the objects of which are given only on a lower level of consciousness. Intentions given on a lower level of consciousness are not unconscious:[6] they remain actions of the ego, of the personality.

Naturally, this shift of emphasis from the subject to the object is only one part of the process of automatization. Two other processes also occur. The effort decreases with each repetition; it does not require the application of new impulses each time. Rather, once I make a decision[7] the action takes its course automatically, though it always remains my action. Parts of the psychological experience are simply eliminated [Kretschmer's (450, 453, 454) "formular abbreviation"].[8] Furthermore, parts not

---

4 Cf. Hartmann's (321, pp. 392 ff.) concept of "automatization," and Lewin's (495, pp. 129–130) concept of ossification. See also Rapaport (658) on "automatization," and Hebb (328, pp. 292–293) on "assemblies."

5 "Innervations" obviously cannot be "attended to"; Schilder apparently means "attending to the movements of the body."

6 On the relation of volition and levels of consciousness, cf. Rapaport (659).

7 Cf. Lewin (495), and Escalona (168).

8 Cf. Hartmann (321); see also Schilder (729, Chapter VII) on Bleuler's concept of "occasional apparatus" (*Gelegenheitsapparat*). The issue Schilder dwells on here seems to be a crucial, but little appreciated and less explored, aspect of learning and habit formation. Learning theories (see Hilgard 348) have hardly touched on it; but see Lewin (495), Schwarz (768) and Hebb (328,

only of the experience, but of the object also, tend to sink to a lower level of consciousness. Not only is it not necessary to will explicitly this or that movement: it is no longer necessary to intend explicitly this or that partial action on the object. For instance, the experienced bicyclist neither thinks that he must now make a movement with the left hand, nor that he must now turn the handlebar to the left. All he has clearly in his consciousness is that he must now avoid this or that object. Indeed under certain circumstances, even this thought will sink to a lower level of consciousness.

The theory of levels of consciousness, developed originally for sensations and perceptions by Westphal (878) and Seifert (770), has great significance in the realm of actions also. Here too there are various middle positions between the simple turning-in-action-toward and the explicit will-actions, the latter of which can always be observed in a new act.

There is no doubt that what in one will-action requires training in order to sink to a lower level of consciousness, in others is already so given; and in all will-actions of adults there is an abundance of "automatisms." Whether or not primary and secondary automatisms[9] are completely identical is an open question. But they are essentially similar, and doubtless there are phylogenetic bridges between them. The multitude of half-conscious actions cannot be overestimated. A spark lights up in the peripheral visual field and is received on a low level of consciousness; the eyes turn toward it, but since the spark is not worth sustained attention, they turn back to the object previously fixated—and this repeats itself thousands of times daily. I feel an itch and my finger goes to it, without my even attending the whole event. It makes no sense to speak here of reflexes. All these are will-actions of a low level of consciousness. C. and O. Vogt (851, 852) have pointed out that there are automatisms woven into every volitional action, but they mean not only what I have labeled from the psychological point of view "automatism," but also bodily processes

pp. 292–293). This issue is a cardinal one of present-day psychoanalytic ego-psychology, of which Schilder must be recognized as one of the pioneers, even though he was not in the position to give a broad and general formulation of the problem which he so clearly discerned.

9 Cf. again Hartmann (321) on primary and secondary autonomy, see also Rapaport (656).

which have no psychological representation. The center for these automatisms must be sought in the striate body. Actually, there is a close relationship between those "automatisms" which have psychological representations and those purely somatic processes considered by the Vogts.

Occasionally the reactions in the psychologists' simple reaction-experiments have also been labeled reflex-actions. A sensory impression is presented and the subject is to press a lever as fast as he can. But the subject has decided, in the moment he accepted the instructions, to do as prescribed. Thus, this is a will-action, though extended in time and particularly simple in its motor phase. These simple experiments show that will-actions apparently have a complex system of preparations. The decision in the reaction-experiment has an outright somatic effect: it sets up motor readinesses. Psychologists distinguish in reaction-experiments between motor and sensory sets:[10] in motor sets it is more the reaction as such which is intended; in sensory sets it is more the kind and correctness of action. Accordingly, in motor-setting the reaction-time is shorter than in sensory, while errors are more frequent and occasionally reaction takes place before the stimulus is presented. But it is obvious that these actions differ only in their simplicity from the everyday variety, and afford less insight than the latter into the psychology of action.

Concerning these matters compare the studies of Lange (476), Grundland (309), and Ach (7).

Wundt distinguishes instinctual actions, volitional actions, and actions implying choice. By instinctual action he means actions arising from a single motive; in volitional actions and those implying choice several motives are involved. But this classification disregards the issue of the level of consciousness of action, and overlooks the fact that instinctual action too may have a broader prehistory. Furthermore, there are actions which take place at the full height of consciousness and are devoid of contrary motives. This classification gives at best an extraneous classification of actions.

[10] "Set" here translates *Einstellung*, a word for which I have usually used the alternative translations: "attitude," "readiness." Only in relation to motor reactions and reaction-experiments does Schilder's *Einstellung* come close to the narrow concept of set in American psychology—usually it has a far broader motivational connotation. Cf. my notes on Lewin (492), Ach (9), concerning the mutual relations of these concepts; see also Allport (24).

In the action we may thus distinguish: 1) intention toward the object; 2) intention toward the innervation.[11] Both are of necessity contained in every action. Furthermore, the effort, the effects of effort, and the temporal course are significant.[12]

Clearly, intentionality cannot be disregarded when considering actions, lest the conclusions be entirely misleading. It is thus out of the question to consider actions as built up of reflexes.[13] The most brilliant investigations, those of Sherrington (779), undertaken to discern the reflex-apparatus of movements, did not succeed in explaining even walking; Graham-Brown had to assume that higher centers are also involved. In the long run even this proves insufficient, and the following general proposition becomes necessary: actions use reflexes, but are not built up of them. Only thus do we gain an understanding of the simple reaction-experiment, which shows us that the decision puts into readiness a somatic mechanism.

b) Movement-plan and movement-impulses[14]

The movement-plan contains the moving bodily part and the goal of movement. The representation of the path is unknown. The movement-plan unfolds from a nucleus. In the course of movement sensory-motor mechanisms come into play. The role of impulses in movement. The disorders of movement-impulses in maladies of the striate body. Primarily the instinctual movement-impulse is affected. Loss of expressive movements is determined by loss of somatic apparatuses. Movement-impulse disturbances due to frontal-lobe lesion. Hyperkinesis. Excess of movement and excess of movement-impulse.

After these preliminary remarks, we turn to a more detailed analysis of action. According to Martin's (535) investigations, at the inception of every movement visual and kinesthetic images arise; in the later course of movement, these play a lesser role.

[11] Cf. footnote 5, supra.

[12] Cf. Wundt's and Schilder's views with Lewin's (495, particularly pp. 144–150), and note the distinction between their concepts of "intention." Schilder uses the concept in the sense of act-psychology, while Lewin uses it as an empirical concept.

[13] Cf. Humphrey's (358) views on this point.

[14] See Schilder (740, Part I, Chapter 10, Part II, particularly Chapter 10 on impulses and Chapter 6 on the postural model of the body); also Schilder (750, Chapter 14), Gerstmann and Schilder (270), and Schilder (744 a). Cf. furthermore Kauders (409), also the few more recent studies in the generally neglected field of motility: Piaget (613), Fries (252), Mittelmann (561), Hartmann, Kris, Loewenstein (319).

The images undoubtedly pertain to the limb which is to execute the movement and to the goal of the movement. It is less clear whether, and to what extent, the path is given in imagery. Nor has it been established whether this complex—which we will call, for now, movement-plan—is already complete at the outset of the movement, or develops only in the course of movement. It is probable that the movement-plan is already present in nuclear form before the inception of the movement, and unfolds in the course of it.[15] In this nucleus of the movement-plan, there are doubtless both image and imageless elements. Once the movement has begun, it is influenced on the one hand by the unfolding movement-plan, and on the other by tactile and kinesthetic sensations which, produced in the course of movement, safeguard its further course.[16] Besides sensory elements, purely somatic excitations, which in no wise reach consciousness, also play a significant role. These regulations are mediated by the cerebellum. Here we have spoken only of the schema of a single movement; but even in simple movements a whole series of single movements is integrated into the action. Therefore, we must assume that the movement-plan already implies the integration of the part-movements which comprise the action. Every single movement itself presupposes an intending.[17] Intending-in-action may also be called the movement-impulse.[18]

At this point, the psychology of action for the first time acquires a significant contribution from pathology. In disorders of the striate body, we find disturbances of movement-impulses. Such patients show a decrease of movement-impulses directed toward the environment. The intact person sitting idly on a chair, looking now here, now there, may get up under the influence of a thought, and then sit down again to rest; but patients of this kind sit rigid and motionless, and do not follow moving objects which appear in their peripheral field of vision. Yet the apprehension of these patients is good, and they answer questions

15 Cf. Schilder and Pollak (713) and Schilder and Kanner (726).

16 Cf. Schilder (752, pp. 532–537), Rapaport et al. (650, I, pp. 249–259, 271–275, 288–291); Lauretta Bender (50), Werner (870, Chapter VII), Piaget (613, 617); see also Wiener's (884) "cybernetic" conception and, for a recent review of motor mechanisms, Stevens (808, Chapter 5).

17 "Intending" translates *sich richten*.

18 "Movement-impulse" translates *Bewegungsantrieb*.

meaningfully. This akinesis fades occasionally, and then the patient moves around in excessively high spirits; the akinesis yields
also to affects and to external stimulation.[19] Yet the lack of
movement-impulse dominates the patient's behavior. Much of
the instinctual movement-impulses on low levels of consciousness
is in abeyance; those involuntary movement-impulses which continuously drive the intact person to action are absent. The patients are, at the same time, quite capable of moving voluntarily.
But even their volitional movements are affected, they are slow,
and such patients often get blocked in the course of a movement.
This occurs most strikingly in eating: they stop with the food
before their mouths and with difficulty get it beyond their teeth;
if they do, it gets stuck in their mouths, or they do not stop
chewing it. But the reflex-act of swallowing is unimpaired.

It seems therefore that this factor, observed in involuntary
actions, must be "built in" in volitional ones also. We owe this
understanding to C. and O. Vogt (851, 852), who formulated it
thus: primary and secondary automatisms are woven into every
action. Though this formulation is undoubtedly of great significance, we must remember that in it the term automatism is not
used in the psychological sense (see above). Expressive movements
too are in abeyance in such patients, though the corresponding
affects are not lacking (cf. Bychowski, 130). Since expressive movements purpose nothing, intend nothing, we are undoubtedly dealing here with a loss of purely somatic processes.[20]

To characterize briefly the akinesis due to lesions of the
striate body we find in it a loss of involuntary movement-impulses
and of somatic auxiliary apparatuses of movement, and an alteration even of volitional motor-impulses and of "impulses of
thought." Though muscle-tensions are frequent in akinetic patients, they do not explain the disorder of movement-impulses.
It is notable that these motor-impulses must be topographically
organized, since their disturbances are frequently limited to certain regions. I hasten to add that there are also disturbances of
movement-impulses due to lesions not of the striate body but of
the frontal lobes, which are less known but in my experience
more far-reaching. The impulse to think may be disrupted by
lesions in any of several central layers.

[19] Cf. Schilder (740, II, 11).   [20] Cf., however, Schilder (752, pp. 525–528).

It is particularly instructive that lesions of these very systems may result in excessive impulse also: the patients are vehemently driven to move.[21] In some cases, this drive to move is comprehensible only physiologically—that is, there is an excess not of impulse, but only of movement; in other cases, an excess of involuntary motor-impulses is at least probable. Such patients are in perpetual movement, grab now at this object, now at that, jump up, run back and forth, etc. The excess of movement-energy may attach itself to voluntary actions also. Gerstmann and I (270) have observed a patient whose speech, once he began, became increasingly rapid. In juvenile cases of encephalitis, there is an excess of volitional movement-impulses which probably has its origin in the basal ganglia. The general bearing of these facts on the problem of psychological energies will be discussed later; here we want to indicate only the role of motor-impulses in action. Action is possible only when there are movement-impulses present.

The theory of movement-impulse-disturbances goes back to Kleist's (420, 422) studies, and was much furthered by the investigations of C. and O. Vogt (851, 852). The studies by Gerstmann and myself took their point of departure from these. For details see "Studien ueber Bewegungsstoerungen," I–VIII (270); for a psychological summary see my paper "Ueber die psychische Energie und ihre Quellgebiete" (708).

c) Apraxia[22]

Definition. Classification of actions into sensory-motor effects, expressive movements, reflexive actions, and handling of objects. Description of motor apraxia. Its varieties: ideokinetic apraxia, innervation apraxia. Apraxia of spatial judgment. Disturbance of body-image utilization in initiation of movements. Disturbance in the use of the body as the goal of movement. Disturbance in utilization of object-apprehension. Movement-melody determines the course of action. The complex action. The total action is given in nuclear form in the movement-plan. Disturbances in the unfolding of an action-segment inhibit the unfolding of movement sequences. Ideational apraxia. Confusion of movements. Omission of movement-components. Are there primary disturbances of movement-sequences? The relation of agnosia to apraxia. Akinetic phenomena of apraxia. Psychological paralysis. Tonic perseveration. Intentional (clonic) perseveration is related to general psychological mechanisms. Summary. Secondary inhibition of cognition by apraxia. Localization of apraxia. Lesion of the supermarginal gyrus. Sympathetic apraxia is due to lesions of the corpus

21 Cf. Schilder (740, II, 10); also Schilder (729).
22 Cf. Schilder (740, I, 8, 9, 11); Weisenburg and McBride (864, Chapters IV, 3, and XIV).

callosum. Lesions of cerebral "association-pathways" do not lead to "associa-
tion-disturbances." Apraxia and the frontal lobes.

The study of action is enriched by yet another facet of
pathology, namely, the theory of apraxia, for the major part of
which we are indebted to the investigations of Liepmann (499, 501,
503). Apraxia is the inability to act. We speak of apraxia only
when a disorder of movement is due neither to paralysis nor to
tension, nor even to a disturbance of coordination. Liepmann
distinguishes four kinds of actions. First, those which require percepts only from that area in which innervation takes place; these
are the self-contained sensory-motor effects, such as clenching of
fists, buttoning, etc. Second, expressive movements related to these,
such as threatening, blinking, etc. Third, reflexive actions, in
which movement is directed toward one's own body, such as
pointing to a body part, fingering one's mustache, etc. Fourth,
handling of objects: here one has to distinguish those actions
performed on the objects themselves, and those which are imitative and performed without the object. In motor apraxia all
these movement-forms are disturbed, without the movement-plan
as such being altered. Motor implementation of the goal-idea fails.
Thus, a patient knows that he should give a salute, but the correctly intended innervation gets derailed (even though the hemi-
apraxic patient can carry it out with his intact hand). For instance, he may wave his hand helplessly, at random in the air,
with the fingers spread, and may even be fully conscious of the
inadequacy of his efforts; if pressed, he may end up by putting
the thumb of his clenched fist against his cheek. Therein the
single movements of the hand, indeed the whole posture of the
arm, become peculiarly rigid, derailed, amorphous; occasionally
the same movement may take a correct course. When such a
patient wants a match from a matchbox, he will, though he correctly recognizes and judges the object, so hold the box as to block
access to the matches; if one pulls out the inner part of the matchbox for him, it does not help, he will now reach not into the box,
but under it. When he finally succeeds in getting a match out of
it, he strikes it against the wrong surface of the matchbox. If the
burning match is put into his hand, he is unable to put it to the
candle; but if he is given one not burning, he may try to light the
candle with it. These patients are motorically stupid, so that be-

fore Liepmann's discovery this disorder had not been separated from dementia. But there is a general disproof of the assumption that these are dementias[23] in that unilateral disorders of this sort exist. The type of apraxia we describe here usually leaves the self-contained sensory-motor effects intact. Liepmann calls it ideokinetic apraxia. Where a disorder of these self-contained sensory-motor effects is in the foreground, we speak of an innervation apraxia (Kleist, 419, 421).

What is the psychological significance of all this? Many patients are unable to utilize in action the spatial cognitions which they undoubtedly have: their grasp misses the object, though they see it in its actual place. In distinction to visual disturbances, this disorder may be one-sided (Balint's, 44, and my own observation) and may appear even when a part of one's own body is reached for. This is a disorder in the utilization of the spatial cognition of the goal.

For the initiation of movements, as mentioned, a knowledge of one's own body is necessary.[24] Under certain conditions this knowledge, though present, cannot be utilized in action. Thus there are patients who cannot indicate right and left, though perfectly familiar with these concepts. For the same reason, they are, under certain conditions, unable to move those fingers, which they are asked to move.

The goal of a movement may involve either one's own body or an object. When the knowledge of one's own body cannot be utilized, then it is primarily the reflexive actions which will be disturbed.

If it is the knowledge of *objects* that cannot be utilized in action, then the handling of them will be disturbed. It is probable that utilization of geometric-spatial relationships in action is not the same as the utilization simply of objects.[25]

Finally, the execution of action itself depends less on the image of the path than on the purely organic sensory-motor movement-melody,[26] which is the very part of action primarily im-

23 For a discussion of dementia, see Schilder (752, pp. 568–570).

24 Cf. Piaget (615) and Spitz (786) for the meaning of the terms "utilization" and "knowledge" in this context.

25 See footnote 24, supra.

26 By "movement-melody" Schilder apparently means the organically determined harmonious coordination of muscle innervations, which permit cer-

paired in innervation apraxia. But the disturbances in the utilization of body-image, in the handling of objects, in the utilization of space, all vary in form from case to case, so we must assume that psychological analysis can really teach us something crucial about the structure of action.

Our discussion so far has dealt only with isolated part-actions. But all actions are composed of a multitude of part-actions. We assume that an entire action is somehow laid down before the inception of its first part, just as in uttering a sentence the total content of the sentence is implicit at the first word.[27] When the unfolding of a part-action fails, this must interfere with further development of the total action. The example given above contains such a failure in differentiation. When the "object-apraxia" patient puts the unlit match to the candle, then a part-action is inhibited, suppressed, omitted; and thereby the movement-plan of the complex action is secondarily disorganized. It is an important law of cerebral functioning that a disrupted function will inhibit otherwise intact ones.[28] The secondary inhibition of the movement-plan is in this way conceivable.

Those forms of apraxia in which the total movement-plan is disrupted are called ideational apraxia. Liepmann and other authors assume that this is a primary disturbance of the movement-plan, and as evidence they point to the omission of partial movements and to the confusion of the total movement. But these occur in "object-apraxia" too; and as in agnosia the miscognition takes the form of a derailment of the cognition-process within the sphere,[29] so in apraxia the action is shunted from movement toward one object to a movement toward a related object. Such patients may, for instance, be derailed from handling a toothbrush toward movements of clothes-brushing. Secondarily, the ability to recognize parapraxes as such is lost. Parapraxis in one area will impair otherwise intact functions in other areas.

---

tain movement components to subside while others arise; this results in a continuous rounded total movement rather than in a jerky sequence of the components or a derailment of the movement into one of its components, as seen in the apraxic cases Schilder discusses here.

27 Compare with the concept of anticipation: Schilder (752, pp. 536–539, 555–558); also Rapaport et al. (650), and Rapaport (658), and Hebb (328).

28 Cf. Hebb (328, pp. 287–289).

29 Cf. Chapter II, footnote 97, supra.

Such a patient may make pouring movements with a basket, or put into his mouth an uncut cigar and drag on it even though it is unlit. Less frequently there occur absurd movement-confusions, such as when the patient brushes off his shoes with a cigar. I regard ideational apraxia as most closely related to "object-apraxia," and leave it an open question whether there exists a primary disorder of the utilization of movement-sequences.

Thus there is a close relationship between agnosia and apraxia. We assert that each sphere of cognition is coordinated with an action-possibility. Consequently, there are disorders of action in space, of action on objects, of action on geometric-visual-spatial relations, and of action on the body-image. It is an additional complication that the body-image is indispensable for the initiation of movements, and that their course is guaranteed by somatic mechanisms. A further complication is the presumably secondary disorder in the unfolding of the total movement which follows upon movement-confusions and derailments.

Two phenomena, very frequently accompanying apraxia, require special discussion. Not rarely akinetic phenomena are seen together with apractic ones—that is, with disorders of the movement-impulse.[30] After our considerations, there is no difficulty in understanding them: in part we may even relate their localization to lesions of the striate body. According to Kleist's recent investigations, the presence of lesions in this system also plays an important role in apraxia. Indeed, it is possible that a part of the awkwardness and rigidity of movements also has its root there. Thus the innervation apraxia would be, in part, traceable to subcortical sources. Still another phenomenon belongs here: from time to time the patients remain motionless in a tense posture—"tonic perseveration." Sudden tensions arise, leading to interruption of movements. Quite aside of the fact that the perseveration of posture presupposes an akinetic factor, the tension itself is probably of subcortical origin. From the akinetic conditions there are bridges to Nothnagel's (579) psychic paralysis: a movement-impulse no longer refers to a certain body-part. This appears as the motor counterpart of the phenomenon

---

[30] Cf. Schilder (740, II, 11), and (729); also Gerstmann and Schilder (270, particularly VI and VII).

of disregard for one half of the body, so penetratingly described by Anton (33).

Intentional or clonic perseveration is a phenomenon of an entirely different order. An action once accomplished recurs again and again. Such a patient is instructed to thumb his nose, and after he has carried this out, if he is then instructed to show his finger, he will frequently carry out the first instruction again. Such perseverations may occur even if in the meanwhile other instructions have been correctly carried out. This is a symptom that has far-reaching significance for general psychology, and is of great importance in speech-pathology also. This phenomenon is not limited to the motor-realm, but obtains for ideas and images also: it is the perseveration described by Mueller and Pilzecker (571)—which will be further discussed later on.[31]

To repeat: for actions too, first a broad schema is laid out. According to Liepmann these are constructed probably of spatial-visual and kinesthetic images, but he does not mean images in the psychological sense, but rather physiological traces of past impressions. The utilization of these visual and kinesthetic residues may become impossible due to a lesion, though knowledge as such is preserved. Psychologically the action-schema appears partly in the form of thought and partly in that of image. But we must distinguish between the thought-components, that is, complete awarenesses, in the schema, and mere knowledge. The schema no doubt contains both the active body-part, that is, the body-image, and the object aimed at by the action. It is an open question whether and how the images, path of movement, and particular movement-sequences are represented in the schema. The schema evolves progressively from a nuclear form to a completely unfolded form. To what extent this unfolding coincides with the execution of the movement is not known. In the course of execution, both conscious and unconscious sensory-motor regulations play a significant role. In apraxia, the body-image is inadequately used either in the initiation or in the consummation of the action. The use of knowledge about the object for the action may also be disturbed. Finally, the executive part of the action may be impaired. Every impairment of action interferes with the unfolding of the movement-plan, and alters the move-

---

[31] See IV, 1, infra; cf. also Schilder (740, II, 12); also Schilder (752, p. 574).

ment-sequence. Furthermore, disrupted actions interfere with cognition, so that otherwise feasible cognitive achievements are inhibited and suppressed for the duration of the action. Consequently it is often difficult to discern whether it is the action as such which is disturbed, or whether misrecognition of objects brings on the disturbance. Whether there are disorders of movement-sequences as such, or whether these are always sequels to interferences with the unfolding of the movement-plan, is an unanswered question.

This analysis of action rests on the basic studies of Liepmann (499, 501, 503) and Pick (620, 624, 628), as well as on my study of the body-image (740).

Returning to our problem, it should be added that according to Liepmann, foci in the supra-marginal gyrus effect motor-apraxia by depriving the motor-apparatus of its influence, isolating it from its visual, acoustic and tactile relationships. Kleist (419–422) assumes a lesion of engrams, that is, of somatically conceived memory-traces (Semon, 773). It seems that an explanation of the disorder in terms of a disturbance of complex cortical functions is preferable to one in terms of lesions of long association-pathways.

Yet I draw attention to the fact that, particularly in apraxia, such hypotheses as Liepmann's have been proven to be admissible in principle. Liepmann demonstrated that lesions of the anterior third of the corpus callosum, or of the fibers leading to it, give rise to a left-sided sympathetic apraxia (see above). Thus the left hemisphere is connected with the right, and the two form an apparatus linked by the corpus callosum. The right hemisphere alone is responsible only for the awkward movements of sympathetic apraxia. This example is also significant in principle, because it shows that the link between the two hemispheres by means of a long pathway has nothing to do with the psychological concept of association: the apraxia does not arise by subtraction of some associations from normal action (cf. section on brain localization), but represents a difference in organization.

In general, the localization of apraxia is controversial, though foci are most frequently found in the supra-marginal gyrus. Monakow (563) and Economo (156) deny a stringent relation between these loci and the syndrome. No doubt the area from which apraxia can be precipitated is much broader. F. Hartmann

(315) localizes it in the frontal lobe. But in frontal-lobe cases akinesis, though frequently accompanied by apraxia, is predominant. Originally Liepmann considered ideational apraxia a non-localized disorder. The localization attempts of most authors pertain only to motor apraxia. Probably Kleist is right, and ideational apraxia too is a local symptom of the posterior parts of the area related to action. According to our view, ideational apraxia is a form of apraxia in which there arise from an object-apraxia inhibitory effects upon movement-sequences. According to Kleist's recent findings, the striate body may be involved in innervation apraxia.

Liepmann (503) reviewed the problem of apraxia in Brugsch's, *Ergebnisse der Medizin.*[32]

d) Expressive movements[33]

Expressive movements as rudiments of actions. Pointing gestures. Imitative gestures. Expressive movements are not a problem of descriptive but of genetic psychology. The principle of association of related feelings. Genetically expressive movements arise from volitional movements by omission of parts, by substitution of opposites, by equation of the object with one related to it in feeling-tone. Individual expressive movements unite several of these. Crying. Expressive movement and affect. Somatic discharge of affect-energy. Wundt's principle of direct innervation.

Expressive movements and mimetic expressions of affects are of great significance for the theory of action. It might be hoped they would lead to the understanding of action; but one gets no closer to its essence in expressive movements than in reflexes. Indeed, Darwin (140) has taken the opposite course in considering some expressive movements as rudimentary actions—for instance, the clenching of the fist in rage as a part of what was once the volitional movement of a blow. He derives many expressive movements from volitional ones. Wundt (897) described a category of expressive movements as image-externalizations; they derive from voluntary actions. Such are the pantomimic movements, which either refer to the object (pointing gestures) or indicate by their form the object and the processes connected

[32] The only recent surveys are those of Weisenburg and McBride (864) and Goldstein (293).

[33] Cf. Allport and Vernon (23), S. S. Stevens (808, Chapter 14), Rapaport (657, 660); see also W. Wolf (891), Spitz (785).

with it. Darwin derives another group of expressive movements by pointing out that their opposite is a voluntary movement expressive of an opposite mood. Thus, for instance, the dog crouches to express submissiveness, assuming a posture opposite to that of attack. Wundt speaks also of a principle of relation of movements to sensory images.

Clearly, expressive movements are not a problem of descriptive, but of genetic psychology.[34] All one can establish descriptively is that changes not only in smooth musculature and secretory organs, but also in voluntary musculature, issue from an affect. Though every posture the mouth assumes on tasting something disagreeable may express disgust, this connection is no longer a psychological one. Naturally, there must be transitional forms between expressive and voluntary movements. Wundt speaks of a principle of association of related feelings: there is an analogy between the facial expression at bitter taste-sensations and that at disagreeable stimuli generally. But the facial expression of bitterness arises in the effort to ward off the disagreeable impression. Accordingly, the facial expression for disagreeable impressions derives from a volitional tendency toward defense.

We arrive at the general formulation: expressive movements derive from volitional movements, but in becoming expressive movement the volitional movement is often altered: first, parts of it are eliminated (clenching of fist); second, it may be replaced by its opposite (crouching of dog); third, it is no longer directed toward its object, but toward another related to it by feeling, by the sphere.[35] These genetic reconstructions appear relevant, because they show us the changes of volitional movements frequently encountered in individual life under the influence of inhibitions. Obviously, the three principles will frequently appear together in individual expressive movements. According to Wundt, the facial expression of crying consists of the following: the mouth is opened, as in response to sour taste, associated with

[34] Cf. Werner (870); see also Spitz and Wolf (785), and Mittelmann (561). Cf. also "Laughter As an Expressive Process" in Kris (461).

[35] For the concept of the sphere, see pp. 12–13; footnote 202, p. 247. In regard to the genesis of affect expressions, Schilder appears to refer here to those expressions which—as "frozen affects," "character armor," and even as individually characteristic affect expression—have been studied by psychoanalysts, particularly by W. Reich (664). Other affect expressions may have a different genetic history; cf. Spitz and Wolf (785), Rapaport (660), also Rapaport (654, Chapter II).

a bitter expression; simultaneously the nasal openings are closed and the corners of the nose pulled downward, as in defense against disagreeable olfactory stimuli; the eye is half-closed, as if to ward off a light-stimulus; changes in tear-secretion and in the blood-vessels take place; breathing becomes spasmodic and interrupted by sudden inspirations caused by dyspnoea.

The changes in blood-vessels and secretion cannot be derived from prior voluntary movements. Here Wundt's principle of direct change of innervation holds. At this point we can penetrate further into the psychology of expressive movements. Every expressive movement issues from an affect. But affects have a definite content and a definite energy. This energy is partly directed toward action, since each image implies a tendency to act; and partly it is discharged into the body, effecting vasomotor-secretory changes. Indeed, it is conceivable that even undischarged energy, without noticeable relation to actual content, should discharge into motility at large: I remind the reader of the diffuse motor-expression of rage.

The theory of affect-expression affords another glimpse into the somatization of processes which were once of a psychological nature. Thus it will not surprise us if gross somatic lesions lessen and even destroy expressive movements. Lesions of the striate body, as well as those of the thalamus, result in such loss of expressive movements. I cannot discuss the finer details here.[36]

e) The phylogenesis of action[37]

Loeb's (515) tropism theory. Differential sensitivity. Varieties of action in infusoria. Jennings's (383) theory of trial and error. But even this assumption is insufficient. The "mood" of protozoas. The inexplicability of protozoan movements. The environment and the internal world of animals.

I do not mean to avoid the phylogenetic history of the psyche, but believe that only a penetrating study of individual experience can make a successful inroad into it: I consider the reverse approach methodologically wrong.

J. Loeb (515) attempted to explain animal behavior by his tropism concept: according to him animals are chemical machines. An animal touched by light on its side turns around automati-

---

[36] For a review of the pertinent literature, see Rapaport (654, Chapter II).
[37] Cf. H. Werner (870), Maier and Schneirla (530), Tinbergen (833), and for a review of the literature, Thorpe (832).

cally until it faces the source of light. Only two factors need to
be taken into consideration in this process: the photochemical
effect of light, and the animal's symmetrical body build (heliotropism).[38*] He speaks of geotropism and galvanotropism in a
similar vein.

Loeb (515) and Bohn (92, 93) distinguish differential sensitivity from tropism. Animals react to differences in illumination,
in chemical composition of the medium in which they live, etc.

But to begin with, even the most primitive organisms show
such a variety of motor behaviors that these cannot be explained
by the simple laws of tropisms and differential sensitivities. Jennings (383) made extensive observations on infusoria; those on
Oxytricha fallax have become particularly well-known. This animal moves from colder to warmer regions; but when reaching the
border of cold and warm it retreats, to begin a second foray
toward the warmer region, and retreat again; and only after it
has repeated this process many times is the desired direction
established. According to Jennings, its movements are thus not
purposive; rather, an excess of movements is produced at random
until an accidentally fitting movement leads to the ultimate goal.
In the trial-and-error method, an excess of movements is produced, and of these the one of proper direction is selected. But
Alverdes (31) has shown that not even the trial-and-error assumption can fully explain the behavior of lower organisms:
the variety of their movements is too great. Not rarely an
infusorium finds the proper movement without prior trials. In
addition, the reaction of protozoans depends on a particular
factor, called "mood." Jennings says these moods depend on
past experience; hunger, satiation, tiredness, and training also
play a decisive role in them. According to Jennings, the principle
of usefulness dominates the behavior of protozoans; according to
Alverdes, the physiological state (mood) of an organism is in
many ways independent of its usefulness or harmfulness. The
change of mood occurs autonomously, and may be intractable to
our methods of investigation. The impulse to locomotion may be
entirely internal. Though a mechanistic view may regard these
moods as physiologically determined, it is precisely these physiological determinants which we do not grasp, and therefore we

---

[38*] Radl (642) reports interesting new findings on heliotropism. For
further literature, see Uexkuell (841). Cf. also Uexkuell (839).

cannot disprove the assumption that a factor of freedom is at play here.

Clearly, in observations of protozoans the same problems are encountered as in those of full-fledged will-actions.[39] True, we cannot expect a contribution to the psychological understanding of action from the study of lower organisms; but if, following Uexkuell, we leave the psychological factor aside and compare only the animal's environment with its internal world, considering the mutual relations of morphology and function, an approach which, besides being methodologically justified, has already proven its value, then it is hard to see how we come back to psychology at all. Uexkuell's conception eliminates psychological problems: it studies the structure of the organism and the nervous system, and infers from these what kind of environment the animal can have.[40] In turn, the reactions of the organism show what aspects of the environment find resonance in its internal world—that is, what its internal world is. As interesting as animal psychology is, it cannot lead to any fundamental psychological insight.

Burkamp (126) analyzed the so-called association experiments of Yerkes and others (900, 901) on lower animals, and found that the associations represent attitudes. This conclusion is in agreement with my views. It seems to me, however, that this conclusion arises from analysis of human behavior.

Details are deliberately neglected here; for them, see Driesch (150), Koffka (438), Uexkuell (841), and Schneider (754).

f) Work[41]

Preliminaries concerning the work-curve. Muscle-sensations and exhaustion-processes in muscle-fatigue. Influence of work on the muscle. Ability to exercise and persistence of exercise. Mechanization of work. Excitability and distractability as central factors.

[39] This point may make Schilder appear as a "vitalist." If being deeply impressed with the idea that no psychology can be built without taking account of those features of behavior which the phenomenologist calls "intentional," then he is a vitalist. His persistent attempts toward discovering the psychodynamics and the organic substratum of behavior phenomena, however, certainly take him out of the vitalist camp.

[40] Schilder refers to Uexkuell (841); see also Uexkuell (839, 840).

[41] On fatigue, see Roethlisberger (675), David (141), Bartley (47); on achievement, Lewin (494); on satiation, Lewin and Karsten (493, 404). Cf. also Menninger (549, Chapter 6, particularly the bibliography on p. 298).

Intactness of action is the prerequisite of work, which is composed of individual actions. Work may be measured by the ergograph. Naturally, a variety of central components plays a role in work. The beginning of work differs from its continuation: first an initial resistance must be overcome; then the effect of exercise becomes noticeable; finally, fatigue, and with continued activity, exhaustion, sets in. Toward the end of a piece of work an increase in impulse makes its appearance. Essentially, we are faced in all these matters with central processes; therefore work-achievements may be studied on arithmetic achievements just as well as with the ergograph. Somatic work-achievements are characterized by sensations of muscular fatigue, and these probably have a determining influence on the physical process of work. Presumably, central exhaustion-processes in the motor area also play an essential role. More important is the fact that exercise involves physiological alterations in the muscle: the working muscle increases in volume, while the non-working decreases. According to Kraepelin, trainability and retention of training are two different things. In muscular work this becomes obvious. At any rate, I believe that changes in central apparatuses play a significant role in somatic training also, as demonstrated by the fact that frequent repetitions of work-achievement lead to its automatization and mechanization.[42] Thus, in dealing with work-achievement we must consider both the psychological factors and the condition of the somatic apparatuses used. In the individual case it is difficult to decide what portion of fatigability, recovery, trainability, and retention of training should be attributed to the one, and what to the other. In contrast, excitability and distractability are always related to central psychological factors, which in final analysis must be considered if everyday work is to be understood. Training and fatigue will concern us again when discussing problems of memory.

2. Speech

a) Thinking, concepts, sentences[43]

The logical nature of concepts. Concept-basis, concept-meaning, and concept-sign. The non-sensory foundations of concept-experience. Verbal images distinguished from meaning. The non-sensory foundation of a concept-experi-

42 Cf. footnote 36, p. 56 and footnote 4, p. 104, supra. See also Luria (523).
43 Cf. Schilder (752, pp. 524–541), and Schilder (707, 750).

ence is not a whole-impression which has a feeling-character, but an awareness (Ach), a thought (Buehler). In the sentence we distinguish the sign, basis, content and meaning of a proposition. The sentence is not simply a sum of words. The sentence as judgment. The sentence represents a predicative relationship. Impersonal sentences. Attributive vs. predicative relations.

A psychology of speech presupposes a psychology of thinking. This will be presented here in brief, though obviously a deeper understanding of it can be founded only on a theory of drives, which we will consider later on.

Formal thinking proceeds in concepts and propositions, and a psychology of thinking must be concerned first with their nature.[44] By its logical nature the concept unites general validity, unchangeability, and timelessness. It confronts the ego as an object; the ego apprehends it, and it remains just as ego-alien as that which is perceived.[45] We distinguish concept-basis, concept-meaning, and concept-sign. The concept-basis of the generic concept *horse* is all existing horses; the concept-content comprises all characteristics contained in the concept horse; and the spoken word "horse" is the concept-sign.[46] The concept has an object-character; it is amenable to objective consideration. The nucleus of the psychological concept-experience is certainly not images. There are no general images, in Locke's sense; there are only individual ones. It is undeniable that images always emerge when concepts are thought of, but they tend to be fleeting, not stable like concepts; moreover, they do not exhaust the concept's meaning. Images stay in the background in everyday life, and with increasing dominance of conceptual thinking they recede further, leaving finally only the verbal images which, due to their paucity of sensory earmarks, have a special position; but it is hard to see how even these could convey the meaning. The concept could be thought of as implying a rule for imaging, so that its meaning would be fulfilled by a series of images. But that too would re-

[44] Cf. Schilder (707).

[45] Concerning Schilder's use of the term "ego," cf. footnote 11, p. 27, supra. Concepts are certainly part and parcel of thought-processes, which in turn are ego-functions. Concepts are not "ego-alien" in the sense in which obsessions, delusions and hallucinations are. Yet the core of Schilder's observation is correct: the subject confronts concepts much as he does objects, and not as he normally does his impulses, emotions and proprioceptions. We do not have the conceptual apparatus to express these distinctions systematically and precisely.

[46] Cf. Schilder (752, pp. 524 ff.).

quire a unifying tie, and to assume a non-sensory foundation of the concept-experience would be inevitable.[47] Gomperz (294) sought this foundation in a total impression of feeling-character. I cannot share his view: the essence of concept-experience is not the feeling. Ach (9) designated this non-sensory thought-experience as awareness; Buehler (121) speaks of thoughts. In contrast to their conception, which I share, G. E. Mueller (569) speaks of unclear images. But how can these be the essence of thinking, when their unclarity and vagueness increases as thinking becomes dominant?

No doubt a number of psychological experiences accompany the arising concept. The concept, which is the final product of thought-operations, implies a demand for a continuance of such operations; despite its logical rigidity, it is immersed in the flux of experience. Concepts are born of intentions directed toward a concept-basis. These intentions have a biological origin; they arise from affectivity, from drives.[48] To build concepts amounts to enlarging the real world by a possible one, in so far as that can become the object of action.

What has been said here about concepts holds for propositions and their meaning-content also. We distinguish proposition-basis, proposition-sound, and proposition-content. The proposition-basis includes those facts which we apprehend in the proposition-content, and are designated by the proposition-sign. The proposition-content is the meaning of what is proposed (cf. Gomperz, 294). A sentence must be regarded as a whole rather than as the sum of the words contained in it, just as a word cannot be regarded as the sum of individual sounds. The grammatical form of a sentence is related to its logical and psychological content.[49]

Sentences contain judgments, and it is with these that we are concerned. According to Erdmann (164), the basic form of the elementary sentence is the verbal formulation of a two-membered affirmation in predicative form. The primordial form of the sentence is: S is P. By judgment, P is subsumed under S. The elementary judgment of formulated thinking is the subsumption

---

[47] Cf. Schilder (751) and (752, pp. 528–530).

[48] Here Schilder indicates how in his view act-psychology (pp. 12; 23–25; 31–144) and psychoanalytic psychology are related.

[49] Cf. Vigotsky (847), Vossler (857).

of one object in the content of another. The sentence, "This paper is yellowed," differs from the attributive connection "this yellowed paper" not only grammatically, but also logically and psychologically. The attributive formulation is not a proposition; the attribute provides only a specific characteristic. The attributive relation must be complemented by the independent predicative connection. Also, the predicative connection is closer to the center of attention. Where the proposition serves as communication, attributive characterization is taken for granted. Even impersonal sentences, such as, there is war, it rains, it thunders, imply predicative relations. In the existential sentence, "There is war," the existence is added as a predicative relationship. In sentences like, "It rains," the activity expressed in the verb is added as a characteristic[50] to the indefinite term.

Clearly the predicative sentence is the basic type of all sentences; it is easy to show that a predicative relationship underlies interrogative sentences and optative sentences also. It is not our goal here to present the details of Erdmann's (164) theory—which is preferable to Brentano's (107), according to whom accepting-as-true and rejecting-as-false is the essence of judgments.[51] Not only judgments but all psychic formations claim validity; thus the special character of verbally formulated sentences would be misrecognized if the claim to validity were regarded as their essence. Thinking put into language takes the form of judgments, yet it would be wrong to equate language and thinking. The distinction between concept-sign and concept-content is drawn to protect us against just that. In turn, concepts and propositions formulated or capable of formulation in language are but crystallization-points in the active and current psychic flux. James (373) saw this clearly, and warned lest the unformed (intransitive) parts of experience be underestimated in favor of formed ones (cf. section on thinking).

b) Development of language in the child[52]

The period of cries. Babbling. Beginnings of language-comprehension. Use of language for communication and for designation. Arising of the meaning-

[50] Here "characteristic" translates *Bestimmung;* another possible translation is "determination."

[51] Cf. Schilder (752, pp. 532–537), also Rapaport (658, pp. 342 ff.).

[52] Cf. Piaget (612, 613, 617); for other recent data see Stevens (808, Chapter 21), Miller (558, Chapter 7), Werner and Kaplan (872).

function. Concept-sign as momentary reaction directed towards an object-category. The road from thought to speech. Speech-sounds as maps of meanings. Speech-sounds and affects. Vocal gestures. Consciousness of meaning as prerequisite of language proper. The child's development of language is a distorted picture of human language-development.

Observing the language-development of the child we note that at first he expresses his sensations and feelings by cries; then follows a period of babbling, then one of voice imitations, then the beginning of language-comprehension, and finally the use of language for communication and designation. There is a period in this language-development in which the child utters speech-sounds taken over by imitation, but their meaning-function as such does not come to his consciousness.[53] In this period the child produces concept-signs simply as memories, and does not conceive of them as signs. C. and W. Stern (801) refer to these as sham concepts, and write: "The child applies his words not only to individual objects exclusively, as for instance to the mother, but also to a series of similar objects, as for instance the word 'uncle' to all men, or 'pip, pip' to all winged creatures.[54] Furthermore, the early phases of the child's language-development particularly demonstrate the change of meaning, that is, the progressive change in the use of one and the same word. Therein meaning is mostly extended to other instances, occasionally it is limited to fewer, or it is transferred to a new instance and the previous meaning is given up." According to C. and W. Stern, the child at this stage is not aware that each word has the function of continuously representing one definite meaning: with him naming is but a momentary reaction, and previous experiences have but a subliminal after-effect. The first word-meanings are only symbols of familiarity based on associations. The child's behavior in extending to insects the "pip, pip" learned in seeing birds may be described as follows: the child directs itself toward a category of things, but has no interest in differentiating within it, and produces for the entire category a concept-sign not familiar to us; but to him it means, more or less, "winged." However, he does not equate or confuse birds and insects. This is an example of how concept-signs change; the problem of meaning-changes in

53 Cf. Piaget (617).
54 Cf. Piaget (612), Werner (870, Chapter 9).

the psychology of language—to be discussed later—is also mostly one of changing concept-signs, rather than of actual changes of meaning. Aphasic disorders also affect the concept-signs primarily, though the disorder of these in turn does affect thinking proper. Thus the view that thinking and speaking are identical (Mauthner, 542) must be emphatically rejected. Rather, there is a path from thinking to speaking (Pick, 623), one to be apprehended only by studying the relation of the word to its meaning.

All languages have speech-sounds imitating sound-qualities of things, but in advanced languages there are fewer. The speech-sound in general does not map[55] the qualities of the object it refers to. Other speech-sounds go with certain affects and moods as suggested by their physiological organization; these are called "vocal gestures." Gestures are closely related to language: there is a natural language of gesture. It is probable that sounds which coincide with gestures of the mouth-region play a role in the genesis of speech.[56]

Naturally, these two factors can explain only the joint appearance of certain psychological contents and certain sounds, but not the meaning-relationships between the sounds and what they designate. To explain this relationship we must assume a specific act, the meaning-function, or as it has been less fortunately called, the symbolic function, of the spoken word. The language training of the deaf-mute Helen Keller was sharply divided into two phases by her shaking experience of suddenly becoming aware of meaning. Yet the process by which the child acquires speech must not be equated with the evolution of speech. It has been proven that the child does not form words independently, but rather builds his language from what adults relay to him. Stumpf's (821) son had an idiosyncratic language, but the basic material even of this derived from the language of the environment. The ontogenetic development of the child's language is thus by no means a reproduction of the phylogenetic development, since the child finds himself given a particular linguistic milieu. Or in the language of biology: a cenogenetic change has taken place in the evolutionary series.

[55] "Does not map" translates *hat keine Abbildungsfunktion*.
[56] Cf. the recent linguistic evidence put forth by Johannesson (385, 386) concerning such "gestural origin of language."

The function of the child's language-apparatus is more transparent than the adult's, and therefore in it we obtain a glimpse not only of how he adopts the language of his environment, but also of the modes of functioning which play a significant role in language-development at large. Romanes's well-known example in which the word "quack" is transferred from a duck to a coin with an eagle on it, and then to all coins, represents in striking form the process of change in meaning which plays such a great role in language-development. It should also be kept in mind that the child's adopting the language of his environment presupposes an internal capacity of his to do so. The growing child's predilection for imitating that particular language, replete with sound imitations, interjections, and vocal gestures, which adults convey to him must rest on peculiarities of infantile language which bear on phylogenesis.

For orientation concerning the child's language, see the extensive monograph of C. and W. Stern (801); also Buehler (122), and C. and W. Stern (800).

c) Aphasia[57]

(1) Sensory aphasia, comprehension of language, and paraphasia

The aphasia-schema for preliminary orientation. Rejection of the view that verbal images are deposited in the brain and are destroyed by lesion. The structure of language-comprehension is many-layered. The relation of disorders of comprehending language to evolution of language. Speech-melody and the affective factor in speech. Comprehending words and sentences. The sentence is not a sum of words. Disturbance of sentence-form in sensory aphasia. Pidgin-style and telegraph-style. Relation between telegraph-style and primitive forms of language. Word-finding difficulties take place in the sphere, which contains on the one hand, those words which are logically and objectively related (super- and subordinated) to the word sought; and on the other, those which are spatially, temporally, and individually related to it. Paraphasia is independent of poor word-comprehension. Patients overlook their own defects. Return of insight into illness and amnestic aphasia. Words which have not been settled are delivered after delay (the mechanism of after-development). The disorder is fluctuating. Word-finding difficulty in motor aphasia. Literal paraphasia. Sensory aphasia due to left-side lesion. Paraphasias as effects of the

57 Cf. Schilder (729, Chapter 5), also (751, 752), Weisenburg and McBride (864), Nielsen (578), Granich (295), Goldstein (293). The problems of aphasia Schilder discusses below are still not definitively settled: a dynamic neuropsychology which could carry out the program implied in Schilder's attempt here is still unborn; see footnote 3, p. 18, supra.

right hemisphere. Pure word-deafness as a lesion of both Wernicke loci. Re-iteration of words spoken by others and transcortical aphasia. Unreflective in-tending of the external world. The function of registration. Registration in transcortical and conduction aphasias. The more rational a function is the more easily it is disturbed. Drive-distant reiteration. Examples of paraphasia.

Language is not accounted for by an associative connection between a speech-sound and that which it designates: rather it implies a definite meaning-relation. Only when we consider this meaning-relation do the important facts of brain pathology be-come understandable. This in turn furthers the understanding of language.

Pathology distinguishes a sensory (Wernicke's) and a motor (Broca's) area. Wernicke's area lies in the posterior third of the first temporal gyrus and extends perhaps to the adjoining parts of the second temporal gyrus. Broca's area lies at the foot of the third frontal gyrus. Lesions of Wernicke's center give rise to sensory aphasia, that is, the patients do not understand what is said: they are word-deaf. They also distort words (paraphasia). The motor aphasic has lost his ability to speak; he cannot clothe his thoughts in appropriate articulations.

The classic theory of aphasia developed an aphasia-schema, that of Wernicke (874) and Lichtheim (496), which I reproduce here because it gives a preliminary orientation (Figure 5). In a rigorous sense it is incorrect.[58] In the following we shall attempt to fill this schema with psychological content. A is the center of word-apprehension; B, that of articulation. A and B are con-nected with a concept-center C, the connection leading from A, through C, to B. There is also a direct connection between A and B, subserving reiteration of heard speech. Lesions below A (1) prevent word-sounds from reaching the word-sound center, and thus no apprehension of words comes about; A, however, can exert its regulating influence on B and C, preventing paraphasia. This then is the picture of subcortical sensory aphasia, i.e., pure word-deafness. Lesion of A (2) causes sensory aphasia. Lesion of the conduction-path from A to C (3) prevents apprehension of word-sounds, but leaves the path from A to B intact: consequently spoken words are correctly reiterated but without word-com-

[58] For a specific critique of this schema, see Weisenburg and McBride (864, Chapters 18–20). For a general critique of this schema see Goldstein (293, par-ticularly Chapter III).

prehension (transcortical sensory aphasia). Lesion of the path from A to B (4) impairs reiteration of heard speech (conduction-aphasia). Lesion of the path between B and C (5) causes inability to speak, though reiteration of heard speech remains intact (transcortical motor aphasia). Lesion of B (6) causes motor aphasia. Lesion of the path below B (7) results in an inability to speak, while internal verbal images are preserved (subcortical motor aphasia).

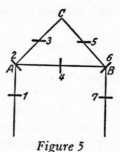

Figure 5

Schema of the "Classical Aphasia Forms"

The original conception was that images are deposited in these centers. The motor-verbal image was supposed to be deposited in Broca's, the sound-image in Wernicke's locus. Wernicke even considered whether each image was not deposited in a single cell. Bergson (63) refuted these conceptions. Sometimes only the first letters of a word cannot be found; and it is always striking that under the influence of affects, the availability of words changes. Aphasic patients, though unable to speak, can sing, and the patient who, when he should say "no," cries out in desperation, "I can't say no," highlights the entire situation. No images are destroyed in aphasia, but the preparatory processes of speech do not develop fully.

In the realm of speech we again find a hierarchic layering of structures. This is particularly and neatly demonstrable in word-comprehension. Pick (622) has shown that, even on the evidence of pure description without dynamic analysis of the phenomena, there is a hierarchic gradation of the processes which when completed lead to word-comprehension.

In the most severe disorders, words and speech are apprehended only as noise; the patient not only does not understand

words, but does not even know that they are words which are
supposed to be understood.

On the next level of severity, the patient understands that he
is dealing with words as signals (word-sound comprehension), but
does not know what they signify; however, he at least comprehends the affect expressed in the speech. He recognizes the speech-
melody without grasping the meaning; he responds to threatening words with apology, to questions with answers. This can be
demonstrated by reading to the patient a neutral sentence, now
in one, now in another intonation. Such experiences put special
emphasis on the speech-melody. Krueger (466) has shown that
changes of pitch accompany speech: no doubt there is a speech-
melody, though the fact established by Koehler (433), that people
unable to recognize pitch and to apprehend music do have intact
speech-comprehension, does make one pause. Koehler himself attempts to explain this by the assumption that vocality and not
pitch is here involved (see above). Be this as it may, an affective
factor, which expresses itself in what we call speech-melody, plays
an extraordinarily important role both in speech and in speech-
comprehension. It seems plausible to assume that this is a primitive and primordial factor of speech-comprehension, closely related to the comprehension of expressive-movements. Animals,
talked to for a while in sad tones, begin to whimper; so do
children. Speech retains a primitive factor, and this we understand quite apart from words. We comprehend immediately the
anguished cries of tortured creatures, grunts of lust, the child's
crying and babbling. Expressive movements and vocal-gestures
play a significant role in the genesis of speech.

On the next level of severity of disorder, according to Pick
(623), we encounter echolalia (compulsory reiteration of words
spoken by others) uttered in a questioning tone. This recalls the
significant role that imitation plays in the child's development
of speech, and it teaches us also that on primitive levels image and
action are intimately related.[59] Every verbal image contains the
nucleus of an innervation.

But speech-comprehension may be incomplete too; this becomes clear if we keep in mind that the sentence is not the sum
of its words, that in speaking the speaker has a general image of

[59] Cf. Piaget (617); see also Schilder (720).

his sentence (Wundt's total image), and that it is the sentence as a whole, and not its individual parts, which is comprehended. Indeed, we frequently see in pathology that word-comprehension and sentence-comprehension do not parallel each other. We have no right to assume that in the child's, or in phylogenetic, speech-development, words precede sentences. To be sure, comprehension of a sentence often begins from a single word, which suddenly illuminates (Buehler, 121) the other words. According to Wartensleben, in translating from Latin sentence-meaning emerges only after the meaning of several words is already there. But comprehension of the whole sentence may emerge before that of single words. Childish exclamations like "water" or "bread" must certainly be considered as single-word sentences, meaning either "here is water" or "give me bread." There exists such a thing as sentence-comprehension, and there are isolated disorders of it. Salomon's patient, for instance, although having intact meaning-comprehension, was unable to distinguish whether a sentence was grammatically correct or not (sensory agrammatism). This was presumably a case of motor aphasia. We have hardly begun to understand these disorders. Isserlin (366) has recently made an extensive study of agrammatism.

Finally, the sentence itself does not stand in isolation; it is connected with other sentences, embedded in a total situation. Everyday expressions, when taken out of their context, are frequently incomprehensible.

Study of disturbances in sentence-structure and word-finding provides even more important information. In sensory aphasia, disturbances not only of speech-comprehension, but also of word- and sentence-construction, are demonstrable. Particular attention should be paid to those disturbances of sentence-construction in which no correct grammatical organization occurs, though the words are used correctly. This may be either because individual words stand side by side with the verbs in the infinitive (telegraphic style), or because grammatizing is disorganized (pidgin). The word-sequence in the telegraphic style may correspond to that of primitives, or to gesture-language, or to the child's aggramatism. Basically, it is a return to a more primitive form of language.

Even more singular are disturbances of word-finding, and

we must discuss these in detail. The most cursory clinical study indicates that word-substitutions in sensory aphasia are not arbitrary.[60] The word is often replaced by one belonging at least to the same sphere. For instance, the word "table" may be replaced by "chair"—that is, by a coordinate concept; or by "cover"—that is, by an object frequently contiguous with it; or by "wood"— that is, by what it is made of; or by parts of it—"foot," "top." Often a superordinate concept, "furniture," and at times even a subordinate one, "cardtable," will appear in its stead.[61] Occasionally the correct word may emerge, but the patient will say, "No, that's not it." In brief: in paraphasia there is a derailment within the logical circle, or within the individual space-time relation. In the first phases of illness the sensory aphasic patient knows nothing of his defect and talks away, displaying a pressure of speech, though as a rule only upon stimulation.[62] It must not be assumed—as was earlier believed—that the patient chooses wrong words only because his disorder of speech-comprehension prevents his recognizing mistakes: some cases show paraphasia when their speech-comprehension is in partial remission. Incognizance of the defect is explicable only on the ground of the patient's attitude toward "talking garrulously." This is an important example of the fact described by Anton (33), that the lesion itself brings about psychological attitudes which lead to incognizance of the defect.[63*] Pick (619) explained pressure of speech by brain-physiology, assuming that the inhibitory effect of the sensory center upon the motor one is in abeyance. At any rate, psychologically the speech has a compulsory character, though the patient remains aware of his being the active speaker. Though neurologically we must assume a loss of inhibition, psychologically the pressure of speech appears as an autogenous product, as an excess of impulse.

[60] "Substitutions" translates *Vertauschung*. For evidence that these substitutions are not arbitrary, cf. Schilder (752, pp. 564–566), where substitution appears as one of the "primary-process mechanisms" of psychoanalysis (see Rapaport, 655, 658).

[61] For the concept of sphere, see Schilder (751, Appendix); cf. also the pertinent bearing of the association-test studies of Rapaport et al. (650, II, Chapter 2).

[62] "Pressure of speech" translates *spricht darauf los*.

[63*] See pp. 70–71; [cf. also Schilder (740, on anosognosia and imperception, pp. 29 ff., 36 ff., 70 ff.)].

Later on the patient becomes aware of his word-finding disturbance: though he intends the right word, his impulse gets derailed to a wrong one. By ever new efforts, he may try to find the right word, and then it becomes obvious how in his search he errs to and fro in the sphere. Finally, in the pure amnesic aphasias, wrong words which belong to the sphere come to the patient's consciousness only as intervening experiences; in milder cases, the correct word is found after a delay, with the aid of these intervening experiences.

It would, by the way, be a mistake to assume that displacements on this level pertain only to the word as a whole; frequently only half of a word emerges, and the other half suffers a transformation which may be of purely vocal character. I will show later that, in all probability, all word-finding passes through such intermediary stages, and that what is said here about concept-signs holds also for concept-content, that is, for concept-meaning also,[64] but the aphasias are disorders of concept-sign and not of meaning-comprehension. It is frequently observed that the very words or word-fragments which have been sought in vain do emerge later on. The quest after the word "lamp-shade" then may be purely schematically conceived as a sequence like: light-shield, light-shalde, light-shade, lamt-shade, lamp-shade. Here the fully developed parts do not suffer paraphasic distortions, while those not yet so developed are subject to transformation.

We see here the mechanism Poetzl (631) found in his dream experiments. In tachistoscopic exposition of pictures, what is immediately apprehended is not further elaborated in dreams; but that which is not yet apprehended, is. This is apparently a mechanism of widespread use; we will call it the mechanism of after-development.[65] In these parapraxes, naturally, perseverative influences also participate. It is noteworthy that a successfully used designation may in the next moment be altogether outside the aphasic's reach. In Naville's (577) interesting report, Dr. Saloz, who had recovered from a total (sensory and motor) aphasia, says "I never knew whether or not I could express myself." The following observations of this medical man are also of interest, "I often felt that I had mastery over this letter, that syllable, or a word, when suddenly the psychological path to it became buried,

64 Cf. Schilder (751).   65 Ibid.

narrowed, made impassable by a sudden onslaught, or blocked by certain conditions." He remembers "that everything was vague . . . except for a few words like yes, no, thanks, as you please. I could neither speak nor write anything; moreover, I had nothing more to say in words. I had all my thoughts and ideas, but not their symbols; I still had the meaning or notion of the word or the letter, but only as a distant echo reminding me of the thing. I had lost the memory for the word, but I retained the consciousness of the place it was supposed to occupy."

This bears out our initial assertation: this is not a loss of memory. This example leads us to the word-finding disturbances in motor aphasia, the literal paraphasias of which can be similarly explained. Dr. Saloz relates that instead of "marasquin" he always had to say "marasquecin" or "mascarin"; he was aware that the word's initial letter was *m*, but unable to find the sequence of the rest. He often had the impression that there was an insuperable discrepancy between letter, syllable, and word. In sensory aphasics' reiteration of heard speech, disturbances similar to the word-finding difficulties of this patient are frequent.

We have given a psychological sketch of sensory aphasia. The question is now: how can we interpret its mechanism as brain-pathology? For good reasons, most investigators at present consider paraphasic speech an effect of the right hemisphere, though this assumption is not completely verified. The effects of the left hemisphere are not simply additional psychological functions, but rather the raising of primitive functions to a higher level. It is noteworthy that paraphasia disappears upon a lesion in the right hemisphere. Bilateral lesion of the sensory speech-center leads to pure word-deafness. This is, by the way, striking disproof of the view that paraphasia results from insufficient control of speech. In the face of these facts, the aphasia-schema proves incorrect. Subcortical sensory aphasia, pure word-deafness, is not due to a subcortical lesion.[66]

Now we turn to the reiteration of heard speech, which again has hierarchic varieties. There is the unreflective immediate re-iteration, called echolalia: Pick (619, 623) has studied it in detail.

[66] Concerning the origin of paraphasia, cf. Goldstein (293, pp. 82–84), whose discussion takes the issue out of the realm of discourse of localization. Cf. also Schilder and Curran (741).

According to the aphasia-schema, reiteration is based on the direct AB connection. Similar reiteration is seen in the so-called transcortical forms of aphasia. Though the schema is not completely apposite here either, it does call attention to a cerebral dissociation of functions which has general significance. There are unreflective intendings of the external world in other pathological conditions also: for instance, patients with certain forms of amentia register experiences in the fashion of a phonographic or photographic apparatus, without any subjective contribution. The counterpart of this type are those amentias in which this registration-function is disturbed primarily and the source of experience becomes mainly intrapsychic. Common reiteration cannot be considered as a primitive function. Bleuler was the first to point out that in the aphasia-schema reiteration goes through C, and therefore the conduction-aphasia[67] of the schema—with severe paraphasia in reiteration as its outstanding symptom—cannot be explained by an interruption of the connection between A and B . . . Indeed, it was actually shown that the white fibers between A and B are not damaged in such cases. In Liepmann and Pappenheim's (502) case the lesion was around the left transversal gyrus.

Now it is noteworthy that though these patients do speak spontaneously, or at least relatively freely, they fail in the apparently simpler activity of reiteration. Liepmann and Pappenheim take the view that a psychological explanation is not possible here; but we must stress that the relation of spontaneous speech to instinctual needs is a quite different case from that of volitional reiteration. Here too the more intentional function is disturbed.[68] The reiteration that is here impaired must not be compared with that which is intact in transcortical aphasia. The latter, closely related to echolalia, is a particularly primitive function, which apparently emerges only when spontaneous speech is destroyed . . .

---

[67] "Conduction-aphasia" translates *Leitungsaphasie*. Cf. Weisenburg and McBride (864), Goldstein (293).

[68] "Intentional" in the sense of "being directed toward something external" as contrasted to a physiological process. Cf. Buerger-Prinz and Kaila (427, footnote 80), which also seems to indicate that the issue is not one of localization of lesion, but rather one of more complex dynamics. See also Schilder and Hoff (714, 715).

The paraphasias of conduction-aphasia are closely related to the disturbances of word-finding and of spontaneous speech found in sensory aphasias. For this reason we will give an example that applies to all these disorders, taken from a case of sensory aphasia in the process of remission.

Object designations [paper]: "Can't say the moment, a paper, a counting paper"; (renewed urging): "a counting pencil"; (renewed urging): "a kite"; (renewed urging): "a white paper." [Pocket watch]: "But I know, I am so nervous, I can't say, the pen." (The patient had correctly named a pen-holder prior to these two tasks, and to a needle shown she first perseverated with pen and then named it correctly.) (Renewed urging): "I know this pe . . . I can't say it, it's always something." (Renewed urging): "I can't say it right away" (very excited). "It's just something sma that one has right away to, in quarter of an hour I have it all well, it is so soft, often very difficult things quite easy." (Renewed urging): "But it is often from home, the patch, the patch it isn't, can't say it this moment." (Do you know?) "Now, surely!" (What is it made of?) "It is just the bottle, and the winder I don't know." (Points with her finger at the watch-hand; picks up the watch.) "The hand and all, I can't say, where it is, I can't see all of it, the glass, the watch, the watch—that's right." (So what is it?) "The watch."

In this example one sees first of all the perseveration-tendency. The word "pen" intrudes repeatedly. More important is the fact that the patient is unable to bring the available word-material into those relationships she means to. Thus, she succeeds only transiently in designating the paper correctly, and then a probably unintended compound-word follows, "counting-paper," which in turn derails to "counting pencil," probably by perseveration, influenced by the after-effect of the pen-holder image. A kite is partly a perseveration, and remarkably enough is already altered by the vowel of the subsequent words, "a white paper." Thus it seems that the next emerging word must somehow have been there. The next example too is noteworthy: here the patient finds instead of "watch" the word "patch," demonstrating again the inability to discern precisely that which is sought and undoubtedly present. In trying to name the glass of the watch, the associatively related "bottle" comes to her mind; only from that does she get to the word "glass" and finally, with the aid of the association, to the correct word.

On further questioning: (What kinds of birds are there?) "Tree . . . glad . . . just the . . . pra . . . just leather . . . just needle . . . just foliage trees . . . not to say . . . bushes too . . ." (Renewed urging): "My God . . . the trees, foliage-trees, needle-trees." (What kinds of animals are there?) "Please consider it entirely differently, not because." (Renewed urging): "Animals: there are, rootan, scatcher, grinzing, poplaree manly." (Renewed urging): "robkin, krokel."

This example is noteworthy for the following reasons: The patient apparently did not understand the question about birds at all, but her answers to the subsequent question about animals indicates that it must have registered. I have already stressed that what is apparently not apprehended may be apprehended in a primitive form. Note also how the intended word "robin" is distorted. In such tests of speech one gets the strong impression that internally there is, so to speak, a correct word-image, which cannot be aroused. In the search for it parts of the word are thrown about, some sounds redouble, others are omitted, and others again are displaced. This matter is important enough to warrant further examples.

The patient is now shown pictures. [Butterfly]: "Matter, mattery, fluttery, I know that it did not make flutter so many years. Flutter . . ." [Lamp and violin]: "Bi . . . dye . . . dime . . . fattub, violin and bow in addition." [Caterpillar and butterfly]: "Ba . . . bat . . . please, not stay at that, fle . . . bat." [Violin]: "Violin." [Cup]: "Pot, coffee cup, a cup."

This example shows how the patient is distracted from naming the butterfly by the associatively related image of the bat. But it seems that the correct word must somehow be extant, since it finds its way through the *tt* into her words, and the *ly* appears in the form of the *y*. It is also noteworthy that the preceding words show up as passing perseverations in the first attempt to name the violin, as in the peculiar word "fattub." Naturally it is not always possible to clarify all the details in such a series, since not even in these patients does every intervening experience take verbal form. The disturbances described here contribute to the understanding of motor aphasia, in which

words are mutilated, letters being cut off from them (literal paraphasia): we must assume that underneath the mutilated words
lies an awareness of the correct ones. We are entitled to assume
that in motor aphasia the same process takes place with letters
and word-fragments as does in sensory aphasia with words and
larger word-fragments. Naturally the details still need to be explored. From this vantage-point, important possibilities for the
understanding of normal slips of the tongue open up. In slips
of the tongue too the correct word is available, but other tendencies prevent it from appearing.[69]

(2) Motor aphasia

Patients who are unable to talk still have single words and sounds, but are
not masters of them. The lack of driving-force in cortical and transcortical
forms. So-called inner speech. The motor aphasic's ability to read and write.
Is this difference one between psychological types? Charcot's classification into
visual, acoustic, and motor types. The type difference is not consistent. Relation between acoustic verbal-image and innervation. General relation between
image and innervation. Identification-type and object-type. Relative separation of image and innervation. The significance of the functional factor in
aphasia. Localization factors must also be considered in explaining various
forms of aphasia. Difficulties in differentiating sensory and motor aphasia.

Let us now turn to motor aphasia. Here the disorder of the
ability to speak and the alteration of the speech-impulse[70] are
in the foreground. The patients are unable to articulate their
thoughts as words. The forming of sequences particularly is
hampered, even in milder cases. Loss of ability to speak is often
complete. Those unable to speak still have single sounds or words
at their disposal, the cadence of which they can modulate. But
if they have several words, they are unable to use them by choice.
The word has them, and not they the word; they are not masters
of their store of words. They may not be able to use a word of a
phrase which they can use. Single words which they have at their
disposal they cannot unite into a sentence. They cannot dissect
and separate.[71] Here too there are cases with intact ability to
reiterate heard speech; these are the transcortical motor aphasias,
in which one quality shared by all motor aphasias is particularly

---

[69] Cf. Schilder (752, pp. 564–566). See also Betlheim and Hartmann (69),
for a similar analogy between organic and functional repression.

[70] Cf. Schilder and Pollak (717), and Schilder (720).

[71] Cf. Schilder on the basic thought-disorder, Appendix, pp. 344 ff., infra.

striking—the lack of speech-impulse.[72] It is possible that in these cases there is a lesion of the frontal lobe, the relation of which to the impulse has been discussed.

Generally, the motor aphasic cannot write but, as Bastian (48) pointed out, there are exceptions: in some, ability to write is preserved though their writing occasionally shows the same word-mutilations as their speech. The ability to read, to write, and to state the number of syllables of a word, is considered indication of preserved inner speech. These cases have been considered subcortical, but this interpretation is anatomically untenable.

It is possible that they are the result of peculiarly localized cortical foci, but there is another possible explanation. Charcot classified man into three types: visual, auditory, and motor. In the visual type, thinking occurs preponderantly in visual-images; in the auditory, in acoustic images; and in the motor, in kinesthetic [out] images. Acoustic and kinesthetic imagery usually coincide in the same individuals. It would be conceivable that motor types with motor aphasia would show greater disturbances of reading and writing. If these assumptions were correct, such patients would also have particularly severe disorders of word-comprehension; but Freud (201) emphasized correctly that in no motor aphasia is language-comprehension completely obliterated. Type-differences, therefore, cannot be thoroughgoing. In fact, G. E. Mueller (569) shows that under certain conditions visual types will use acoustic-motor images, and vice versa. In the overwhelming majority of people the various types of imagery coexist and outweigh each other only to a small extent.

Concerning imagery-types see Baerwald (41) and G. E. Mueller (569).

That motor types show mostly acoustic imagery is also noteworthy because it points to an important relation between the sensorium and motility.[73] But we must first clarify what we mean by motor-images, since obviously, besides images in the narrower sense, rudimentary innervations which carry feelings with them are also involved here. It was in this sense that Stricker (818)—obviously an extreme motor type—pointed to the significance of

---

[72] See footnote 70, supra.
[73] Cf. Hebb (328).

motor speech-images. Every thought or word that is apprehended strives, as it were, towards its motor realization.[74] This demand is more urgent than that implied in visual images, though the latter too have a close relation to motility. The demand for innervation may vary greatly: for instance, some psychotics will utter loudly or act out what they hallucinate acoustically. In the visual realm this is rare, though I have observed a patient who hallucinated a cow and simultaneously made grinding motions with her mouth. This is the identification-type of hallucination: action is not directed *toward* the image as it is in the second type, but carries out only what is experienced *in* the image. The identification-type contrasts with the objectivation-type.

Generally, however, every image implies an action. In turn, every action presupposes a sensory impression. Exner (170) spoke of sensory-motility, implying that without sensory stimulation no movement would come about. One cannot swallow with a palate anesthetized by cocaine. Bergson (63) elaborated these ideas. He assumes that only what can become the object of an action becomes tangible and appears in sensory form. Experience with aphasias contradicts this, showing that sensory and motor phenomena are to a certain extent independent of each other: though disturbances of speech, i.e., of comprehension, do appear in motor aphasics, they are in general minor. To be sure, in motor aphasias articulation is suppressed rather than destroyed. Bergson's assumption, per se improbable, is shaken by the empirical material, but the existence of a close relation between sensorium and motility is probable.

The attempt was also made to explain the difference between reading and writing disturbances in motor aphasia by the inexperienced reader's dependence on muttering the words to himself, and the experienced reader's independence of it. Thus, when motor aphasia sets in, the inexperienced would have more severe reading and writing disturbances than the experienced.[75] In other words, the functional factor was invoked for explanation. Bastian (48) and Freud (201) have used it extensively in explaining aphasias: when a center suffers a general lesion, a habituated function

[74] For recent experimental evidence cf. Crafts et al. (136, Chapter 24); see also M. Washburn (859).

[75] Cf. Orton (594).

would be better preserved than a non-habituated one, and one earlier acquired better than one acquired late; furthermore, a center no longer responsive to volitional decision will still be responsive to associative stimulation.[76] It was thus that the transcortical aphasias were to be explained. By now, however, it appears certain that the differences between cortical and transcortical aphasias rest on different loci of lesion. Bastian's assumption must be at least amended. Functional factors, the role of which is unquestionable, do not alone determine the form of aphasia; it is determined also by the destruction of brain-structures which correspond to functional units turned into organic structure.[77] I have already stated that in final analysis even these organic functions may become psychologically comprehensible.

I have based this presentation upon a division of aphasias into sensory and motor, but I must make the point that this distinction belongs among the most debated questions of brain pathology. P. Marie (533, 534) recognizes no such thing as a motor aphasia, and the significance of Broca's locus is questioned by other authors also. Certain disturbances of language-comprehension are demonstrable in nearly all cases; in turn, remission phases of sensory aphasia are often hard to distinguish from motor aphasia. The relatively intact speech-sequences make a distinction just possible. In spite of these difficulties, the presentation above seems to me to come closest to the facts.

d) Reading[78]

We read with a resting eye. The role of word-connections in reading. Reading is not a serial linking of letters. More on pure word-blindness. The role of unimpaired speech in reading. Apractic agraphia.

Understanding of reading disturbances in aphasia presupposes the psychology of normal reading: I call attention to Schumann's (764) survey of it. Reading is not learned letter by letter. First the total word-complex is surveyed by the resting eye (Erd-

[76] Cf. Hebb (328) on early and late brain injuries; also Rapaport et al. (650, I), on the preservation of verbal concepts in functional disorders.

[77] Cf. footnote 36, p. 56; footnote 72, p. 74; footnote 4, p. 103 supra, referring to various ramifications of this view of the relation between function and structure, which is central to Schilder's thinking and seems to be the predecessor of the "automatization" concept of psychoanalytic ego-psychology (321).

[78] Cf. Orton (594), also Woodworth (893, Chapter 28).

mann and Dodge, 165). During eye-movements nothing is perceived: we speak of a central anesthesia of the retina during eyetions may become psychologically comprehensible.
movements. In tachistoscopic perception, many more letters of words can be cognized than letters without a word-connection. The gross whole-form issuing from determining letters can arouse the acoustic-motor verbal image as a whole. At any rate, reading is not a serial compounding of letters.

Pathology shows that reading requires a specific visual apprehension. In pure alexia, which we have already discussed, the letter-form as such is not apprehended: the Gestalt is not perceived. Yet there are patients who apprehend the letter but not the word, and others who apprehend words but cannot dissect them into letters.[79] Digits are always more easily read than letters, because the digit as a Gestalt is more directly coordinated to a concept than are letters. Neither the psychology of normal reading nor its psychopathology has, to date, anything to say about the processes involved in reading sentences.[80] Naturally, reading presupposes the reader's ability to apprehend the word as language. In motor and sensory aphasia, where this ability is disordered, reading and writing cannot be flawless.

Let us add that, just as there is a disorder of reading independent of that of speech, so there is an independent disorder of writing also, which is to be regarded as apractic, though other action-disturbances may be absent. Here patients cannot find the appropriate writing-movements, and fail to form even individual letters.

The modern conception of aphasia goes back to H. Jackson (367). He stressed that aphasics, though speechless, are not wordless. Patients bereft of speech do not have command over their words. They have not lost their "images." The conception that psychological processes occur on various levels was put forth by Jackson and was taken up again by Head (326, 327). Jackson demonstrated that damage encroaches first on the highest level. Thus, for instance, volitional, rational speech may be disordered, while affective speech persists: a patient who cannot speak may

[79] Cf. Schilder, on the basic thought-disorder, Appendix, pp. 344 ff., infra.
[80] Cf., however, Rapaport et al. (650, I), and Rapaport (658), on "anticipation."

have good expressive movements, but be unable to imitate expressive movements because such imitation is "volitional, rational speech." "Yes" and "no," being especially anchored in affectivity, are very often preserved in aphasia. The aphasic can say "no" when the situation demands it, but cannot reiterate it after someone.

Recently Head has continued Jackson's line of thought, stressing that in aphasia the "intentions" and the "formation of propositions" is disordered. The aphasic has the words but cannot use them intentionally, "propositionally." It is symbolic thinking, the use of words and signs which do not directly designate an object, that is disordered in aphasia. Besides the disturbances of symbolic thinking and expression, others are also present: spatial wholes are not apprehended, and the meaning of the big and small watch-hands is not appreciated. The closer a "symbolization" comes to being intentional, the more difficult it is for the aphasic; while the closer the task sticks to the sensory image, the less likely it is that the former will be impaired. Symbolic acts of a more complex structure tend to become more impaired than those of a lesser "intention-level," of a lower "propositional value."[81] Head's classification of aphasias differs from the classical one in many points, but to my mind has no advantage over it.

At any rate, Head's investigations support the views here presented: in aphasia the thought-act as a whole is disordered, and it loses command of its apparatuses.[82] But different lesions encroach on different partial functions of "symbolic" thinking in differing degrees.[83] To me it seems that the particular involvement of spatial apprehension (orientation on the watch, etc.) is related to lesions of special apparatuses. In any case, the "functional conception" of agnosia and aphasia seems at present to be securely founded. Bergson (63) has definitively shown that no

[81] Schilder here equates the "intentionality" of act-psychology and the "propositionality" of Head. Since he derives "intentions" from drive-dynamics, and since "propositions" pertain to reality-relevant thinking, this equation does not solve but only raises the question: How does brain-injury disrupt the usual balance between the drive-directedness and the reality-relevance of thinking?

[82] Concerning apparatuses cf. Appendix, pp. 350 ff., infra, also Schilder (752, pp. 577–580).

[83] The term "symbolic" is used here apparently not in the psychoanalytic sense, but rather in the broader one of logic.

images are destroyed; in Germany, Pick's (619, 623) studies yielded
comparable conclusions. Rieger (669) has demonstrated that
brain-lesions cause a gross basic disorder: the patient can no
longer differentiate between legato and staccato; he cannot volitionally analyze experiential sequences, he cannot dissect them,
is compelled to repeat the whole sequence (compulsory legato)
or cannot tie together fully apprehended parts (compulsory staccato). Clearly, these formulations differ little from those of Jackson.

It is not easy to assimilate the literature on aphasia. Heilbronner's (330)
article in the *Handbuch für Neurologie* provides a good orientation. Monakow's (340) extensive volume orients one to the basic problems and presents a
broad bibliography, but his views often differ from those here presented.[84]

e) *Phonetic and meaning-changes*[85]

Analogies between literal paraphasias of motor aphasia and phonetic
change. The significance of speech-speed. Role of affects in the pronunciation
of consonants. Phonetic-change in the German language. Meaning-change as
change of concept-sign and its relation to meaning-experiences.

The theory of aphasia offers analogies to the phenomena of
phonetic and meaning-change. In phonetic change these analogies
are less obvious and have been little studied, yet the same laws
appear to operate in them as in the articulation-defects of motor
aphasia. Contiguous sound-articulations influence each other: not
only does the preceding one influence the subsequent, the reverse
is also true. The not yet uttered sound seems to be already given
in consciousness. This holds in slips of the tongue of normals
also. Just as perseveration may exert its effect over several intervening words, a sound too may influence another one over several
intervening sounds. The alterations wrought on a sound by one
succeeding it are easiest to understand. *Adtrahere* becomes *attra-
here,* apparently due to the striving not to decrease the speech-
speed too much: under the pressure of the attitude directed at
maintaining the tempo, the articulation-mechanism fails.

Thus here attitude and speech-apparatus are involved in the
phonetic-change. Language is closely related to sound-gestures;
therefore when affectivity changes, the sound too must change.

84 The more recent surveys (864, 293) have already been referred to above.
85 Cf. G. Stern (804), Bloomfield (90).

Actually, when the subject experiences affect, various consonants are now more sharply, now more softly uttered. Thus, when a phonetic change takes place, we may infer a change of total attitude. The question arises: what brought about the change in internal attitude? Thus, for instance, a changed relationship to other languages and people may be held responsible for that phonetic change in Germanic languages by which voiced stopped consonants (mediae) were changed into voiceless stopped consonants (tenues), voiceless stopped consonants (tenues) into aspirated stops (aspiratae), and aspirated stops (aspiratae) into voiced stopped consonants (mediae). In addition, new cultural attitudes and new habits of life influencing the tempo of speech also come into play. Besides these attitudinal factors, the physiological condition of the apparatus plays a role: this is seen in the, to be sure, fluctuating, phonetic change of the paretic's speech; he says artillery, or even ratrillery, instead of artillery. Finally, similar phenomena are frequent in the child's language also: here too both physiological and psychological factors must be considered.

The child's language helps us to understand meaning-changes also. When the child applies to all coins, and even to everything shiny, the expression "quack" which applied originally to a bird on one coin, this example of name (sign) change occurring within an individual life may be compared to meaning-change. The Romans' naming their first minting-place Moneta, from the nearby temple of Juno Moneta, is meaningful only in the light of the specific experience; if that is forgotten, then the names "monnaie" or "money" for the medium of exchange is as senseless as "quack" for something shiny.

Wundt (898) calls this meaning-change "singular" and he considers it the main line of development in the history of words. He contrasts this singular meaning-change with regular meaning change, an example of which is the history of the conceptually related word *pecunia:* it means money as possession and not as a single coin. It too is the product of a meaning-change: as *moneta* meant originally "the admonisher," *pecunia* meant "herd of cattle." But while there is no conceptual relation whatsoever between money and "the admonisher," *pecunia* = "herd of cattle" and *pecunia* = "money" both originally meant the same thing: mobile possession used for exchange. The mobile possession of

Romans in the earliest times consisted mostly of cattle, which were used as the general exchange-medium in barter. Later, when barter-trading was replaced by money-trading, the name of the generally used barter-medium spread to minted money.

According to Wundt, regular meaning-change, in contrast to singular, is the history of a concept. But in both changes of the concept-sign occur—in the first through an objective relationship, in the second through contiguity. This formulation underscores the similarity of meaning-change and the word-substitutions in sensory aphasia. If we sort out the different forms of meaning-change, by establishing the conceptual relationship between primary and secondary meanings, we find that a meaning may expand, contract, or be replaced by a coordinate one. Thus, the expression *limb* is transferred from the limb of a tree to a limb of the body. In our terminology: the meaning wanders within the sphere. Later on I will demonstrate that individual factors as well as logical and objective ones partake in the formation of the sphere. These individual factors can be classified into those determined only by spatial-temporal contiguity and those implying affective interests. No wonder that meaning-change may "improve" as well as "degrade" the meaning. Thus, for instance, the word rogue,[86] originally very derogatory, underwent an improvement of meaning.

In meaning-change the original word often retains its meaning, while the phonetically changed word has a new meaning. Thus the word *Rabe* (raven) meant originally a black horse also, but not after the word *Rappe* (black horse) split off . . . In meaning-change we deal primarily with a change in the designation of things already apprehended; at least, this is so in pure cases, though the new word often makes a more exact grasp of the concept possible. The word-substitutions in sensory aphasia are not conceptual changes at all (though in them constancy of designation is not preserved), but we know that—due to the language-disorder—thinking and acting are often severely disturbed in sensory aphasics. Pick (623) has emphatically pointed up the influence of speech on thinking.[87] Though thinking and

---

[86] "Rogue" translates *Schelm*. The "improvement" of the word "rogue" seems more equivocal than that of *Schelm*.

[87] Cf. Whorf (883).

speaking are by no means identical, finer differentiations of thought are made possible only by differentiated speech, and meaning-change is a means of conceptual differentiation. Though it is in the study of language-development that we encounter meaning-change in particularly clear forms, nevertheless, even after the child's language-development is completed, we find a continual restructuring of meaning connected with the differentiation of concepts. The severe disorders of thinking found in aphasics must warn us against underestimating the role of speech in thinking.

For data on phonetic- and meaning-change, see Wundt's *Völkerpsychologie* (898).

3. MOTOR- AND SPEECH-DISORDERS IN PSYCHOSES, AND THE PROBLEM OF PSYCHIC ENERGY[88]

Disorders of motor impulse in psychoses. Hyperkinetic and akinetic conditions in schizophrenia. Disorders of motor impulse originating in the striate body and in the cortex. Waxy flexibility has a psychogenic explanation. Hyperkinesis, particularly that of speech. Verbigeration. Principle of the double path. The psyche has energy. The various depots of psychic energy. The relation of psychic and somatic energies. Displacement of affective energy to lower levels. Displacement of lower-level energies to higher levels. Role of the total brain in psychological functions. Localization principle and unity of psychological experience.

Though motor- and speech-disturbances of mental disorders become understandable only by insight into drive-dynamics, our preceding discussions throw some light on them. Disorders of the motor-impulse not only accompany circumscribed lesions of the mentioned parts of the brain; they play a significant role in psychoses also. Probably a part of the akinetic- and tension-states in schizophrenia is referable to a direct lesion of the striate body; but the motor-impulse may be inhibited or disturbed from cortical apparatuses also. The motor aphasic speaks little, has no impulse to speak: this becomes particularly clear where reiteration of heard speech is good.

Here a possibility for the understanding of such disturbances is open. Conceivably we could be dealing with direct damages as in transcortical motor aphasia; but undoubtedly only a small part of tensions and of flaccid motionlessness, as in various forms of

88 Cf. Schilder (729), also (708, 709).

waxy flexibility, in which passively given postures are retained as in wax, can be explained by direct damage to primitive brain-apparatuses. These symptoms more frequently arise directly from a psychogenic sequence; so we assume that the brain apparatuses are not directly damaged, but only altered or switched off by psychological influence. The symptoms which arise closely resemble those organically determined, yet their general organization shows significant differences.[89]

The same applies to conditions characterized by an excess of movement. The movement-excess of chorea is no doubt a purely organic happening. In certain forms of epidemic encephalitis we see restless movements, which do not arise from psychological causes, though it is not impossible that the excess of motor "impulse" is represented psychologically. An excess of expressive movements is frequently observed.[90] In sensory aphasia there is unquestionably an excess of speech-impulses which often manifests itself in movement-impulses in general: the patients are very motile, hang onto every person's arm, stroke it, and the like.

But even if the hypermotility of the mentally ill, particularly schizophrenics, occasionally may come about in this direct way, it is mostly determined by psychogenic sequences and their effect on brain-apparatuses. The lingual-motor phenomena are particularly varied.[91] At one moment the patient speaks only when stimulated, though he may glide into an avalanche of words; at another moment he quite spontaneously chatters away, whispers, speaks, shouts, and sings. Now their speech is monotonous and machine-like, and now rhythmic. Their words and sentences may remain meaningful, or may become distorted, their grammar quite loose, their words disfigured—the last resembling aphasias. Perseveration and repetition of entire sentences, meaningful or meaningless, grammatically correct or incorrect, play a great role (verbigeration). If the material of the verbal avalanche is understandable, it is found to derive partly from experience and partly from external impressions. Neologisms too are prominent. If speech- and movement-pressure is accompanied by manic elation. it becomes obvious that it is being fed from affective sources, and

89 Cf. Schilder (729, Chapters 7 and 11); also (702).

90 Cf. Schilder (729, Chapter 10); also Gerstmann and Schilder (270, VIII).

91 Cf. Schilder and Sugar (716); also (717, 720).

is unlike the phenomena described here which can be apprehended neurologically. But the catatonic pressure of speech, as already mentioned, often suggests that in it the function of anatomically well-known apparatuses is altered by psychological attitudes. This function may be altered by both psychological attitude and anatomic lesion (principle of the double path).

If the conception that the function of a somatic apparatus can be influenced psychologically is correct, then we must attribute to the psyche a particular energy which interacts with purely somatic energies.[92] We have already developed this view in the introduction, and wish to elaborate it in relation to this material. There are forms of hypermotility which take their course outside of consciousness, and in which, dependent on the position of the body, now this and now another muscle-group shows excess of movement. Gerstmann and I (270) have observed a case in which hypermotility manifested itself now in continuous bending and stretching of knee- and hip-joints, now in outward and inward rotations. It was as though a given mass of excitation were flowing first into one and then into another channel.

The somatic hypermotility of chorea is increased by psychological excitation; therefore it must be assumed that affective energy can be switched to a deeper level.[93] Something like this also happens when a relatively akinetic Parkinson patient is brought into lively motion by affect or external stimulation. Here a purely somatic deficit is first of all made up, but the patient also acquires primitive movement-impulses which he did not formerly have: psychological energy is displaced partly into the somatic, partly into another psychological, realm. In turn, it is probable that the obtrusiveness and the rage-attacks of juvenile encephalitics are due to a displacement of subcortical movement energies into other realms.

The evidence for this I have presented elsewhere (270), and here wish to offer only the general conception which arises from these and similar findings: there is a psychic energy, and it is in an exchange-relationship with energies of a purely organic cerebral nature. This energy is bound to certain brain-apparatuses

92 Cf. Schilder (708) and (750, Chapter 21); concerning the standard psychoanalytic conception of psychic energy, see Bibring (71), and Rapaport (657).

93 "Deeper level" translates *Tiefere Station;* the implication is apparently that a displacement from a cortical to a subcortical center takes place.

in a particular manner. These brain-apparatuses are hierarchically arranged, and it seems that only those higher up in the hierarchy are related to experiences that can be apprehended psychologically. Between the various levels of the hierarchy, continuous energy-exchanges take place. From this point of view, the individual brain-apparatuses appear as collecting and distributing depots of organic and psychological energy. Though this whole conception is tentative, it may serve as a point of departure for future attempts to comprehend more exactly the relationships and nature of psychological energy.[94]

After this elaboration, let us return to the role of the total brain in psychological experience. It makes no sense to say that a psychological function as such is localized. The total brain, indeed the total organism, is the prerequisite of psychological experience; but the execution of functions requires an intact brain, and localized brain-lesions result in strictly specific disturbances of the course of functions. Each of Vogt's cortical fields is necessary for a certain function, even though we do not yet know the role of every field. Some functions may require the cooperation of several fields. Perhaps lesion of one field may be compensated for by the function of another. Psychic experiences involve not only cortical apparatuses—for instance, the organs of motor-impulse are in their essential parts subcortical. Besides the division of functions according to fields, there is probably a division of functions according to the layers of the cortex: the six layers are by no means functionally equivalent. But assuming a strict localization of disturbances does not mean assuming a localization of the psyche. Psychic acts are and remain achievements of the total personality, even when the course of psychic processes is altered by brain-lesion.

Concerning cortical layers, see C. and O. Vogt (850). Concerning motor disorders of the mentally ill, see Kleist (420). Concerning schizophrenic speech-disorders, see Pfersdorff (606). See also Jaspers (382).

94 Cf. Schilder (729, Chapter 7), also (708, 709).

IV

MEMORY[1]

1. Registration, Learning, Association

Similarity and contiguity associations. The latter cannot be reduced to the former. Associations by similar initial links must be distinguished from associations by similarity. Associations rest on affective-volitional attitudes and presuppose an ego. Memory investigations: Ebbinghaus's method of saving. Registration and retention. Subsequent intensive mental activity weakens what was registered. Inhibition of registration when the initial link has other prior associations (generative inhibition). Newly acquired associations inhibit previous ones (effective inhibition). Experiences tend to re-emerge (perseveration tendency). The association and memory mechanism has organic foundations, but is in the service of the total personality. On perseverations.

The problem of memory is closely linked with that of associations. When I hear the opening lines of a poem which I have always heard as a whole, the rest of the poem comes automatically to my mind.[2] On hearing the name *Werther*, memories of scenes of the novel immediately emerge. On hearing the name of the cathedral of Cologne, not only does its more or less complete image arise, but also that of the neighboring houses, and of one experience or another I had in Cologne; and perhaps also that of other Gothic cathedrals, and in connection with them the difference between the Gothic and the Romanesque style. This re-emergence appears to be impersonal, occurring without my contribution, obeying a rather mechanical lawfulness which we speak of as association-laws.

Ebbinghaus (154) summarizes these laws as follows: when any psychological formations have filled consciousness simultaneously or in close sequence, the later return of some parts of the

1 For recent surveys of the field, cf. Woodworth (893, Chapters 2, 3, 4), Stevens (808, Chapters 15–20), also Hebb (328).

2 Cf. footnote 82, p. 144, supra, and Schilder (729 Chapter 7), on automatized apparatuses, and Hebb (328), on "assemblies."

experience will arouse the others, even though the original causes for their arising may not be present. Associations are customarily divided into those of similarity, contrast, and spatial or temporal contiguity; or simply into those of similarity and contiguity. Some psychologists try to reduce associations by similarity also to contiguity: the valley is beside the mountain, the deep beside the high, the sublime beside the ridiculous. When the memory of the cathedral of Cologne brings with it the memories of other Gothic cathedrals, this occurs because for the most part we have thought of these simultaneously, we have heard about them at the same time: here too association by similarity reduces to contiguity. But just as similarity cannot be reduced to partial identity, association by similarity as a particular form of association cannot be denied either. Reproduction *through* similar initial links, as distinguished from reproduction *of* a link similar to the initial one, is often mistaken for association by similarity. Thus, when seeing some other Gothic church one may be reminded of the surroundings of the cathedral of Cologne.[3] Strictly speaking, an experience never repeats itself, and in final analysis therefore the initial link of a reproduction is never fully identical with the original initial link: it is either partially identical with or similar to it.

The original conception of associations was that they are, so to speak, a soulless mechanism. The ego was supposed to be built of such associations.[4] But pure association is an abstraction, which is never encountered in actual psychic life. When associations occur, it is the total ego which makes use of the mechanism, and the right-of-way it gives this mechanism always implies a psychological attitude. We will later discuss in detail how every association implies an affective-volitional happening, which emanates directly from the total personality.[5]

The total personality is presupposed by everything that we designate as memory-laws. These laws must be discussed in greater detail. The study of memory gained decisive impetus from the

---

3 Cf. Bartlett (46) on "schemata," Rapaport et al. (650, Vol. I), on "memory frames of reference" and (Vol. II) on association-studies.

4 It is not clear in what sense Schilder speaks here of the "ego"; probably he means "cohesive experience" in Claparède's sense (135).

5 For similar views cf. Stern (806), also Allport (26, particularly pp. 170 ff. and pp. 187 ff.).

investigations of Ebbinghaus (154), who was the first to introduce experimental methods into research on memory. He used the method of saving: a series of items (words of a poem, single words, nonsense syllables) is repeated until learned to perfection; then it can be established whether the number of repetitions is identical in various individuals, and how the material learned is retained. For instance, it can be demonstrated that on the second day learning to perfection takes far fewer repetitions, and that this saving in number is diminished after a week or a month. Thus the weakening of associations can be exactly followed.[6] I reproduce here a curve of Ebbinghaus's, which presents in percentage-form the savings in learning as a function of the time elapsed since learning took place (Figure 6).

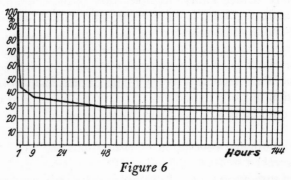

Figure 6

Percentage of saving as function of the time elapsed since learning

The problems of registration are of great importance for experimental psychology, but are of less interest to us. In registration the number of repetitions and their distribution, the kind, articulation, meaningfulness or senselessness of material, and finally the speed of learning and efficient distribution of material, all play a role. Individual differences are significant. The weakening of associations has already been mentioned, but there are many processes which can interfere with retention. Any intensive mental activity following learning interferes with what was learned, but there are specialized inhibitions also. If in learning a poem I have registered a wrong phrase, I will learn the right

6 This statement of Ebbinghaus's work and the associationist view is sketchy and partial, though not in essence incorrect. For more recent statements cf. Hilgard (348), and Stevens (808, Chapters 15–20).

one with much greater difficulty than if I had never learned the wrong one: the association AB inhibits the correct association AC; but once AC has been learned, the association AB is more difficult to reproduce.

The inhibition of previous impressions by newly acquired ones we term effective inhibition; the inhibition of new acquisition we term generative inhibition. It appears that anything once acquired has, for a while, a tendency to appear. These are the perseveration tendencies described by Mueller and Pilzecker (571).

That what once existed tends to re-emerge, and that an impression is not done with when it fades away a moment later, is obviously a basic law of our organization: the perseveration tendency is a clear expression of this. But even if what has been experienced does not reappear in its direct form, it still influences all that follows. O. Gross (307) has spoken of a secondary cerebral function. The influence of preceding impressions, the tenacity of retention, their after-effects in general, are basic psychophysical phenomena, and pathology sheds ever new light on them. In aphasias and agnosias, the perseveration tendency is always striking: the invalided apparatus retains previous impressions and actions with particular tenacity. Intending of new impressions and new action is thereby hampered. In epileptic dementia and in epileptic states, the tendency to psychological perseveration is particularly great. It may be assumed that the paucity of new material, combined with the compulsion or impulse to react or to perceive, leads to perseveration. But without a sticking of impressions as such, perseveration would not come about. Recently Freud (236) expressed the view that there is a "repetition compulsion" in the life of every individual; he regards this as a tendency of the organic material to maintain its state unchanged.[7]

Poppelreuter (633) has correctly pointed out that all the phenomena of learning and forgetting are extensively determined by psychological attitudes. The customary learning experiments do not study associations as such, because in them registration and reproduction are both volitional; in addition, such experiments imply continuous selection and testing.[8] Thus experimental psy-

[7] On "repetition compulsion," see Bibring (72); on perseveration and iteration, cf. Schilder (752).

[8] Schilder means that the volitional registration and reproduction selectively suppresses the associations which are not "correct" in terms of the material to be learned.

chology overlooks the wealth of subtle intervening experiences: indeed, it conceives of chain associations and reproductions as products of volitional ordering. Aall (1) demonstrated that retention is totally different when one decides to learn the material for a short while, and when one decides to learn it for good. One continuously observes in memory experiments that the mechanism subserves higher purposes: but that there is a mechanism is certain. Experimental psychologists have established that associations of identical reproducibility fade more slowly when they are older and have been reinforced more often by new registration. We observe this in cases of Korsakow psychosis—which, as is known, appears with any gross brain-lesion, and the physiological prototype of which is the memory of seniles; these cases retain events and experiences of youth with tenacity and faithfulness, while recent experiences soon fade and vanish. This, no doubt, is an organically anchored mechanism.[9] The laws of association and learning give us a glimpse into the mechanism, but do not explain the nature of memory-phenomena. In most cases the point is not that reproduction takes place, but that it is either willed or follows recognition.

2. RECOGNITION,[10] REMEMBERING,[11] FORGETTING[12]

The feeling and quality of familiarity are not simple feelings. Recognition presupposes remembering and a germinal thought containing reference to the previous experience. Remembering of forgotten names. The déjà vu as a congruence between a pre-stage and the end-product of experience. Déjà raconté. Extraordinary memories and complex-formation in learning. Schemata and diagrams. Extraordinary memories are based on the meaningful articulation of material into complexes. Special memories and types. Forgetting in organic brain-disease as inhibition. Forgetting in hypnosis and in hysterical special states as a symptom of repression and as flight in general. Not even experiences in epileptic special states are lost. Forgetting as a consequence of attitudes and inhibitions. Biological factors determine forgetting and remembering. Latent and overt determinations. Memory-span.

Wundt (895) reduces recognition to a feeling, Hoeffding (350) to a quality of familiarity, and both maintain that familiarity is

9 For a review of the memory impairment in Korsakow psychoses, cf. Rapaport (654, Chapter VII, particularly pp. 226 ff.), Betlheim and Hartmann (69), and Buerger-Prinz (123).

10 Cf. Claparède (135).

11 Cf. Bartlett (46).

12 Cf. Pear (598), and Rapaport (654).

indicated by a definite feeling-factor without a memory of the earlier experience being present.[13] But in the moment of recognition we have not only an impression of familiarity; we also know where to seek for the previous experience. In other words: a germinal thought is given, which, as we shall discuss later, contains the previous experience, though in a particular form. The old "rationalistic" view, that when recognition takes place the previous experience is recalled, is the more correct one. When the previous scene is remembered by a volitional act of reproduction, then what was already there in germinal form merely unfolds. But, obviously, the same happens when I attempt to revive an experience without previous recognition. This can be well observed in remembering forgotten names, where we do have the inner rhythm of the word, we know its "psychological locus," and our search puts us in possession of something that already belonged to us.

There are illusions of the feeling of familiarity also. Of these, déjà vu is the best known.[14] The person affected believes that he previously experienced what is now happening to him: everything seems to take its course mechanically, as if pre-determined. The individual feels strange and distant from himself. Though déjà vu appears in certain psychoses, particularly and strikingly in epilepsy, it is not rare in normals. Fatigue and alcohol favor its occurrence. But such recognition is not merely a feeling, not just an illusion. Every thought, every image, before it is full-fledged goes through developmental phases, like those of the embryo. Now if the continuity of the developmental series for some reason decomposes, then a pre-stage and the end-product of the thought coincide, and the impression arises that one has experienced all this in the same way before.[15]

The counterpart of déjà vu is déjà raconté. Freud (224) demonstrated that the impression of having already spoken of something is based on an earlier intention to speak about it. Here too remembering arises due to coincidence with a previous experience, and thus the quality of familiarity has justification. Again the experience has two facets: an earlier and a later ex-

13 Cf. Claparède (135), both for recognition and "déjà vu"; for the latter, see also (69, 224) and (752).

14 Ibid.

15 Cf. Schilder (751).

perience are being related to each other. (Concerning déjà vu, cf. Heymans, 344, 345; Grasset, 296; Bergson, 60.)

In remembering there emerges first an outline, a vague sense of the previous experience, from which the details unfold. According to Poppelreuter (633), reproduction is not a successive progress by means of images coming and going, but rather an increasing imaginal clarity of the parts of an experience, which forms throughout it a unitary whole. He speaks of "a progressive emergence of the imaginal parts from total presentations."

Particularly clear insight into the conditions of learning and retention is gained through the study of extraordinary memories. Rueckle learned a series of 204 digits in 7 minutes and 27.8 seconds, and a series of 504 digits in 39 minutes and 30 seconds.[16] This amazing achievement was possible only because he articulated the material meaningfully and recombined it continuously. The virtuoso of numbers is intimately familiar with their characteristics; he continuously creates new relations between them. Rueckle has the ability to discover quickly, and to register, the mathematical characteristics of any complex of numbers. The complexes so developed he unites with others into complexes of higher orders. In this process, visual imagery plays a preponderant role. The main point, however, is that groups which have mathematical characteristics are for Rueckle something of extreme interest. It is instructive to compare Rueckle's achievements with those of another virtuoso of numbers, Miss Bergh. She has little talent for numbers as such and therefore images digits as persons, objects, stripes; against the background of an imagined landscape she creates remarkable figures, situations, and chains of actions. Accordingly, her achievements were particularly astounding when she was given series of words with easily imaged meanings.

To explain the achievement of Rueckle, Mueller (569) refers to his many endowments: low mental fatigability, high concentration of attention, excellent retention, and extremely rapid apperception and reproduction. Furthermore, he uses natural aids to an unusual degree in learning. Finally, there is his particular interest in his field. Mueller correctly refuses to assume a congenital phenomenal memory for numbers. In turn, Hegge (329) considers Bergh's combinatory activity as a remarkable

16 Regarding Rueckle, see in G. E. Mueller (569), and in Schilder (752).

achievement of constructive visual fantasy. It appears that memory achievements depend much on combinatory processes, and are not mechanical registrations in an apparatus which reproduces what it takes in, like a phonograph.

In learning generally, natural aids, the creation of relationships, subsumption into schemata and diagrams, all play an important role. The diagrams may be simple spatial figures, or complex pictures such as maps; they are spatial schemata, the various points of which are associated with the terms to be learned (Froebes, 258). Henning's main diagram included the numbers 1–700 and a line which ascended progressively in definite whorls, had a break at 70, then partly descended; some points of it were dark, others light. In this diagram he located historical dates, coins, weights, mountains according to their heights, etc. Such diagrams derive from individual experiences, mostly of childhood; in their formation, symbolizing fantasy plays a great role.[17]

All this, however, does not solve the problem of memory. We have to settle the problem of special memories also, which coincides in part with the problem of types. The older psychopathology assumed that the circumscribed losses of visual, auditory, verbal and other types of memory, were due to specifically localized brain-lesions. In the preceding chapters we saw that there is no loss, but only inhibition, of memory-images. With this restriction in mind, we can speak of special memories. A central psychic function, in this case memory, needs apparatuses to exert its effect. Brain-lesions deprive it of these. This is similar to Bergson's view of memory. If the theory of types has any meaning after the restriction mentioned, it would obviously be that individuals have different kinds and degrees of command over the various apparatuses.

We are familiar with an array of memory-inhibitions of another kind, namely, the memory-losses in hysteria and the inability to remember the experiences of deep hypnosis. These open an avenue to the understanding of memory-disorders in general. The memory-gaps in hysteria rest on repressions. These patients turn away from their psychic contents, they want to know nothing

[17] For more recent literature, cf. Bartlett (46), on the relation of schemata and interests; Hebb (328) on "assemblies"; Rapaport (658, Part VII), on thought and anticipation patterns.

about certain experiences: this is a flight. Breuer and Freud have
shown that experiences with an unpleasant affect-tone are repressed.[18] The amnesia for experiences in hypnosis is also a
turning-away, carried out by the individual partly to demonstrate
—for the sake of the hypnotist—the singular character of the
hypnotic state, and partly because he is ashamed of his erotic-
infantile attitude toward the hypnotist. The essential similarity
of hypnotic and hysterical amnesia is indicated by the fact that
memories of the experiences in hypnosis, and those of hysterical
amnesia can both be recovered by appropriate suggestions.[19]
Memories of certain epileptic special states, too, can be aroused
in hypnosis (Muralt, 573; Ricklin, 670). The amnesia of epileptic
special states was considered by many to be absolute, and its
contents lost to the individual for good. But traces of experiences in the twilight-state can always be demonstrated, partly by
recovering them in hypnosis and partly by Ebbinghaus's method
of savings; and this is true whether the consciousness of the
twilight-state was more like that of the normal state, or of the
dream, or of confusion. Thus here too the loss of memories is
only an apparent one: the memories are suppressed, inhibited,
but not destroyed.[20]

Moreover, Brodmann (109) and Gregor (297, 298)[21]* were
able to show that in Korsakow psychosis, in which, according to
clinical observation, recent experiences are apparently not retained but lost (disorder of registration, according to Wernicke),
the method of saving demonstrates traces of learning and experience. How these traces are represented psychologically is at present an unsolved problem; but it has been demonstrated beyond
doubt that even in these severe memory-disorders there is no loss
of experience. It may also be surmised that the memory-impair-
ment following skull-fracture, both that of experiences prior to
the trauma (retrograde amnesia), and that of experiences subsequent to the recovery of consciousness, is not a memory-loss
but only an inhibition of the memory-material, which should be

[18] For a critique of this formulation and for a review of the pertinent
literature, see Rapaport (654, Chapters 3 and 5).

[19] For a review, see Rapaport (654, Chapter 6).

[20] Cf. Schilder (710, 711).

[21]* We are in Gregor's debt also for other penetrating studies into the
pathology of memory. [For references see (654).]

recoverable in some way. Thus, there are probably transitional forms between the organically and the psychologically determined inhibitions which prevent the re-emergence of memory-images. But these forms seem to vary in the extent to which organic and psychological factors contribute to them, and in the psychological representation of the inhibition in them.[22]

At any rate, one arrives at the general view that organic conditions do not simply destroy the memory-material; and this raises again the question of whether there is a normal destruction, a using up, of memory-material. The curve of loss has already been presented above. Here the question is not to what extent the trace can be utilized, but whether it exists. This, I believe, must be assumed.[23] In psychoanalysis we experience almost daily how the apparently long-forgotten rises to the surface, and in one case Freud was able to trace memories back to the age of one-and-a-half years. C. and W. Stern (801) report the case of a child who must have acquired words of a dialect before he was able to speak properly, but certainly before he was one-and-a-half, and had command of these at five years of age. I refer here also to the amazing memory-feats of certain hypnotized people and of people in trance. There was the servant-maid who began to speak Aramaic, an incidental memory which originated in the years of her childhood, spent in the house of a preacher.[24] The hyperamnesia of dying people, particularly of those drowning, must be mentioned here too.[25]

But if it is asserted that nothing once experienced is lost, the question must be raised: why then should anything be forgotten? When we turn with interest to an object, we brush a manifold of others aside. To think means not only to arouse something, but also to shove aside an infinite number of other thoughts.[26] Ach (7, 9) has demonstrated that every emerging idea arises from a determining tendency, from a will-attitude. This will-attitude not only brings about the emergence of a certain thought, but also inhibits associative and reproductive material.

[22] Cf. footnote 8, p. 155, supra.
[23] This is one of Schilder's persistent assumptions. For a particularly striking statement of it, see Schilder (703).
[24] Schilder's reference is apparently to Pfister (607).
[25] Cf. Stratton (816).
[26] Cf. Pear (598), and Hebb (328).

Koffka has shown that there are also latent determining tendencies. If we are accustomed to settling tasks in a certain way, this form of behavior becomes ingrained, and we always apply the same schema. When I ask people which is the lightest town in the world and suggest the answer Agram (i.e., a gram) or Kagram (i.e., no gram), then ask them which is the biggest town in the world, most people will hesitate in answering, though they know full well: they are set for a joke, not for a factual answer. Every situation sets us certain tasks and arouses certain attitudes, which in turn regulate the memory-material that is to come forth. Indeed, even after the memory-material already has arisen, the attitudes exert a selection over it: in a learned discussion the idea of lunch does not arise at first, but once it has arisen it is pushed aside. Our entire thinking and remembering is determined by attitudes. Attitudes, however, follow (biological) interests. Accordingly, it may be said that remembering depends on attitudes and biological interests.[27] In hysterical amnesias, the biological interest is negatively determining: it wants certain things not to be remembered. But the wish to remember something definite simultaneously pushes everything that is not pertinent into the background of experiencing, into forgetting. We may therefore assert that not-remembering rests on an explicit or coincidental lack of interest in whatever is not remembered.

Bergson (60, 63) correctly distinguishes between the attitude directed toward pure remembering, and that which intends a memory which is to serve a certain purpose. Thus, in learning a poem by heart I do not retain the differences between the second and the eighth readings, because they are of no interest to me. But the term interest designates a variety of psychological processes: we mean by it partly something which can be rationally directed, and partly instinctual interest-orientations which cannot. It would be impossible for me at present to recover my psycho-

27 For a purely "attitudinal"-dynamic-view of remembering, see Lewin (490, 492, 493) and for a critique of his views see Gibson (272); note also the parallel trend in Hartmann's (321) recognition of ego-apparatuses, in contrast to the earlier pure drive-dynamic conception of all perceptual memory phenomena in psychoanalysis (654, Chapter 5). Note also the critique by Klein (417, 418) of the "new look" trend in perception-experimentation; he shows that this trend, absorbed in the study of the effects of need in perception, disregards response-characteristics (apparatus) and controls (individual perceptual styles).

logical experiences at my various readings of the first Faust monologue; a particular psychological constellation would first have to arise. But I am convinced that such a constellation could arise, and that then the experiences would be aroused by it. Clearly, my conception of biological interest reaches into the organic realm. I am inclined to assume that the inhibition of the arousability of impressions which occurs regularly after a lapse of time, is nothing but an organic expression of such interests. I wish to point out again that the disturbances of registration in normal senescence go with a vanishing of interest in new things.

Once one has come to the view that what is once experienced cannot disappear, one must raise the question whether this holds only for experiencing as such—that is, experiences—or also for the relation of single experiences to each other, and thus naturally for the relation of the person to his experiences. I admit that I hold the latter and broader view, though I cannot bring stringent proof of it. But these discussions have brought us close to the realm of drive-life, a real understanding of which is prerequisite to understanding the psychology of memory.

3. PSYCHOLOGICAL PRACTICE-PHENOMENA

Practice and habit. Practice and interest. Attitude, fatigue, work-curve, stimulation.

The problem of work-achievement we have already met in our discussion of action. It borders on physiological problems. But there is psychological work also: memorizing, calculating, thinking, etc. The factors of practice, habit, fatigue, must be taken into consideration here too. I will present a few data taken from the results of experimental psychology.

Practice effects are rapid in the beginning, but very slow later on. This holds in all psychic activities—adding, memorizing, etc. If the practice of the achievement is interupted, the skill attained by practice is mostly lost. Practice of a function improves similar functions . . . Practice and habit are closely related. According to Ebbinghaus, practice facilitates the emergence, improvement, and acceleration of psychological achievement by frequent repetition; and habit is the resulting integration of achievement into a certain system of connections. Practice is the improvement of the "associative basis" brought about by fre-. quent repetition; habit is the firmness of the associative connections thus gained.

In the course of practice, moreover, the material is again and again re-thought and apprehended in ever new relationships. Our discussion of the phenomenal memories is in point here. New aspects of the material are continuously apprehended, and thereby the task as a whole is better mastered. With practice, a deepening of insight into the structure of the material also occurs, and therefore Ebbinghaus was right: an increase of interest goes along with it. But when we reach the insight that can be gained, interest fades. Still, let us not forget that things offer many possibilities. Muensterberg (572) interviewed a woman who had the boring occupation of wrapping lamp-bulbs into advertisement sheets; she stated that she finds the work interesting, and is full of excitement as to how many boxes she can complete by the time of the next work-pause.

In the course of time certain approaches become dominant, a certain form of thought and action prevails again and again. We speak of attitudes. After we have lifted a heavy weight repeatedly, a lighter weight is lifted with such striking ease that it appears even lighter than we expected. The impulses are, without our directly noticing it, set in accordance with preceeding tasks. Obviously, these attitudes are stands taken concerning the total situation; they are latent determining-tendencies. Interest- and willfactors enter into even the simple function of weight-lifting mentioned above.

Practice is counteracted by fatigue. The effect of mild degrees of fatigue may be limited to specific activities; high degrees affect all activities. Dulling of interest, in the sense discussed above, here plays a great role; but definite feelings of displeasure and disagreeable sensations also appear. For all this, muscle fatigue may serve as the paradigm; mental fatigue is not different. The effect of fatigue is a decrease in work-achievement. The factors of practice and fatigue are present in every continuous workachievement. But the "work-curve" (Kraepelin, 444) indicates yet other influences. In the beginning and toward the end of a piece of work there appears a particular impetus, but from the work itself there also arises continuous stimulation (Kraepelin).

V

DRIVES, WILL, AND ACTION[1]

1. GENERALITIES CONCERNING DRIVE AND WILL

Classification of drives, their varieties. Ego-drives and sex-drives. Freud's view: ego-drives are to be equated with death-drives. Repetition-compulsion. Sadistic impulses as links between ego- and sex-drives. Drive and will have a common root. The differences between drive and will lie in the object, in the kind of motivation, in the level of consciousness, and in the quality of direct-edness. The somatic resonance of drives in comparison to that of the will-action. The differences in resonance are pre-formed by the character of the percept. The somatic resonance of the sexual percept is strong. The somatic resonance of the drive-object is strong. The level of consciousness of the will-object. The act of wishing and the act of willing. The motivation and the effect-value of experiences. The real and the pretext motivation. The activity of the drive. More about active and passive attention. The specific act of will (Ach). The feeling theory of will rejected.

While until recently psychology had little to say about drives and action, now, thanks to Freud, it can offer fundamental information.[2] A discussion of affective life is basically nothing but a presentation of psychoanalytic theories; but we must hasten to add that no part of psychology can be studied thoroughly without taking into consideration the phenomena of drive and will. If therefore a psychology wishes not to by-pass its tasks, it must be based on psychoanalysis.[3]

There is a great variety of strivings. They can be grouped, to begin with, according to their goals. I may crave a noon-meal, or my goal may be to influence the fate of my country decisively, or I may have the urge to empty my bladder, or I may wish to write a good book, or I may long to be close to a beloved person, or I may have a need for sexual gratification. Obviously, the

[1] For Freud's early views of the concepts drive and will, see his *Collected Papers*, Vol. I, particularly (203); see also Freud (231). For his views on action, see (216). Compare also Lewin (495) on action.

[2] Later on Schilder leaned heavily also on Lewin's experimental psychology of action and affect. See Lewin (493, 495), also in Ellis (163).

[3] Cf. Hartmann (321) for a more recent and amplified form of this claim.

manifold of goals, drives, and volitions is immense. Nevertheless, attempts have been made to bring order into this manifold.
According to Balzac, man strives toward three goals: he wants
love, money, and food. Even superficial consideration shows that
attainment of money banishes the danger of hunger too; and one
comes to the simpler formulation that man's goals serve partly
the gratification of his ego, that is, the preservation of the individual, and partly the preservation of the species. It is easy to
find the transition from Balzac's formulation to this.

But the designations "preservation of the individual" and
"preservation of the species" are, of course, incorrect. Fundamentally, as we see at every step, the individual is never satisfied
with preserving what he has. Satiated, we yearn again for hunger;
having reached sexual satisfaction, we feel the desire anew.[4] The
rich man is not satisfied with preserving his possessions, he wants
to have still more; and the ambition of the politician strives for
the maximal power. Thus, in all manifestations of man we find
something strangely immoderate and excessive, a continual dis-
satisfaction, a magnificent extravagance, which appears to us as
the basis of all volition and drive. Neither is it correct to speak
of a drive for the preservation of the species, because this is not
our immediate goal: we are striving for the sexual object and
for the gratification of our sex-drive. We know that the preservation of the species is connected with these, but that is not the
direct motivation of our actions.

Thus we distinguish between ego-drives and sex-drives.[5] This
distinction in principle should be maintained, though there are
basic homologies between the two which have seduced Jung
(394, 395) into speaking of a unitary psychic energy, the psychological expression of which he sees simply in interests. Later on
we will see that there are energy-exchanges between ego- and
sex-drives. Yet psychoanalysis has always maintained that the
two must be distinguished, though it has never clarified exactly
what it means by ego-drives. Originally it used this term to mean
the functions which subserved the preservation of the individual,

4 For the continuous character of drives, see Freud (226, particularly pp.
61–64); on satiation, see also Lewin's collaborator, Karsten (404).

5 This distinction corresponds to that phase of development of psychoanalytic theory reflected in Freud (225, 226, 231). For more recent conceptions,
see Kris (460), and Hartmann (320).

the need for nourishment, the maintenance of social status, etc. In the course of the development of psychoanalysis, more and more of these drives have been conceived of as libidinous, that is, of sexual nature.

According to Freud's (236) most recent discussion, the ego-drives would consist only of the tendency to maintain the present state, and to let this state tend toward its natural end, that is, its pre-destined death. Thus, Freud equates ego- and death-instincts.[6] In the tendency to repeat what has been experienced earlier (such as the repetition of the traumatic scene in the dreams of traumatic neurotics, and the repetition of the scene that drove them into neurosis, in the fantasies and dreams of neurotics while in psychoanalytic treatment), Freud sees a repetition-compulsion[7] pertaining to the ego-drives. The opposition between ego- and sex-drives I consider to be a fact, though I cannot agree with this description of the ego-drives.[8]

In a recently published article, Freud maintained that the death-instincts imply destructive tendencies against one's own ego.[9] These destructive tendencies may be turned outward in the form of sadism. The question arises, do the destructive tendencies in sexuality pertain to ego-drives? My subsequent discussions will closely touch on this question, because to me too sadism, the drive to grasp, to hold, to subjugate, appears to be the connecting link between ego- and sex-drives.[10]

So far we have spoken only of drives. We started from the premise that drive- and will-phenomena share fundamental properties. Indeed, it could be said that in final analysis will-actions rest on drives. The energy-source of drive- and will-actions are the same, but there are qualitative differences between the drive and the will which require attention. These differences lie in four directions: first, in the object toward which the drive or

[6] For a precise statement of Freud's views on this point, see Freud (245), Bibring (71), Fenichel (180).

[7] For a survey of the literature of "repetition compulsion," see Bibring (72).

[8] The psychoanalytic theory prevailing at present uses neither the concept of death-instinct (drive), nor that of ego-instinct (drive); cf. Fenichel (178), Bibring (71), Hartmann, Kris and Loewenstein (319), Hartmann (320).

[9] Presumably Freud (240).

[10] Though this formulation remains within the framework of an earlier phase of psychoanalytic theorizing, in it Schilder anticipates later developments: cf. Hartmann et al. (319), Erikson (166), and Mittelmann (561).

will is directed; second, in the level of consciousness; third, in the relation between the motivations of drive- and will-actions; and fourth, in the quality of directedness.[11]

Many psychologists deny that drives have an object; nevertheless, there is given in each drive a direction toward something, the psychological locus of which is to some extent known to us. Moreover, this object is before us, even if only in vague outlines. The constitution of objects will be discussed in further detail, but it should be pointed out here that they are frequently represented by symbols or symbol-like images. Furthermore, they often appear on a lower level of consciousness. This concept too will be discussed below in greater detail. A further characteristic of drive-like strivings is their great somatic resonance: the drive-object, so to speak, pulls close to the body. The exposition of this point requires some more general considerations.

The following may be considered the prototype of will-actions. The vase that stands on the table arouses my interest; I reach for it to get a closer look at it. While I observe the object, I have a clearly circumscribed picture of it which is definite in all of its particulars; my will and my intending of the object are also given.[12] In addition, a series of sensations—for instance, tension-experiences in the neighborhood of the eye—occur against a background of a complex of coenesthetic sensations.[13] In other words, there is always a somatic resonance coupled with the feelings which are alive in me. Stumpf (822), in order to express the close relatedness of certain sensations to feelings, spoke of feeling-sensations.[14] Undoubtedly, reaching after the object must be considered a voluntary action. Such elements will be found in the analysis of drive-actions also, but when in my hunger I throw myself on the food, grab for it and devour it, the qualities of the food recede, and my sensations and gratification are in the foreground. The drive-object has an *a priori* closeness to the body, and does not stand apart from it as does the object of the voluntary action. When a hungry person sees food, his somatic

[11] "Directedness" translates *sich richten*. Cf. Lewin (495), and Rapaport (658).

[12] "Intending" translates *sich richten*. Schilder speaks here of the "givenness" of both content and intentional act in perceiving.

[13] "Coenesthetic sensations" translates *Gemeinempfindungen*.

[14] "Feeling-sensations" translates *Gefuehlsempfindungen*.

reactions are *a priori* more vehement (salivation, etc.), and claim him in a quite different way.[15]

The processes of perception and sensation provide the foundations for the drive-like or voluntary intending of the object. When I am pricked by a needle, I perceive that I am dealing with a pointed object; yet my somatic reaction, my sensation, my pain, is more important. The same holds for a tasty dish: here too my sensation, rather than the dish as such, is in focus. This is even more true for coenesthesias: for cold, hunger, thirst, comfort, discomfort, etc.

In every percept both perception and sensation play a part. Even discomfort has a residue of an object-perception: there is something about it which comes upon me from the outside. When weights are put on my hand, I can get set to the weight of the objects, or to my pressure-sensations, or, if I lift the weights, to my effort-sensations (cf. Friedlaender, 251). Even in visual percepts, a visual sensation is also present besides the sensation factor already mentioned: the tension in the neighborhood of the eye. Naturally this does not usually become manifest; we infer the sensation-factor of the visual percept only from the simple experiment, that when the eyes close we no longer see objects. In the perception of tridimensional colors, and in the postoperative vision of people who were born blind (see pp. 54, 71–72, above), this sensation-like factor does become apparent. In sexual experience also, there is a powerful sensation-resonance connected with the visual-tactile-kinesthetic sexual percepts. Here too one may be oriented either more toward the object or more toward one's own experience. But without doubt the object here is close to the body—and not only spatially so: it tends to shade into sensations. It is readily seen that drive-objects have a stronger somatic resonance than will-objects, and that they are, as it were, closer to the body.

As a rule we speak of will-actions only when the drive-object is on a high level of consciousness; in connection with drive-objects of a lower level of consciousness we usually speak of instinctual, drive-like, attitudes. This distinction is roughly

[15] Here and in the following the means of "act-psychology" enabled Schilder to delineate drive-objects from the objects of the secondary process more sharply than hitherto had been done.

correct; that it disregards observations about hypnosis will be
discussed later. But drive-actions can take place also at full
height of consciousness, even in the waking state.[16]

These remarks about the object of drive- and will-actions may
be transferred unaltered to the object of the drive-wish and the
volitional wish. These objects may be given as percepts, as images,
or as thoughts. But in both the drive- and the will-act, the act of
wishing or desiring is replaced by that of realization, or action.
This is a specifically different intending of the object. Let us
also remember that everything which emerges in psychic life,
every so-called association, rests basically on drive-like or volitional attitudes. Imagination and thinking should then be considered as internal drive- and will-attitudes.[17]

It has been correctly pointed out that the role of motivation is different in drive-actions and in will-actions. But first
let us consider the nature and meaning of motivation in general.
A hand-grenade zooms over my head, and I duck "instinctively."
A fruit lies before me and I grab after it. Every object, every
situation arouses in me a reaction, an action. May one speak of
motivation in such events? Every impression carries within it,
of necessity, an action-like intending.

Every experience has, as we have said, an effect-value, and a
part of this effect-value becomes manifest in the subsequent
action.[18] But we do not usually speak of motivation in this connection, unless the experience is explicitly conscious as the reason
for the action. For instance, I go from the room because it is too
cold. The experience of the connection is very often deceptive,
however, as has been demonstrated particularly by psychoanalysis.
The disagreeable cold effects my flight. This is a causal connection. I can understand it, but the understanding may be absent,
too. In turn, when I understand an experience to be my motivation, I may deceive myself concerning the true connection.

This much may be said: when a motivation comes to my
consciousness as such, it must follow from another psychological

16 Cf. Rapaport (659).

17 It is unclear in what sense imagination and thinking can be considered
as any kind of attitudes. It is possible that what Schilder meant was that
imagination and thinking should be considered either as organized by drive-
and will-attitudes, or as their expressions and manifestations.

18 Cf. Lewin's (495) concept of "valence."

series. A motivation appears[19] as such only when there is another cross-cutting psychological causal series, as it would, for instance, in the above example if I should be waiting in this room. This becomes much clearer when analyzing actions in which the motivation is given in the form not of a percept, but of a new goal. It may even be said that a motivation appears[20] only where contrary impulses are present.

When I make a decision on the ground of a motivation, the experienced motivation, the fully conscious motivation, need not be the real cause of the action. In fact, it will very frequently be a pretext, and the action will have arisen from the effect-value of other experiences. In will-actions the motivations are in general more often conscious, while drive-actions follow the effect-value of experiences more free of inhibition. Though the man who throws himself on a woman in violent craving may well mention some attribute of hers as his motivation, his action is nevertheless a drive-action. If a psychology takes into account only that which is clearly conscious, it neglects the complicated transpositions of drive-energies which underlie all percepts, images and actions.

Consequently, Wundt's classification of actions, according to the number of their conscious motivations, appears schematic and does not do justice to the difference between drive- and will-actions. Though I consider that the experience of a connection is the same as the connection of experiences, this holds not for the experiences analyzed, but only for the drive-attitudes which emerge from the analysis.[21] In a deep and fundamental sense, however, I experience the former as my real motivation, namely, that my action arises from a definite wish; I experience the latter as a pretext motivation; and simultaneously I am somehow aware of what motivates me to this "motivational displacement."

A drive, as Freud (226) also has stressed, has a pressure charac-

[19] Schilder presumably means "appears in consciousness"; the subject of this discussion is usually treated in the psychoanalytic theory under the heading "overdetermination," or more specifically as "rationalization." Schilder's conception of "motivation" does not become systematically clear. Yet a central conception of his here comes to expression: consciousness arises when an impulse is checked—delayed—by another impulse (cf. Schilder, 751).

[20] *Ibid.*

[21] The point is that the experience of a connection arrived at by a patient in the course of analysis is regarded as a recapitulation of the genetic connection between the "drive-attitudes" underlying the experiences in question.

ter. It has been maintained by many that we are passive in relation to drives. In action I experience myself as active. It is
therefore incorrect to hold that we are passive in drive-actions
and in drive-like intending. We experience a directedness of ourselves. The impression of passivity is an appearance, due to the
fact that often a group of other volitions counterposes itself to
the active drive, and is overwhelmed by it. But the ego is active
both in the drives and in the counterposing "parts" of the
personality.[22] Attention-attitudes too must be considered as drive-
phenomena.[23] Even in so-called passive attention I turn "actively"
toward an object, except that I have not prepared this intending
by a decision of will.[24]

Attitudes, experienced intendings, rule our thinking. But
the inner will-action consists of my explicit willing of a thought,
of a decision. The external will-action also contains an explicit
"I will it." Ach (7, 9) has shown experimentally that this is a
specific experience, present even in simple reaction-experiments.
He demonstrated it clearly by having his subjects learn series of
nonsense syllables, and later presenting the first syllable of each
pair with the demand that the subject rhyme it, etc. Here the
decision to perform the demanded operation had to struggle
against the reproduction-tendencies created by learning. It is in
such situations that the "I really will it" is experienced. It may
be accompanied by tension-experiences in the head. Here the
goal-presentations (Rhyme!) are present either in words or in
imageless forms. The volition is experienced as the doing of the
ego. According to Ach, feeling does not play a significant role here
Michotte and Pruem (556) have carried out similar experiments.[25]
Thus, it must be maintained that there are distinct will-experi-
ences. Though feelings may accompany actions of will, they are
neither an essential nor crucial factor. The feeling-theory of will-
action, developed by Wundt (897), must therefore be rejected.

[22] The formulation "the ego is active . . . in the drives" is confusing.
Schilder may have meant to convey that drives too act through the ego, because the ego not only controls but also executes drive impulses.

[23] This formulation is at odds with the usual psychoanalytic conception
of attention. Cf. Rapaport (658, particularly pp. 321–322); see also (659).

[24] On active and passive attention (attention and concentration), see Rapaport et al. (650, Vol. I), Rapaport (658), and Diethelm and Jones (147).

[25] Cf. Lewin's (490, 492) similar experiments and his analysis of "will";
concerning the latter, see also Lewin (495).

Volition cannot be reduced to intellectual processes, either. In will-action I experience myself as a doer, as a determiner; I am conscious of activity. This state of affairs, which—viewed phenomenologically—is entirely unique in its kind, cannot be explained away.

According to the above considerations, the main differences between drive- and will-actions lie in the constitution of the object towards which they are directed, and in the phenomenal character of the directedness. Though the level of consciousness and the motivation-formation differ in the two, these differences are not of a principal sort.

The effect of will- and drive-attitudes, that is, the dynamics of will and of drive, will later be discussed in detail.

A careful survey of the recent studies on the psychology of will was published by Lindworsky (507). I cannot follow him in his refusal to recognize Ach's determining tendencies. Our present discussion, indeed this whole part, is based on the findings of psychoanalysis. Freud (231) gives an orienting glimpse of the psychoanalytic treatment of the theory of drives; see also his (226). Though my point of view differs from that of Jung, nevertheless I recognize the significance of his studies (393, 394, 395). But it should be mentioned here that Steckel's (793, 794, 796) studies, perhaps with the exception of (795), represent a shallowing of psychoanalysis, in spite of some telling observations in them. They neither give a correct picture of psychoanalytic thinking, nor have a theoretical or factual value of their own.

2. SEXUALITY AND ITS PARTIAL DRIVES[26]

Visual, oral, anal, urethral, mucous membrane, and muscle-erotism and object-erotism. Libido-development. Narcissism. The oral eroticism of the infant. Preliminaries about the Oedipus-complex. Infantile sexual exploration. The castration-complex and its sources. The birth- and sexual-theories of the child. The latency period. The pre-pubertal phase. The development of vaginal sensitivity. The relatedness of all mucous membrane sensations. The morphology of excretory and sex organs points to their function. Ambivalence and ambitendency.

The sexual act proper is preceded by the beholding of the sex-object, which arouses pleasure. Touching, pressing, kissing, biting, hitting, follow. Sexual excitement manifests itself often in an increased urge to urinate and occasionally to defecate. Sex-

[26] The formulations of this chapter are not an adequate sketch of Freud's views, and there is some question whether they were not meant rather to be Schilder's marshaling of the material to suit his integrative purposes. Cf. Freud (206); for more recent systematic formulations, see Sterba (799), Fenichel (180, Chapter 5), and for a genetic as well as ego-psychological treatment, Erikson (166).

uality thus seems to have many auxiliary apparatuses and components. Freud (206) spoke of partial drives of sexuality. We distinguish between oral, anal, and urethral partial drives; between mucous membrane, skin-, muscle-, and motor-eroticism; between sadistic, masochistic and homosexual partial drives, and finally between autoerotism and alloerotism, which turns to other objects.

This fairly planless enumeration needs complementation and ordering. We arrive at the above by considering the development of sexuality in the individual. Sexuality begins with the first breath of man, and ceases with the last; we must add that perhaps the embryo already has sexual excitations. In the moment of birth, sexuality is diffusely distributed over the entire body. The newborn infant is satiated sexually: he needs no external object, and has little or no interest in the external world. His interest is claimed mostly by his own body, and we refer to this as primary narcissism; it could be called self-love or, even more correctly, self-absorbed love.[27]

In the course of feeding, in sucking on the breast, there is an influx of new erotic experiences. After feeding the infant falls asleep, satiated like the adult after sexual gratification: his expressive movements suggest this analogy. This is oral eroticism, which, when not gratified by the feeding, creates for itself new gratifications in the infant's sucking on parts of his own body. Soon the excretions become the source of new sexual sensations. The child learns to increase the pleasures of defecation by specific practices. Masturbation in infants is a common phenomenon: they discover new pleasure possibilities in their own genitals. Naturally, one must not assume a primacy of the genitals as in adults. Later on, the child learns to appreciate his own body as a source of gratification and a secondary narcissism supersedes autoeroticism; it is retained throughout life, together with its primary background. We never give up the love for our own body, though from it arises that love which pertains not only to the body but to our own ego in general. Indeed, we turn a great part of that primary love toward an ideal picture of ourselves, which represents us not truly but rather as we wish to be. We speak of

27 For the standard psychoanalytic formulation cf. Freud (225), and Fenichel (180); but see Hartmann (320) for a more recent view.

an ego-ideal and a superego. Having drawn a dividing line between object and subject, let us remember that not only the body, but images, thoughts, feelings, and strivings fall on the subject side.

Between the third and fifth years of life a particular period of sexuality sets in, which has more clearly circumscribed objects. It might be stressed, however, that the child's object-love is permeated by much stronger autoerotic components than that of the adult. The people who take care of the child, his immediate environment, his parents, present themselves to him as love-objects. They offer him food and kisses, they caress, press, and stroke him, and in the course of the cleansing of the genital region, provide him with sexual sensations.

The first indications of sex-differences appear here: the attraction to the parent of the opposite sex is greater. This attraction rests on somatic impulses. The parent of the same sex early becomes a burdensome, indeed dangerous, competitor. The child wishes him, or her, away. At this level of thinking, "to be away" and "to be dead" mean the same thing. Psychoanalysis speaks of the Oedipus-complex, and means thereby the child's wish to possess the parent of the opposite sex and to kill the parent of the same sex. In the latter wish cruelty, a sadistic attitude, already finds expression. The hate against the parent of the same sex is a mixture of hatred and love. On the most primitive stage of this phase, the homosexual-sadistic attitude is even preponderant. Simultaneously, a particular anal interest comes also to the fore.[28]

This period of sexual activity is simultaneously one of increased interest, curiosity, and urge toward sexual explorations. The child is interested in the genitals of the other sex. The boy cannot imaginatively realize the differences between the sexes, and assumes that women have male genitals. If experience proves his assumption erroneous (often he does not let himself be informed), he may develop the view that girls are robbed of their penises by violent intervention (castration-complex). We are less familiar with the corresponding developments in girls.[29] Yet we know that when girls become aware of the difference, they ex-

[28] For the later developments of these psychoanalytic views, particularly on sadism, see Freud (245, Chapters 3 and 4), Freud (247), and Fenichel (180).
[29] For a later contribution on this problem, see Freud (245, Chapter 5).

perience the lack of penis as a defect (penis-envy feminine castration-complex).

Naturally, the castration-complex has still deeper roots in the ambivalence of sexuality. Everything sexual implies vivid yearning, together with an obscure and powerful contrary impulse. Added to this, the incestuous and sadistic inclinations within the Oedipus-complex evoke guilt-feelings closely linked to the anxiety about the father's vengeance, which naturally will smite that part of the body which has sinned. The narcissism, the love of one's own body, centers in the genitals. Every threat to the body somehow arouses the castration-complex.

About now the child is preoccupied also with the problem of the origin of children. There is a typical infantile theory of birth, which is that the child comes from the anus. Consequently, it is equated in essence with feces. It is easy to comprehend that the child ascribes the ability to bear children to the father also. The subsequent theories of birth are more varied; they take into account the problems of conception also, they distribute the roles between the parents; but the anal zone usually retains a particular significance in them. Thus, Reitler reported the following theory of a child he observed: children are made by the parents putting their buttocks together and flatulating.

After the fifth year of life a period ensues in which sexual interest and excitations recede. It is in this period that the child accepts the parents' stork-story, even though somewhat ironically. Only in puberty does there arise a new and powerful wave of sexuality. This too has its peculiarities: uncertainty about the sex-roles is great, and it seems to be the rule that homoerotic impulses first come to the fore, even if in the form of fanciful friendships, but in final analysis founded on somatic eroticism. The genital zone attains primacy, the sexual excitations center on the genitals, and their stimulation-need, accompanied by object-libidinous imagery, leads to masturbatory self-gratification. In this period the woman must accomplish a particular achievement. In the boy, his penis has had a sexual emphasis since earliest childhood, and pre-puberty brings about only a quantitative intensification of emphasis. In the woman, however, initially the clitoris is the leading part of the genital, and in pre-puberty sexuality must be transferred from the clitoris to the vagina.

Thus a reorientation must take place, and this, as is well known, frequently misfires, resulting in vaginal anesthesia. [30]

Traces of this development are demonstrable in the sexuality of normal adults, but there the erogenous zones of the mouth, nipples, anus, and urethra, are subordinated to the genital sphere. Sexuality is genitally centered, and at the same time directed toward the heterosexual object. The evidence for these assertions of Freud's will be given in subsequent discussions. For the present, a few principal comments must suffice.

The sensations mediated by the various mucous membranes are, beyond doubt, phenomenologically related to each other: a series may be construed reaching from the sexual to the anal. Muscle contractions, secretions, skin-sensations too, play a role here. Evolutionally, the urethra, anus, and sexual organs derive from related matrices, and one need not go back very far in the evolutionary series to reach a place where the organs of excretion and sex all had a common outlet in the cloaca. It is important that this evolutionary continuity is re-presented psychologically. The close relation between sexual excitement and urinary urge, drastically expressed in the phrase *castus raro mingit,* is also in point. It is within the normal range when sexual excitement results in increased intestinal peristalsis. In turn, excitations in the intestines and the bladder react upon the sex organs.

A consideration of the gross morphology of the organs of sex and excretion readily suggests that their spatial closeness, and the partial sharing of their auxiliary organs, have a psychological significance. Morphology here too may prove to be a guide for psychology. We may assume that the psychology of the sex-drive permits a glimpse into its biology also. The sexual tension which manifests itself in the sexual drive is something entirely organic.[31] In the pre-menstruum, sexual excitability is increased.

When we speak of libido we mean primarily something psychological, but also the organic-biological side of the sexual process. Furthermore, our general discussions of the structure of drive-life apply to sexuality. Somatic excitations always play an essential role in the sexual process. The somatic resonance is par-

[30] Cf. Freud (245, Chapter 5).
[31] For a survey of the psychoanalytic view, see Bibring (71); for an independent and confirming view, cf. Beach (49), but see Kinsey et al. (411), and Ford and Beach (195).

ticularly powerful when the libido is turned toward an object. We may add here that the more intense the somatic resonance, the closer to one's body the object is experienced. In the sexual act one's own body seems to merge with that of the partner, and we may consider the inference generally justified that in the sexual experience body and world are permitted an exceptional closeness. But even the most obscure sexual drive implies an object and an intending of it.

Sexual strivings are accompanied by counter-strivings, the forces of attraction by those of repulsion: something drives us away from sexual pleasure, and we gain it only when we surmount these counter-strivings. The temporal relations between striving and counter-striving vary. The counter-striving may manifest itself before the goal is reached, or make its appearance as disgust of sexuality afterwards. These strivings and counter-strivings are accompanied by external feelings as indicators, and it can be said that the feeling-tone of ambivalence attaches to sexuality to a particularly great extent. However, a general theory of drives must point out that ambivalence belongs to the necessary and general characteristics of drive-life.

There are practically no unequivocal strivings, and the bipolarity of drive-life obtains for the alimentary drives also: after satiation the craved-for dish arouses indifference or even disgust. It may be even asked whether or not full satiation *per se* amounts to disgust. Be that as it may, ambitendency and consequently ambivalence are particularly striking in sexuality. From this follows the fundamental point, that from sexuality itself tendencies arise which strive to suppress sexuality. These tendencies are then reinforced by the ego-drives.[32]

The preceding is the essence of Freud's *Three Contributions to the Theory of Sex* (206). The extension of the concept of sexuality aroused strong opposition (most recently by Kretschmer, 453). But the close relation of the "partial drives" to sexuality, in the everyday sense of the word, is an established fact, and there is no reason to limit sexuality to genitality. The theory of perversions speaks too convincingly against it. The development from Krafft-Ebing (447) to Freud is obvious. Freud described

[32] Concerning the relation of ego to sexuality and drives in general, cf. A. Freud (200).

the child as polymorphous-perverse, and this too was found objectionable. But the relation of perversions to childhood sexuality is an established fact. The felicitousness of the term may
be questioned, but it has already established itself. Psychoanalysis
has given up its original thesis that perversions correspond to
revived or persisting partial drives, though as Binet already knew,
perversions make their appearance mostly in early childhood
(ages three to five). According to more recent investigations, childhood perversions arise from childhood neuroses, which are themselves results of complex neurotic transactions. I refer to the
discussion of homosexuality below and to Rank's (647) significant
study, which represents the recent stand of psychoanalysis and
shows how complex these matters are.[33]

3. THE EGO-DRIVES[34]

The physiological apparatuses of the ego-drives are the higher organs of
sense. Prehension. With the ego-drives there is a clearer separation between
body and world. Hunger, thirst, grasping, holding, fending off, repelling. Grasping, making-it-one's-own, as a connecting link between ego- and sex-drives.
Narcissism is related to the ego-drives. Sadism as mediator between ego- and
sex-drives. The relation of destructive drives to Eros is secondary in origin, according to Freud.

We must conceive of the ego-drives as particularly connected
with certain physiological apparatuses.[35] We think of sexuality in
relation to both the sex-organs and coenesthesias. Seeing and hearing too imply drive-like intendings. An object in the peripheral
visual field arouses a drive-like intending of it—in other words,
it arouses the drive to look at it.[36] The road is not long from seeing and hearing to grasping. Schuster (767) observed the revival

[33] Cf. Fenichel (180, Chapter 16).

[34] Concerning the concept "ego drives," cf. footnotes 5,6,7, supra.

[35] While present-day psychoanalytic ego-psychology has abandoned the
concept of ego-drives (for a discussion of energies at the disposal of the ego,
see Kris, 460; Hartmann, 320; and Rapaport, 658), it has come to adopt a view
much like Schilder's, or even one deriving from his, as to the relation of the
ego to physiological apparatuses. Cf. Hartmann (321), see also Rapaport (656).
See also Schilder's conception of the "means layers of the psyche," Appendix,
pp. 347 ff., infra.

[36] Schilder clearly does not refer here to the scoptophilic partial drive, but
to ego-impulses (intentionality) connected with the sense-organs. Whether his
conception is like that of Buehler's (122) "function-pleasure," or more like that
of Mittelmann's (561) "motor drive," remains unclear.

of the archaic grasping-reflex in brain-disorders. I myself have seen compulsive pointing and grasping movements associated with hallucinations. In apraxia, movements are often derailed into primitive grasping movements. The same occurs in hearing. All this leads to the assumption that the higher senses too have drive-functions; and in turn, to the inference that the drive-functions of higher senses are in a closer relation to the ego-drives than to the sex-drives. Even if in these realms there are also drive-like intendings, they are recessive as compared to the clearly conscious ones; and this strongly suggests that drive-like intendings play a more decisive role in sexuality, the level of consciousness[37] of which is lower, than in seeing and hearing. At the same time, it must be pointed out that the seen object appears to us most clearly as an object: in seeing, the separation of body and world is particularly clear.

Yet it must not be overlooked that here too there is a somatic resonance, as in the sensations of eye-muscles and in the changes of blood-distribution never absent in attention. Here again we have an opportunity to deepen our concept of attention. An object appearing in the peripheral field of vision is immediately charged with attention. This charge is an expression of a drive-intending, which is finally followed by action—in this case by eye-movement, in others by grasping. We are once more in the borderlands of physiology, and only by taking attention into account can we explain that while the picture shifts over the retina, the object itself appears to remain at rest (see above).

In speaking of a charge of attention, we imply that attention is something passive, something that follows intending. In this respect it is comparable to feelings. The difference between active and passive attention is that in passive attention the drive-attitude obtrudes either from the inside or from the outside; in active attention the drive-attitude is determined by a volitional decision. But even active attention requires a participation of drives. Thus, we must distinguish between drive-like attention-intending (which is an "active experience" of intending both in active and passive attention) and the attention experience it-

---

[37] Concerning "level of consciousness," cf. Silberer (782), and Rapaport (659).

self (which follows the intending, and is no more active than are percepts).[38]

By ego-drives, we mean primarily those which are related to the maintenance of the individual. He needs food and protection from enemies and dangers. Eyes and ears prepare on the one hand for intake of food, and on the other for the struggle against enemies and untoward events; they also subserve sexuality. Hunger and thirst we must class among the ego-drives proper.[39] Food intake, however, presupposes grasping. The hand and the mouth are the organs of this grasping and incorporation. (Grasping with the hand is itself basically incorporation.) Not only grasping and incorporating, but also rejecting and repelling are in point.

What holds for intake of nourishment may serve also as a pattern for possession-relationships and relationships to the human environment.[40] To possess something means to incorporate it, to count it as belonging to one's own person, to one's own body. To have social power means, basically, to make other people the organs of one's own will. The protection of one's own body may even be considered of crucial importance in the genesis of social organization.[41]* The wish and will to maintain the integrity of one's own body presupposes a drive-like love of it. In other words, ego-drives and narcissism are closely related—that is, narcissism mediates[42] between ego-drives and sex-drives.

There is another and broader realm common to both. We have recognized the importance of grasping and holding for the ego-drives, which subserve the gratification of the needs of the body. But grasping and holding are also essential components of sexuality, and, we may add, so are being grasped and being held. The essential characteristic of sadism is that the sadist wants unconditional power over the other person. He wants to

[38] Concerning the theory of attention of psychoanalysis proper, cf. footnote 23, supra.

[39] Schilder subsumes these under "ego drives" apparently because of their relation to survival; their relation to the oral organizations of libido he seems to disregard here.

[40] Here again Schilder points to a relationship between bodily and social behavior patterns, which has not until recently been appreciated or conceptualized; cf. however Erikson's (166) concept of "organ-modes."

[41]* These considerations are tentative.

[42] How Schilder conceives of this "mediation" remains unclear. For Freud's somewhat similar assumptions, see (239, pp. 62–67) in his discussion of the relation between narcissism, sublimation, and "neutral displaceable energy."

lord it over him, and he causes him pain only to ascertain his unconditional power. But does he not thus deny the independent existence of the other? Does he not destroy it? Here we have a destructive tendency. According to Freud's (236, 240) recent views, this destructive drive, which belongs to the death-drives, becomes connected only secondarily with Eros. In turn, by his sufferance of pains, the masochist expresses only his unconditional dependence. This too suggests that ego- and sex-drives arise from the same ground.[43]

4. REPRESSION AND THE RETURN OF THE REPRESSED[44]

The concept of repression. The relation of repression to ego- and sex-drives. Repression in the narrower and broader sense. Determining tendencies and repression. It is the drive-representation that is repressed. The penetrating power of the repressed. The return of the repressed: examples. The similarity of the returning images to the repressed, and their determination. The similarity of appearance and feeling-tone. The censorship arises from the ego. Repressing forces have an energy-cathexis; as this cathexis decreases, images increasingly similar to the repressed arise. The theory of free association. Countercathexis. Slips of the tongue. An example of parapraxis. The forgetting of names and the determination of forgetting. The repressed reappears piecemeal.

The wish to gratify hunger and thirst, the tendency to avoid harm to one's own body, the striving after power and possession, are recognized and exert their effects in the light of day. These drives are not silently tolerated or rejected; society builds on them. Indeed, we may surmise that society is only the structuralized[45] expression of them. But the sex-drives are not publicly recognized, they are considered at best as private matters; they are in fact proscribed, and considered indecent and sinful. In other words, the attempt is to exclude these drives from the array of phenomena.

This is the reason that repressions are directed primarily toward sex-drives. The concept of repression originated with Breuer and Freud (108). They discovered that disagreeable experiences are excluded from consciousness, are delivered to forgetting; one turns away from them. We have already encountered

[43] The implications of this statement are unclear; cf. Bibring (71).

[44] Freud's theory of repression which Schilder leaned on was stated in (227, 229); the one prevailing at present derives from Freud's *The Problem of Anxiety* (244).

[45] "Structuralized" translates *formgeworden*. Cf. footnote 72, p. 74.

the phenomenon of repression in our discussion of memory. The original Freud-Breuer concept did not point to the relation between repression and sexuality. Only Freud's later investigations made this relationship clear. It is quite conceivable that non-sexual material should also be repressed, but experience has again and again shown that, surprisingly often, it is sexual material which succumbs to repression. In his recent studies Freud has recognized that broad segments of the ego and the ego-ideal may be "unconscious"—that is, repressed.[46] For instance, there are "unconscious" guilt-feelings, which evidently belong to the ego-drives and to the ego-ideal.[47] But if repressions can occur here too, then the repressed ego-drive energy too must be capable of displacement.[48] The mechanisms to be discussed therefore have quite general significance.

Nevertheless we must distinguish repressions in the broader sense—the non-emergence of what lies off the line of prevailing interests—from repressions in the original sense, the repelling of experiences and drives which continuously attempt to emerge. Here we must recall what was said about determining tendencies: they exclude all that does not pertain. The question arises: what is it that is repressed? Primarily it is the content, the image, the object of the drive, the drive-representation; and it should be questionable, *a priori,* whether the drive as such is repressed.[49] Freud (227, 229) speaks only about the repression of drive-representations.[50]

A further question is: what becomes of the repressed drive-representations? According to Freud, they are unconscious. We will return to all these problems later in detail. Here I want to stress only the empirical fact that the repressed experience, or rather the drive which manifested itself in it, does not lose its penetrating power. Freud (203) speaks of a return of the repressed. The repressed returns not in its original, but in a distorted, form.

[46] The apparent implication that all which is unconscious is repressed, certainly does not hold; cf. Freud (239). But that does not seem to be Schilder's point; it seems rather that like Freud before his *The Problem of Anxiety* (244), Schilder uses the term "repressed" as synonymous with "defended against."

[47] This formulation is unclear; cf. Freud (245, Chapter 5).

[48] On the theory of countercathexes, see Rapaport (658, Part VII).

[49] Cf. Rapaport (654).

[50] For Freud's later formulations, see (239, 245, 246).

A few simple examples will illustrate this basically important fact, and give a glimpse into the mechanism. One of my patients, a streetcar conductor, resolved firmly that he must suppress all his sexual thoughts, in order to retain his semen and increase his efficiency. Prior to this he would have nocturnal emissions, accompanied by dreams of sexual intercourse with women. Now the following dream replaced these: he conducts a car, which collides at great speed with a loaded coal-car. In the moment of collision he has an emission. Without going into detail, it can be asserted that the seminal emission gives evidence that the dream was caused by sexual drives. We will not be mistaken if we regard the collision of the cars as a representation of intercourse, in which the male element is represented by the fast-going streetcar, and the female by the heavily-loaded coal-car. The struggle of our patient against his sexuality did not destroy the energy of his sexual drive, but only forced it to find fulfillment in other images. These images are not arbitrarily chosen, but have a certain similarity to those actually intended; it is by virtue of this similarity that they can represent them. This fleeting observation shows that even the choice among the variety of similar images is determined: as a streetcar conductor he conceives the meeting of sexes as a collision of trains. We must assume that the feeling-tone of the experience is also significant: the collision of the trains is anxiety-laden, terrible. Apparently, sexuality must have the same feeling-tone for the patient. We must assume that not only the similarity of appearance of images, but the similarity of their feeling-tone too plays a determining role.

Another example: to her first sweetheart, a young girl expressed curiosity about the looks of the male genital. He explained jokingly that it is red and has green dots; and the naive girl, greatly astounded, believed him. The dream took place a few months later when the girl was struggling against an overwhelming curiosity, which took the form of temptation to cheat her sweetheart with other men; in the meanwhile she had had occasion to convince herself, with him, that the male genital is not thus colored. This dream occurs in a period of unwillingly suffered sexual abstinence: she is in a meadow by a swamp; there is a multitude of snakes coming from the swamp, one after the other; they coil around her thighs; there are dotted and undotted ones; the dotted bite, the others do not; she is afraid of the dotted. Her immediate association is that the dots correspond to those she had imagined. She had asked her sweetheart, half-jokingly, "But are there not perhaps other men who are dotted there?" The dream was anxiety-laden. We can formulate this dream thus: the dreamer has a desire for the penises of men other than her sweetheart. The ego fends against this wish. Freud (204) tellingly describes the censorship which admits the objectionable only in distorted and disguised form. The distortion is only partial. Penis and snake are similar, and of the same ambivalent feeling-tone; and the identifying sign, the dottedness, is unchanged.

A third example: an anxiety-neurotic patient dreams that there is a bed in his room, the posts and boards of which are broken. Associations to the dream reveal that the patient has repeatedly had the fantasy of the bed breaking down while he is having intercourse and injuring his penis. The inference can readily be made that the drive-orientation is directed to the scene in which the genital gets injured. Here censorship has permitted only a fragment to pass, and deleted the rest.

One more example, from a schizophrenic who in the course of several breaks developed delusions of influence. At the time of the episode reported, he had these corrected. He complained that the previous afternoon he had experienced a compulsion to lick the edges of a book. This idea was very troublesome, because he felt he might cut his tongue on the pages. Toward evening another burdensome impulse made its appearance: to go over the rough bedsheet with his tongue. He gives the following associations: before these impulses arose, his girl-friend had visited him; he had the impulse to perform cunnilingus on her, but suppressed it. We see then the original impulse, an objectionable wish; this is suppressed and a less objectionable arises in its place, while the image pertaining to the original impulse is also replaced. Books and female genitals have in common that they open; the bedsheet is contiguous with the original goal. Simultaneously, the patient had the association that the roughness of the book-edge and the bedsheet is as disagreeable to the tongue as that of the female genital.

Here it is noteworthy that the first substitute-image is more disguised than the later one, and that the original tendency obviously persists. It is related to this that any weakening of restraining forces, any lessening of repression-energy, permits the revival of the repressed. Such weakening of repressive forces may come about in various ways: by a natural slackening of attention, or by a slackening of attention in sleep, or by voluntary suppression of directed thinking, which is then replaced by free associations.[51] The latter possibility is the theoretical justification of the psychoanalytic method. In this method we oblige the patient to associate freely, with the expectation that the repressed, which has not lost its effectiveness, will reappear when the countercathexis is lifted.

Our everyday object-directed thinking, which has the objective of adaptation to society, represents such a countercathexis;[52] thus, when this is eliminated, the repressed must reappear. Spontaneous slackening of attention manifests itself in slips of the tongue, slips of the pen, and parapraxes of everyday life.[53] These conditions are particularly amenable to analysis in slips of the tongue. If somebody says "things are becoming queer" instead of "things are becoming clear,"[54] a second train of thought has broken through which, for propriety's sake, should have been suppressed. In such cases, the speaker's self-observations usually give a sufficient insight into the situation. The same holds for slips of the pen. One of my patients complains that recently she has been making particularly frequent slips of the pen. For instance, she wrote Beethoven as Beetopen. The associations show the meaning: bed-open, and its connection to unfilled sexual wishes . . .[55]

The slackening of censorship in dreams will be discussed in connection with them. We may add here that forgetting also plays a role in the psychopathology of everyday life. In the section on memory, we stressed that the corollary of the assumption that

51 Cf. Freud (204, Chapter VII), and Silberer (782).

52 In what sense everyday thinking "represents" coutercathexes is not clear; usually rationalizations are regarded thus, and goal-directed thinking is *safeguarded by*, rather than *representative of*, countercathexes. For a discussion of the psychoanalytic theory of thinking, see Rapaport (655, 658).

53 Cf. Freud (205).

54 This slip replaces Schilder's German, *es sind Dinge zum Vorschwein gekommen.*

55 Schilder's next example is omitted here because it does not lend itself to translation, nor does an analogous English slip readily offer itself.

all experience is indelibly imprinted in memory is the question, "Why are these persisting experiences suppressed and not used?" One of Freud's (205) examples should give an overview of this important problem. He could not remember the name of the painter of the frescoes of Orvieto; instead, the names Botticelli, Boltraffio, Trafoi (a village in Tyrol), arose persistently. Then came an association to the recently received news that a patient, whose impotency had defied treatment, had committed suicide in his despair over it. From here Freud's thoughts glided to a conversation of the preceding day, concerning the peculiarities of Mohammedans. They are engulfed by any misfortune or sickness that befalls them or their closest ones, and exclaim, "Lord, what are we to do!" They are stricken by misery beyond all speech when impotence befalls them. "Lord" in Italian means "Signor," and now Freud finally found the name sought: "Signorelli."

Our conception is that there was a repression-tendency directed at the painful memory of a patient's suicide. The motivation of the suicide was impotency, which in turn was the theme of the conversation about Mohammedans; the conversation therefore was prone to arouse the painful memory. Thus, the repression tendency extends to this conversation and to the expression "Lord," which may be considered its representation. With it, everything of similar or identical meaning—thus also the word "Signor"—is suppressed. This is the reason that only the "Signor" part of "Signorelli" is lost. It is noteworthy that the word is broken up mechanically, without regard for its meaning; one part, the most innocent, escapes repression and appears in the substitute "Botticelli." At this point, the forbidden "Trafoi" (forbidden because it recalls the painful event)[56] comes to the fore in the name "Boltraffio," preparing the definitive break-through of the repressed.

We have here a complicated system of transactions, which may be summarized by saying that the repressed reappears piecemeal in consciousness, in such fashion that those parts of it which have already found conscious expression do not recur any more.[57]

[56] I.e., the suicide of the patient.

[57] This is one of Schilder's central conceptions concerning recall; see p. 191, infra; cf. also Schilder (751). It derives partly from Poetzl's (631) experi-

In the avoidance of the repressed, similarities play the same role as they did in the preceding examples. The essence of these considerations is: the repressed is that which is not consummated psychologically. Everything unsettled and drive-like strives to reach settlement, and in final analysis there is only one kind of settlement: drive-gratification. Until this is attained, the process has not reached closure; therefore the tendency is to produce images ever more similar to that originally intended. The similarity may be either objective or in feeling-tone. Similarity may be replaced by partial identity, and that which is intended may be replaced by something spatially or temporally contiguous with it. These are the possibilities within which one intended image may yield to another.[58]

Freud (227) assumes a primal repression taking place in childhood, in which the drive-representation is denied entry into consciousness. This is accompanied by a fixation (206). The representation in question persists from here on, in a state of repression, with the drive fixated to it. The next phase of repression pertains to psychological derivatives of the repressed representations; consequently, repression proper is after-expulsion. Besides the repelling force which exerts the repressive effect from the side of consciousness, the attraction which the primally repressed exerts on anything that becomes related to it also plays a role here.

For a summarizing statement on repression, see Freud's paper "Repression" (227). Concerning slips of the tongue and forgetting of names, compare Freud's *The Psychopathology of Everyday Life* (205). Ranschburg's (649) objections to Freud's theory of name-forgetting I regard as having no foundation. The theory of repression has, to my mind, anticipated essential discoveries of Kuelpe's (470) school concerning determining tendencies (7, 8, 9), tasks, etc.

5. SYMBOLISM[59]

Non-settled psychological material is delivered after a delay. Poetzl's dream-experiments. The generality of this rule. How does the repressed manifest itself? Formal consideration of images: they either point beyond themselves or are self-contained. Condensations, symbol-like images, symbols, allegories, meanings. The symbolic overtone of all images.

Everything psychological which is not settled[60] strives for settlement; the incomplete strives for completion. This seems to

---

ment, and partly from Schilder's observations on organic cases; cf. Schilder (752). Later on Schilder used Lewin's (495) experiments and theory—on the resumption and recall of interrupted activities—to support this view.

58 Cf. Schilder (752, particularly pp. 528–530).

59 Cf. Silberer (782); Schroetter (760); Roffenstein (676); Nachmansohn (575); and Jones (388, Chapter 3); also Schilder (745).

60 By "not settled" Schilder means: an ideational representative, the drive-cathexis underlying which was not discharged; that is, a not-consummated idea, action or impulse.

be a general law which holds for perceptions too. Poetzl (573) has demonstrated that everything which in tachistoscopic exposition of a picture is immediately apprehended, fails to appear in subsequent dreams; those parts of the picture which at the time of exposition were not apprehended, do find their way into subsequent dreams, even though in partly distorted and condensed form. Similarly, Allers (776) has demonstrated that non-apprehended parts of pictures re-emerge in subsequent association-experiments. Finally, Poetzl has demonstrated that this mechanism plays a role in hallucinations also: in a case of alcohol hallucinosis, only those parts of pictures were hallucinated which at the time of tachistoscopic exposure were not perceived. Here too the subsequently delivered parts showed distortions. There is an analogy here to repression. It may be said that the perceptual process progresses in stages, may suffer interruption at any of these, and has the tendency to reach its goal in spite of this.[61]

It is necessary to form a more exact conception of how the repressed delivers itself in spite of repression. First, a few formal comments. There are images (both perceptual and imaginal) which are completely self-contained, and do not point beyond themselves. Thus, the snow I see on the window-sill is simply snow. An imaginary picture of the Danube does not point beyond itself either. But there are others which arouse a certain disquiet in us, which have the tendency to arouse images and thoughts beyond themselves. From the previous examples, the image of licking the edge of a book is pertinent here. If we consider its genesis, we note that it is built of the same components into which it tends to decompose. On the other hand, we could say that in its origin two spheres of images interpenetrated and condensation took place. But we must hasten to add that the condensation-product is in this case actually a façade: only one of the images appears in the final product, while the other—apparently the more important—is given merely as a tendency.

In such cases it will be useful to speak of a symbol-like image, and to distinguish this on the one hand from condensations in the narrower sense, in which the final image clearly indicates some components of the repressed also, and on the other hand from symbols. Examples of these symbol-like images are abundant

61 Cf. Rapaport (654, Chapter VIII, particularly 1 A and B).

in the mixed compositions of dreams . . .[62] Clearly condensations are a step closer to the complete decomposition of the image than are the symbol-like images. We speak of symbols only when the image points beyond itself.

Symbol and meaning must be sharply distinguished: it does not mean the same thing when I say that an image symbolizes a thought, as when I say that it means this or that. In the symbol there is a wavering back and forth between that which is symbolized and the symbol, there is no one-to-one relationship; but the image of the triangle drawn by the mathematics-teacher means the concept of the triangle. The allegory may be classed between symbol and meaning. It may be said that it is the essence of allegory that, though that which is allegorized is unequivocally given, the image which serves as allegory retains some value of its own.[63]

In general, in the series which leads from perception to the meaningful image, the image loses in value progressively; in the case of the triangle only the concept has meaning, and no longer the image. In the symbol, the image is still the essential. We might, therefore, set up the following gradations: 1) self-contained image; 2) symbol-like image; 3) condensation-image; 4) symbol; 5) allegory; 6) meaningful image.

Let us note that once repression has taken place, the image that appears no longer has the self-certainty and self-containedness of those images that are not built on repression.[64] Moreover, it must be asserted that the repressed is in some form present in any image that represents it. To decide in what form it is present is an important issue. These formal considerations have a limitation. The conception of a sharply circumscribed image is but a theoretically postulated limiting case; it will never exist in reality, because every image and every percept is the consummation of drive-attitudes; and in final analysis, my prior attitudes enter every perception and memory of mine, without my being fully conscious of them.[65] In this sense, every image has a "symbolic" overtone.

[62] Cf. Schilder (691) and the references in footnote 135, p. 217.

[63] Cf. Silberer (782).

[64] Here Schilder attempts to combine act-psychological and psychoanalytic considerations. This subtle analysis, though promising, has not been carried far either by Schilder or by others; cf. Sartre (684).

[65] Here drive-attitudes of psychoanalysis and intendings of act-psychology are equated. Moreover, the conceptions that became common with the advent of the "new look" perception psychology are here anticipated.

There are always pre-phases in which condensations have taken place, and since nothing psychological is ever lost, the image is surrounded with this prehistory as a halo.[66] We have now gained a tentative survey of the theory of repression.

6. PSYCHOLOGICAL ENERGY AND EFFECT-VALUE[67]

The relation of drives to time. Drive-energy. Drive-determination of association. The indestructibility of psychological energy. The transformation of repressed psychological energy into somatic processes: conversions, anxiety, disgust. The hysterical attack as conversion-symptom. The embeddedness of psychological experiences into the total happening. The effect-value of psychological experiences. Effect-value and voluntary effort. The effect-value and the apparatuses it affects. The psychological causal chain is not crossed by somatic influences. The dependence of effect-value on the past. The repressed experience and the image in general as occasional apparatus (Bleuler) and as distributor of energies.

Now we turn to the most important problem of psychological relationships, which we touched on in the first introduction. Drives take their course in time, and a theory of drives which does not treat of temporal relations neglects the most important problems. Every drive strives towards its gratification, and the first effect of mounting drive-tension is the clear appearance of the drive-representation.[68] Thus, the sexual desire will at first manifest itself as a dull excitation with an unknown object, until finally perhaps the image of a woman's naked body will appear. To this image may be adjoined a series of actions which lead to the gratification of the sex-drive. Under certain circumstances, the drive will be aroused only by the naked female body. We might say that the drive has a certain energy which is spent by the sexual activity. Obstacles encountered by the drive-gratification decrease this expenditure. But it is conceivable that the energy so saved is spent in other ways. In the sense of our previous discussions, we might say that this series is amenable to causal treatment: the onset of drive A results in image B and action C, provided that no other causal factors interrupt their causal series.

It must be stressed again and again that the so-called association issues from drive-like sources. The course of thoughts is

66 I.e., Schilder's "sphere."
67 Cf. Schilder (709, 708), and (750, Chapter 21).
68 Cf. Freud (216).

causally determined by experiences and the drive-attitudes attached to them.[69] The post-hypnotic command is carried out when
the patient has had the experience in hypnosis that he took the
command upon himself. It is this acceptance of the command
which is dependent on drives, and which determines the execution.
We have thus a rigorously knit causal system before us.

This system is connected with the assumption of psychological energy, because A can affect B only if it expends a certain
energy.[70] To assume such an energy is as justified as the assumption of energy in physics.[71] If this comparison is justified, there
must follow from it as a further assumption the indestructibility
of these energies. Now, all observations bespeak this assumption.
When the sex-drive is not gratified it persists, causing psychological and somatic phenomena—restlessness, tiredness, sleeplessness—
and the frustrated person will obsessionally produce sexual ideas.
But what happens when these sexual ideas are repressed? The
drive will produce others which originate in the same sphere. For
instance, instead of the intended image an apparently more harm-
less one will arise; but the unsatisfied drive will be gratified only
when the sexual image is again reached, and is followed by sexual action. It was Breuer and Freud (108) who first recognized
this relationship. Affect-toned painful experiences succumb to
repression, and are prevented from exerting their effect and reaching discharge.[72] The psychic energy which is not used up pushes
substitute-formations to the fore.

At this point these investigators hit upon a phenomenon both

[69] Here Schilder does not find the link between his conception of memory
as an apparatus, and reality-adapted memory functioning, and the drive-
determined phenomena of memory functioning. For a theory similarly defi-
cient, see Rapaport (654). Indeed, only recent psychoanalytic ego-psychology
has found ways to meet this problem; see Hartmann (321), Rapaport (658);
compare also Klein (417, 418).

[70] The issue implied here is that of the nature of energies at the disposal
of the ego. Cf. Hartmann (320), Rapaport (658, Part VII).

[71] The grounds of this justification which have been continuously taken
for granted by psychoanalysts have not been clarified to this day, though it
seems both plausible and tempting to treat the phenomena Schilder discusses
in such terms. For a similar treatment, see Lewin (493, 494, 495), and Rapaport
(657).

[72] For a critique of this formulation, which is frequent and was used occasionally also by Freud (205), see Rapaport (654). The formulation is misleading in that it suggests that the affect-tone is the dynamic cause of repression.

remarkable and important. A part of the unused psychic energy is transformed into not psychological but physical phenomena, paralyses, contractures, vasomotor phenomena, seizures. Freud designated this process as conversion. The transformation of repressed affects into anxiety and disgust also belongs in the realm of conversion.[73] A typical conversion is the representation of the desire for the sexual act in the hysterical seizure; a close study of its mechanisms is instructive. Originally the position and movements of intercourse are intended. But this posture is censored, and only the exaggerated pushing forward of the lower part of the body is retained. Corresponding to the rejection, head and neck are retroflexed in the extreme. Thus, the hysterical seizure represents a condensation of contrary wishes, of which the wish for intercourse must be considered the driving force which provides the energy for staging the seizure. Naturally this does not exhaust all the factors involved; more thorough study would probably show that infantile combinations of movements also play a determining role in the seizure.

Here we are concerned only with establishing that the psychic energy of the intercourse-wish is not lost.[74*] The psychic energy of the wish for intercourse originates in very tangible somatic influences; and we may at once add that the causal structure of psychic life stands in direct causal relation to somatic effects, and is thereby joined to the general causality of nature. Naturally, the hysterical seizure is not arbitrary but follows somatic laws. To avoid for the time being the issues involved, let us point out only that in individuals so disposed, hysterical seizures may be replaced by epileptic ones, the organic relationships of which are unquestioned.

We must keep in mind that the emergence of an idea too is dependent on a multitude of somatic factors, which is easiest seen in how the intoxicated person permits uninhibited emergence of ideas which others suppress. The intoxicated person

[73] For the later theory of anxiety, see Freud (244); cf. also Rapaport (660).

[74*] Energies pertaining to the sexual drives we term libido. But psychoanalysis means by the term "libido" not only the energy but also the experience. [This comment is certainly confusing. "Libido" in psychoanalytic theory is definitely an explanatory and not a descriptive concept. It is possible that Schilder meant: not only drive-actions but experiences (ideas) too are treated by psychoanalysis in terms of the explanatory concept "libido."]

reacts differently to immediate experience than the sober person. The execution of a plan of revenge may be arrested by tiredness suddenly setting in.

These examples should make clear the tremendous and continuous influence of somatic changes on the effect-value of experiences. Digestion, sleep, internal secretion, are all involved, and single somatic changes are intimately interwoven with the total somatic constitution. Every so-called association is determined by the effect-value of the preceding ones. The concept of effect-value is such that it points only to the theoretical ordering of connections between experience. It disregards totally whether that which dynamically regulates the course of the experience in question, that is, whether the energy (by analogy to the concepts of natural science) which determines the course of events, is or is not amenable to internal perception.

The effect-value is presumably reflected in the manner of intending, in the kind of qualitative coloring of the act-experience. Thus, an event which elicits deep and long-lasting sorrow would, in the course of the experience itself, arouse the consciousness that this event will lastingly affect one's life. The experience-quality of sorrow itself implies this. A voluntary decision already bears the possibility of its realization. But it is a mistake to assume that decisions of will which are particularly difficult have a particularly great effect-value. Strong volition is marked rather by the fact that a decision, once made, implies smooth action without exertion and without renewed decisions.[75] The will must have a well-functioning apparatus at its disposal, and this suggests that, strictly speaking, we must distinguish between two components of effect-value: on the one hand, the effect-value itself; on the other, the apparatus which the effect-value influences. While we can assume that the effect-value itself is represented psychologically, to assume the same for the apparatuses would be difficult.[76] At any rate, effect-value is not a descriptive concept.

[75] Cf. Lewin (495, particularly II. 2).

[76] The use of the concept "apparatus" here again implies considerations like those from which Hartmann's (321) concept of "automatized apparatuses of secondary autonomy," and Hebb's (328) concept of "assemblies," arose.

The similarity of Schilder's conception of "affect-value" to Lewin's "valence" has been already commented on. It is a conception of situational causality in which experiences are not traced to their genetic and dynamic sources for the understanding of their motivational role, but are treated as irreducible units having motivating power: "effect-value."

Thus, we come to the view that all drives, both ego-drives and sexual ones, have energy; that this energy is related to the somatic sphere; and that the causal sequences of drives cogwheel into the biological chains, and are dependent upon somatic conditions. Psychological experience, therefore, may be considered a causal sequence. It is due to drive-motivation that experience arises from experience.[77]

The psychological causal chain has its own peculiarities: present experience is the causal consequence of preceding ones, and the somatic conditions may alter only the form of it, but cannot sever psychological causality.[78] Thus, in a sober state hostility may breed only ideas, in drunkenness it will spit forth words; but in both cases the hostility attached to previous impressions is the cause of the subsequent psychic happening. It may be asserted that, in psychological life, drives are the sole causal determiners. But how do we conceive of this causal series? The drive as such is not to be considered as the causative A, any more than gravitation causes stones to fall. Rather, the stone falls because it was loose; and in our case, a certain experience which aroused hostility is the cause of the hostile thoughts or utterances.[79]

Every experience has a certain effect-value. The effect-value depends in part on the experience itself; every experience elicits drive-impulses which are partly molded by the experience. But as will be discussed later, every experience passes through layers of past experiences, arousing new drives anchored to them. The effect-value is therefore dependent upon the entire past, which we can trace by means of psychoanalysis. At the bottom of all experiences lies the drive-constitution; therefore, the effect-value of experiences depends always on constitutional factors also.[80] This factor too is psychophysical: it manifests itself in a certain physique, pattern of internal secretion, brain-formation, and

[77] This formulation takes only the primary-process connections of experiences into consideration, and disregards those of the secondary process; cf. Rapaport (655).

[78] Cf. Schilder (752).

[79] These relationships of causality and precipitation imply the issue of overdetermination. Lewin's (495) theory gets around this issue by assuming that it is the needs that give valences to objects and events.

[80] Cf. Rapaport's presentation of this issue, which is much influenced by Schilder's views (658, Part VII, particularly Section XII).

finally a certain temperament. Kretschmer (456, 457) has pointed to the close relation between psychological temperament and body-build. Besides these constitutional factors, determining the effect-value, there are somatic influences of other kinds also.[81]

Thus, the assumption of a psychic energy proves heuristically valuable, although it raises many—at this time, unsolvable—questions. Is the psychological energy of a person constant? Does it change in the course of life? These questions require thorough study.

Does not the hysterical seizure discharge energy? Is it correct to assume that psychological energy manifests itself continuously in such seizures? Where does the energy manifested in these seizures come from? Why does the energy discharged in seizures work differently from that discharged in real gratification? Bleuler (83) too concerned himself with these important questions, and maintained that one cannot speak of abreaction here, but only of occasional apparatuses which are assembled and rebuilt. But what about psychological energy?—are the conceptions we developed above false? We must assume that the psychological image is an energy-receiver. It directs and conducts psychological energy in a certain direction, in that of the seizure. When it has expended its energy, it replenishes itself by attracting new energy from the total organism.

The repressed is therefore an accumulator-apparatus for psychic energy. This is why it retains its effect-value as long as it is not dissolved. This conception is important: it leads to the assumption of many small energy-reservoirs. This holds for the gross organic apparatuses, the cortical and the subcortical. The speech-pressure of sensory aphasics, as well as the motility-pressure of hyperkinetics with subcortical lesions, must continuously attract new energies. About every experience we must ask therefore not only its effect-value, but also whether or not it serves as a continuous energy-receiver. It can do this only if it is connected with certain drives, which continuously replenish its energies. Ob-

[81] While the assumption of constitutional foundations of psychological individuality seems to become more and more a necessity (Freud, 246), the typological approach to these constitutional foundations seems to become less and less promising; this is shown by Sheldon's (775, 776, 777) adverse critique of previous typologies, and the increasingly dubious results others (353, 354) have obtained with Sheldon's method.

viously, experiences and images serve as energy-distributors. Indeed, the function of the brain at large might be thus conceived of.[82]

The ideas developed in the preceding I have attempted to substantiate in a series of articles, particularly (704, 699); cf. also (707, 708). The views here expressed are entirely "voluntaristic" and lean closely on psychoanalysis. Specht (748) too takes a voluntaristic view of psychological happenings; his report on the pathology of attention is otherwise also well worth reading.

7. THE TRANSFORMATIONS OF DRIVE-ENERGY[83]

Libido and ego-drive energies. Repression presupposes a counter-cathexis. The transformation of image into percept by means of additional energy. The transformation of repressed energy into compulsion-cathexis. The repressed impulse changes into a compulsion-cathexis. Sublimation. Sublimation as utilization of repressed drive-energies in the service of the ego-ideal. Fluid boundaries between neurosis and sublimation. Displacements of energies between sexual drives. The utilization of libido by ego-drives and vice versa. The significance of sublimation. Psychogenic and phenomenological structure. Psychogenetic study is not a devaluation.

The energy of sex-drives we term libido, in contrast to ego-drive energies. We must assume that ego-drives and sex-drives oppose each other. Freud's original assumption was that repression is effected by ego-drives, and this view was our starting-point too. In the meanwhile, however, the concept of narcissism was developed, which embraces much that had been ascribed to the ego-drives. In the presentation above, no sharp line was drawn between ego-drives and sex-drives;[84] and the ego-ideal in particular, upon which so much energy centers, must not be related to the sex-drives alone. In any case, repression originates from the ego-ideal.[85] The question is: what are the energy relationships between repression and the repressed? Obviously, it takes energy to maintain repression, and since we see that it is maintained, we must assume that the repressing force is balanced against the tabooed drive-impulse. Psychoanalysis speaks of cathexes and countercathexes.[86]

Thus, though repression keeps certain contents out of con-

82 Cf. Schilder (708, 729).

83 Cf. Freud (226, 230) and (245, Chapters 3–4).

84 Cf. however Hartmann's (320, 321 a) conception, according to which the countercathexes used in defenses would originate in aggressive drives.

85 "Ego-ideal" is used here as a synonym for superego.

86 Cf. Freud (227, 229).

sciousness, it by no means destroys their energy;[87] and the repressed does not even suffer changes, except that now it appears in
substitute formations. In general, when impulses unacceptable to
society are repressed, energy must become free which is then
displaced to other formations. An example of this is the hysterical seizure—a substitute of intercourse: it is a successful displacement, not valued by society, but tolerated as a necessary evil. Now
the transformation into pathology need not be somatic; the undischarged energy may be transposed to other psychological
functions. Thus, ungratified sexuality may intensify images into
hallucinatory perceptions, as is the case in hysterical and hysteri-
form wish-deliria: for example, a young girl's rocking a piece of
wood as though it were the longed-for child. The unused energy
may become the cathexis of a compulsion. Obsessional ideas, as
is well known, are those which obtrude continuously on the
individual against his will. Where do such thoughts get their
energy?—from repressed impulses, repressed drives.[88]

Here repression leads to illness: the energy of the repressed
is transformed into pathological phenomena. In such cases, the
ego-ideal cannot make use of the repressed energy, and so this
energy evades the positive demands of society. All pathological
phenomena derive their energies from drives. When the compulsion-neurotic speaks of obsessional thoughts and images, he conceals from himself and others that their contents are more or
less distorted drive-goals. The formal change, whereby that which
is wished for appears as mere image, is the effect of repression.

This can be well demonstrated in individual cases. Two of
my patients had the impulse to utter obscene words. They suppressed the impulse, but could not overcome the obsessional
idea that they had indeed uttered them. Here the change of the
impulse into the cathexis of the obsession is obvious. In hysteria
too, we can easily demonstrate that it is the drive-wish which
turns the image into perception. Besides these formal changes
of drives, repression makes for changes in content also. We have
not exhausted even the possibilities of formal changes.

Yet pathology is not the only outlet for repressed drive-
energy. It can be turned to socially useful goals; we then speak of

---

[87] But cf. Freud (246).
[88] Here again the term "repression" is used synonymously with defense.

sublimation,[89] and mean by it the use of the sexual energies in the service of the ego-ideal. It may be considered sublimation when the sadistic partial drive is inhibited and its energy makes its bearer a surgeon, a vivisecting biologist, or a good butcher.[90] We also speak of sublimation when the homosexual partial drive is repressed, and reappears in the inclination to social activity with others of the same sex.

Obviously, the dividing line between neurosis and sublimation is entirely fluid. If such a large portion of a sadistic partial drive is sublimated into occupational ambition that no room is left for erotic gratification, we have a neurosis before us. A second factor that distinguishes neurosis from sublimation is the fixation of libido in neuroses; the person who sublimates can easily withdraw a part of the libido tied up in sublimation and use it for direct drive-gratification. There is, however, one common point to neurotic displacement and sublimation: the new goal is related to or partially identical with the original one, it belongs to the same sphere, it originates from the interference of two drive-impulses and satisfies both simultaneously. The homosexual satisfies his sublimated partial drive in social activity, which on the one hand brings him together with men and on the other satisfies strivings of his ego-ideal.[91] In other words, the new goal is a compromise between the two drive-impulses. This is true for both sublimations and neuroses. A unitary drive-impulse brings forth the image which corresponds to it, and does not point beyond itself. The sexually aroused person will imagine or dream of naked bodies, of partners of the other sex; but if there is a multiplicity of drive-impulses present, the image produced will have the tendency to disintegrate that was described above.

For instance, in the earlier example, the book is thought of

89 The concept of sublimation is a most confused one in the pschoanalytic literature. Sometimes it appears as a "vicissitude of drives," as in S. Freud (226), sometimes as a mechanism of defense, as in A. Freud (200), and sometimes as a category all by itself, as here and as in the survey of Sterba (798) and critique of Levey (487). In the treatment of artistic and other creative processes, the concept is slowly being replaced by more complex and more specific conceptions; cf. Kris (461).

90 The understanding of the complexity of the factors which enter occupational choice may well contribute in due time to the clarification of part of what was crammed into the concept sublimation; cf. Ginzberg et al. (281).

91 Cf. Freud (237).

instead of the female genital, and ego-ideal and sex-drive are equally satisfied. This is a symbol-like image, and such images are compromise formations. When a symbol-like image becomes a meaningful image, the drive has succeeded in exerting its full effect. In our example, the patient became aware of his impulse, in final analysis. Even when the impulse and the drive-goal proper are already conscious, the symbol-like images may still surround the unequivocal image as live residues of previous inhibition. It is now clear that the formal considerations I have put forth help us to understand drive-processes.

Which drives succumb to repression? What is transformed and sublimated? The displacement of energies occurs under the direction of images, and is made to related images. The energy connected with sex is readily displaced amongst the partial drives. Repressed genital libido may appear as anal or urethral libido; therefore, sexual excitement may manifest itself as a urinary or retentive urge, and may appear as a conversion symptom in hysteria. Hysterical vomiting is a conversion into the oral sphere. Accordingly, the exchange of energy amongst the sex-drives is frequent. Transpositions of energy take place between sex- and ego-drives also. Sublimation is the utilization of sex-energy in the service of ego-drives and ego-ideal.[92] Ego-drives and narcissistic libido repress genital sexuality and its partial drives; and every partial drive represses the others, once it has secured the support of the ego-drives and ego-ideal. Narcissistic libido thus supplies repressive energy against object-libido. We know, for instance, that the overt homosexual represses his heterosexuality.

Just as sex-drives can be repressed by the ego, however, the unused energies being put into the service of ego-drives, so too ego-drives may be repressed and their energy used to subserve sexuality. In such cases, ego-drive energy is transformed into libido: in orgasm all energy is converted into sexual, the world submerges, and the energy usually invested in it is turned toward the sex-object.[93]

I add here one more indication of the importance of sublima-

[92] Cf. Kris's (460, 461) conception of "regression in the service of the ego," which dispenses with the concept of ego-drives and offers a different explanation (bound and neutralized cathexes) of ego-energies.

[93] Ibid.

tion. While the child lives out its sexual partial drives, we adults have learned to renounce their full gratification. It is only by this renunciation that we became capable of culture. The child must give up its pleasure in feces and urine, must curtail his lust for cruelty, must not let his homosexuality unfold. The energies so gained become available for cultural purposes: the homosexual impulses attain a decisive role in cementing associations of men,[94] from which in turn—according to Schurtz (766)—issue the formation of states; energetic defense against enemies, and the pleasure in attack too, are probably related to sadistic impulses; the role of repressed partial drives in art and science must be discussed later in greater detail. One general comment: states, like art and science, have a complex structure, the nature of which is by no means revealed by discovering the sources of the energy involved in creating them. This is easier to see in objectified formations than in psychological phenomena, for which it also holds. Thus, if we succeed in demonstrating that saintliness and the bliss of resting in God are rooted in repressed sexual energies, we do not thereby explain the phenomenology of these experiences; nor does psychogenesis crucially contribute to understanding the order of value they possess.[95]

Concerning sublimation, cf. Bernfeld's (64) article.

8. REGRESSION[96]

Concept of regression. Sexuality and its partial drives are organically-biologically rooted; but the role of experience must not be underestimated. Regression as arousal of drive-attitudes and rearousal of past experiences. Formal regression. Regression pertains both to ego-drives and sex-drives. The basic biogenetic law.

Our discussions so far have by-passed a very important principle. If the main stream of sexuality is obstructed, the partial drives, the abandoned side-runs, fill up again. When the neurotic's sex-life is frustrated, his mature sexuality has no outlet; a back flow of libido comes about, and infantile partial drives, as well as an infantile world of images, revive.[97] For instance, the

[94] Cf. Freud (237).
[95] This is apparently Schilder's formulation of the issue of functional autonomy; cf. Allport (25, 26), Hartmann (321), Rapaport (656).
[96] Cf. Fenichel (180, particularly pp. 53, 65, and 159 ff.).
[97] Cf. Freud (206), also (204, Chapter VII).

mouth may again be experienced as the locus of sexual excitement. The fantasy of pregnancy induced by a kiss may be the background of hysterical abdominal pains. Every inhibition of libido brings a revival of its abandoned positions, that is, a return to a previous stage of sexuality. We refer to this as regression. Regression of libido vitalizes partial drives because they are primitive levels of sexuality, predecessors of genitally centered sexuality.

The question continuously arises, which factors determine that a certain partial drive or drives be revived in a given regression? We assume that the partial drives have organic roots. Research in genetics has demonstrated that heredity plays a certain role in homosexuality; therefore, it may be regarded as biologically rooted. We relate every other partial drive also to an organic-biological factor, i.e., to sex-constitution. We may assume that constitutional formation of the drive will determine whether or not, and in what fashion, regression will take place.

Biological quality is not an abstract notion for us: it must manifest itself in definite experiences. In the third to fifth years of life, the period so crucial for sexual activity, sexual experiences are extremely varied as regards partial drives. We also have reason to assume that the sexual constitution is not alone responsible for this, but that it may be crucially influenced by concrete experiences, since at this age it is so malleable. For instance, it makes a difference whether the child's sadistic or masochistic impulses are reinforced by spanking, or whether he is exposed to inordinate sexual stimulation by excessive tenderness of the parents. Experience and sexual constitution are of equal weight here.[98] We have repeatedly stressed that every drive has an object; accordingly, the revival of infantile partial drives does not occur in the abstract, but rather implies the emergence of infantile drive-objects also. With the revival of partial drives, specific childhood memories also arise. The concept of regression denotes both that (1) early drive-attitudes arise, and (2) previous drive-objects emerge.

This regression in drives and drive-goals is usually accompanied by a formal regression also.[99] In the shaping of drive-objects, symbols and symbol-like formations play an increased

[98] Cf. Erikson's (166) treatment of the nature of regression. See also Freud (210, 230, 233).

[99] Cf. Freud (204, Chapter VII).

role. The concept of regression must not be limited to sexuality, though it is most easily seen there. There is regression in the development of intelligence also, which we will speak about later. Regression to an earlier stage may be partial, and need not mean a return in every respect. Finally, a complete identity between the products of regression and previous developmental stages is neither theoretically expected nor empirically found, because new functional connections and new modes of apperception have since come about.[100] Head's (324) view of the process and apparatuses of sensation is in point here: the hierarchic layering, so exactly demonstrable psychologically, exists also in the purely organic realm. However, a complete understanding of the concept of regression must take into consideration all the objections to, and limitations of, Haekel's basic biogenetic law.

9. THE DREAM[101]

a) Dream-stimuli, hallucination, projection

Influence of external stimuli on dreams. Stimuli cannot explain the specific dream-content. The psychoanalytic method. Significance of attitudes. Resistance. Complexes. Fact-diagnosis. The problem of hallucination. Fluid transition between images and percepts on lower levels. Eidetic images more frequent in youth. Drives and perceptual world. Wish-dreams and dreams of comfort. Image vs. percept: dependence on libido-cathexis. Attitudes determine differences not only in content but also in form. Projection. Examples of projection in dreams and hallucinations. Transformation of projected material. Example. Transitions to projection: compulsive ideas, fabricated ideas. All affective mechanisms are related.

The foregoing considerations have prepared us to understand the dream—the main field of psychoanalytic research. Before Freud (204), dreams were considered meaningless sequences of images, and even Hacker's (313) paper, which deals with the formal phenomena in dreams, sees in them a lack of determining tendencies. Many authors, primarily Mourly Vold (854), were concerned with the influence of external stimuli in dreams. They report that stimulation of the legs arouses dreams of walking, running, dancing. The following celebrated example comes from Maury (541). He dreamt about the Terror in the French Revolu-

---

100 Cf. Erikson (166).

101 Cf. Freud (204, particularly Chapter VII); also Schroetter (760), Roffenstein (676), and Nachmansohn (575).

tion, partook in awesome scenes of murder, and was then himself
called into court. There he saw Robespierre, Marat, Fouquier-
Tinville, and all the other sad heroes of that terrible period. They
questioned him, and after various interludes, which he does not
remember, he was sentenced and taken to the place of execution,
accompanied by an endless mass of people. He ascended to the
guillotine, the executioner tied him to the board, the board tilted,
the knife came down, and he felt his head being severed from
his body. He awoke in terrible anxiety, to find that the bed-board
had fallen and hit the back of his neck just as the knife did in
the dream. The stimulus impinging upon the sleeper is apprehended in the dream in a symbol-like fashion. On the one hand,
the sleeper obviously tends to apprehend percepts; on the other,
there must be opposing tendencies, not revealed to us by a
formal study of dreams. Neither does such formal study explain
the choice of one symbol-like image from among the many possible.[102]

Yet we know a way to approach these opposing tendencies.
We must induce the patient to associate freely. The method of
psychoanalysis demands of the patient that he let his associations
come freely, regardless of their sense, while centering upon a
detail to be analyzed. Our thinking is bound by a multitude of
determining tendencies. Messer's (550) studies have demonstrated
that experimental subjects, when they associate, set themselves
quite detailed tasks. Likewise, our entire existence is directed by
tasks set by society and our own ideals. We simply cannot be
aimless.[103]

To think logically and objectively, and not to abandon ourselves to drive-determined musing, is one of these tasks. In free
associating we lift this compulsion, and thereby liberate the
drives.[104] The psychoanalytic method anticipated the findings of
Kuelpe's school of the psychology of thinking. The authors of
this school have shown us penetratingly that tasks and attitudes
determine the course of thought-process.[105] The method of free
association is a practical substantiation of this theoretical view.

102 Cf. Schroetter (760, particularly footnote 31).
103 Cf. Freud (204, pp. 482–483).
104 For a more precise statement, see A. Freud (200).
105 See Ach (9), Messer (550), Kuelpe (470).

Yet we must hasten to point out that an attitude directed at suppressing certain drive-impulses and experiences cannot be expected to disappear instantly; rather, it continuously obstructs the emergence of the repressed, and when it fails in this, it interferes with its direct expression. The stubborn attitude which maintains repression we term resistance; and we recognize it by the abeyance of associations and the failure to communicate those which occur. If there were no resistance, or if it were lifted, the repressed—which, as we know, retains its energy—would rise to consciousness. Under certain conditions, resistance may manifest itself by the appearance of something close or similar to the repressed. Due to the complex interplay of drive and counterdrive, these transformations take a relatively long time.

Experiment, as well as everyday psychoanalytic experiences, supports these conclusions: Jung (392) demonstrated in the association-experiment that words referring to repressed, affect-toned experiences elicit different reactions than do others. Such associations are slow, peculiar, occasionally accompanied by laughter, and occasionally in abeyance. Repressed, affect-toned experiences Jung calls complexes, and speaks of complex-reactions. Indeed, if the subject is given a sufficiently broad and appropriately selected series of stimulus words, the complexes may be inferred from the associations. Some have sought to use this procedure in criminology, and assumed that culprits presented with stimulus-words related to their crime would give complex-reactions betraying their guilt (Wertheimer's fact-diagnosis). As interesting and theoretically correct as this procedure may be, it founders on the fact that the complex is purely psychological and does not presuppose a preceding action. Occasionally, vivid preoccupation with a crime will itself elicit complex-reactions.[106]

Thus, even for those who do not practice the psychoanalytic method and have no direct experience of its value, compelling evidence is available for its correctness. With this method we will now approach the study of dreams.

A preliminary remark seems in place. In dreams we are faced with a new world of percepts. Dream images are, in spite of the objections of some, hallucinations. Therefore the first problem is:

[106] Cf. Wertheimer (875), also Freud (208), and for a review of the literature, Rapaport (654, Chapter III, 3, particularly sections E and F).

how can hallucinations come about at all? For us, the answer is facilitated by our not recognizing a basic difference between imagery and perception. Nevertheless, a few comments seem necessary. Imagery and perception differ in that while to some extent we are in command of our imagery, perception—again, within limits—is beyond our will. On the other hand, we can defend ourselves against threats from the perceptual world by attack or flight; but imagery belongs to the body, to the subject, and thus is harder to withdraw from, even though it is subject to our will. We have good reason to assume that the distinction between imagery and perception is less sharp on lower levels: the hungry infant is satisfied by a pacifier stuck into his mouth—the milk he apparently hallucinates.[107]

The child plays with objects which only in their contours are like the objects he means them to be; the rest he adds by means of his fantasy. Reality and fantasy shade into each other. Jaensch (372) and Kroh (462) have demonstrated that eidetic images, which are related to perceptions, are much more frequent and clear-cut in children. Separation of fantasy and reality is not only ontogenetically a late acquisition; even primitives fail or only partly succeed in it.[108] We have reason to assume that primordial psychological states do not separate imagery and perception. For creatures which do not have to maintain themselves by purposive action, this distinction is of no relevance. We may surmise that there are states in which body and world are not sharply separated. We have seen already, in our discussion of drives, that the more the individual is impelled by them, that is, the more saturated by sexuality, the more the world loses its independence and threatens to merge with the body. We must also assume that there are exceptions to this unity of body and world: the form in which the perceptual world appears to us depends on drives, but we have seen that a part of these drive-processes is already structured into organization.[109] Nevertheless, we may assume that alterations of drives do bring body and world closer

107 Cf. Freud (204, pp. 508–509), and Freud (216); also Schilder (694, 739).
108 Cf. H. Werner (870), also Rapaport (658, Part 5).
109 Schilder here points out the continuous transition between the primary and the secondary process (this is also one of the implications of his "sphere" concept), of which the mainstream of psychoanalytic theorizing has only recently become aware. See, e.g., Kris (460).

to each other. Imagery by its nature belongs to the body to begin with.

In other words: alterations of drive-attitudes are the prerequisite for the transformation of images into percepts. The factors which change image into percept may be studied first of all in certain dreams and hallucinations. There is a type of dream which is quite clearly wish-fulfillment. Dreams of children are like that. For instance, Freud reports that a child, who because she had been vomiting had to fast a day, then dreamt: Anna F . . . eud, st(r)awberry, highberry, egg . . .[110] The two-year-old dreamer spoke these words in her sleep. Dreams of convenience have a very similar structure. We are familiar with the dream of the student, who dreams in the moment of being awakened that he is already in the class room; and with those dreams in which, the sleep being threatened by a need, one dreams that the need (hunger, thirst, urge to urinate or defecate) has been satisfied. In these a wishful image is turned into reality. Quite analogous are the hysterical wish-deliria in which what is wished for—e.g., a marriage, or a child—appears as reality, is hallucinated as an actuality.

Wishes are thus capable not only of arousing definite images and thoughts, but also of giving them reality-value and perception-character. They surmount all obstacles. The transformation of images into percepts appears dynamically as the consequence of greater affective libido-cathexis. Obviously, this is again the very general issue already encountered; attitudes can alter not only the content, but also the formal aspect of thought. Above I spoke advisedly of reality-value, because affects can make a thought appear correct and its content real.[111]

If we consider the image as belonging to the subject—and I believe we cannot do otherwise—then transformation of an image into a percept is an externalization of part of the subject into the object. Fundamentally this is a projection. Yet we speak of projection in the narrower sense only when this externalization takes place without far-reaching transformations of content and

110 See Freud (204, p. 214).

111 See Freud (204, pp. 492–497); also cf. Rapaport (659), where it becomes clear that the cathexis which gives perceptual reality-value to the image is obtained by means of condensations of images or displacements of their cathexes.

form.[112] The mechanism of projection plays a great role in dreams. Frankl-Hochwarth had a dream in which he was to pull a soldier's teeth, and awoke with a toothache. At another time he dreamt that he was called to perform an ileus operation, and awoke with abdominal pains. In these examples, experiences one would wish not to have are displaced to other people. Freud[113] reports a patient who in her sleep threw away the cooling-apparatus which she was supposed to wear continuously because of an ailment of her jaw; when questioned, she explained that in her dream she sat in the opera, free of pain, while a certain Mr. Karl Meyer had terrible headaches. Here too the motivation is transparent: what one wants to be rid of is projected.

This mechanism of projection is not limited to the dream. One of my patients suffered a severe shot-wound in his right arm, which resulted in a rigid paralysis and was accompanied by a septic delirium. All the people he saw in his delirium had crippled arms and legs: when they approached him the crippled limbs were on their left, and when they turned away, on their right. That is, he projected his defect outward by the shortest path. I have often encountered projections of body-defects in false perceptions also.

In all these cases, transformations take place in the course of projection: the patient with toothaches dreams of the headaches of Karl Meyer; the patient with a crippled arm sees people with crippled limbs.[114] These alterations in the course of projection must have a definite meaning: they seem to express still other affective attitudes. Their break-through points to the particular malleability of projected material. The interplay of various impulses can be readily studied in the transformations in these projection-dreams and in simple wish-dreams—that is, in the change of images into percepts in general. Freud,[115] after a very salty meal, would awaken thirsty at night, but first would dream that he was drinking water in big draughts. Once he had another attack of thirst after he had drunk his glass of water; to get more, he would have had to rise and take it from his wife's night table. Accordingly, he dreamt that his wife gave him water from an Etruscan ash-

112 Concerning the problem of varieties of projection, cf. Rapaport (661).
113 See Freud (204, p. 210).
114 See Schilder (740), also (732, 735).
115 See Freud (204, pp. 209–210).

urn which he had brought back from one of his trips and had since given away. The water of this urn tasted so salty from the ashes that he awoke. We see how real thirst supersedes hallucinatory gratification, how the salty drink expresses both strivings, and finally thirst proves stronger than the need to sleep and enforces awakening.

A compulsion-neurotic patient of mine dreams she is imploring me to help her, then she goes crazy; then suddenly I am crazy, and she wants to rush to me and put her arms around me, but the nurse restrains her, saying it wouldn't do. In the beginning of her treatment this patient actually experienced a compulsive urge to put her arm about me; also, the fear of going crazy plays a great role in her thinking. Here the dreaded insanity is experienced, but is immediately projected onto me. The patient also gains the fulfillment of her wish to put her arm around me; yet her hesitance too is embodied in the nurse who warns against it. It is hardly necessary to point out that any experience of the subject, sensation, perception, image, or thought, can be projected. In the process, not only changes of content determined by intervening drive-impulses may occur, but also all changes of form which can be brought about by changes in affect-cathexis.[116] Compulsive ideas, fabricated ideas, and the like, may all be projected onto other persons.

Interesting transitional forms of projection are those instances in which somatic pain is apprehended as a result of external influence. A patient suffering severe pains due to a tumor of the adnex had a brief confusional episode in which she complained that people were beating her back and pulling her hair. Here an embarrassing and painful somatic sensation is attributed to an external influence. Similarly, an untidy senile demented female patient explains that a man was in bed with her, he soiled the bed, and she will beat him up for it: here a projection determines a confabulation. These few examples indicate the tremendous role which projection plays in psychological life. It determines what belongs to the subject and what to the object; the drives in turn determine how this dividing line will be drawn.[117]

There are still other pre-stages of projection which deserve

116 Cf. Rapaport (660).
117 Cf. Schilder (740), also (751, pp. 515–516).

our attention. When I have a thought or image, it is always my
thought and my image; and I experience my own activity in them.
But when I struggle against the thought and it impinges on me
nonetheless, then it is a compulsive thought, and it appears strange
to me. This attempt to expel my own thought is the first stage of
projection. A further stage is the so-called fabricated ideas of
schizophrenics, in which their own thoughts appear as products
of foreign influence. When the neurasthenic feels tired and dour
and in no mood to do anything, this lack of impulse appears to
him as a heaviness of the limbs: the body is closer to the external
world than the psyche, and thus such somatization of psychological
conflicts (termed conversion) must be regarded as a pre-stage of
projection. In spite of these relationships, it is purposeful to
limit the concept to projection proper. But we are warned that
there is a deep relatedness between all affective mechanisms.
Finally, it may be mentioned that according to Head (327), the
affliction of internal organs causes pains and oversensitivity on
the surface of the body. It might be surmised that we have an
analogy to projection here in the organic realm.[118]*

   Cf. my study of hallucination (694) and (707). Jaspers (378) has a good
review of the hallucination problem.

b) Identification and appersonation.[119] Latent dream-
    thought

   Appersonation of tools and clothing. Identification. From the analysis of
a homosexual. Role of identification in sexual and social life. Ego-ideal as
sediment of identifications. Identification is not role-playing. Personality projection. Identification in dream. Identification and cognition of others' psychological life. Comprehension and empathy. Manifest dream-content and
latent dream-thought. Nature of dream-thought.

   Besides projection, we find in dreams another mechanism
which is its counterpart: identification. We speak of identification when we make another's experience into our own, indi-
cating our wish to take that other person's place.[120] Besides identification there is also the mechanism of appersonation: something
that belongs to the outside world is accounted to one's own ego,

   118* Here I follow a discussion comment of Federn's.
   119 Appersonation is a concept put forth by Schilder (696). Concerning
identification, cf. Fenichel (181), also Axelrad and Maury (38). Schilder's definition here is unsatisfactory.
   120 Ibid.

to one's own body. The most primitive example of appersonation is when, pushing with a stick against the floor and having a sensation of hardness and resistance, we locate this sensation in the end of the stick. Jewelry, clothing, tools, are all appersonated more or less explicitly. This process is even clearer in psychotic patients when they assert that the suffering of the patient in the next bed is their own, or when they experience a change which occurs in the outside world as happening in their own body.[121] Thus, the appersonator may make into his own the objects or experiences of other people. Identification is a particularly important process, and I will first represent it by an example.

The case is that of a homosexual,[122] 37 years of age at the time of therapy. His objects were boys between 13 and 14. He would begin a conversation with them on the street, and have them tell him about what happened in school; it gave him special joy when they reported that the teacher thrashed them, or had them stand before the benches. At such times he would get an erection, with occasionally the impulse to beat the boys or pull their ears, but he did not usually yield to it. He felt toward these boys a motherly tenderness, tried to help some of them, and would have best liked to take them home with him and raise them. On occasion he actually did take care of the education of such boys. In psychoanalysis, it was learned that the patient had his first erection at nine years of age when thrashed by his mother. He was unaware of its sexual significance at the time, and until therapy did not fill this gap in his knowledge, though he was a landowner and cattle-breeder. He still considered erection an indication of shame, and assumed that the boys who were thrashed were ashamed when talking about it and had an erection. In other words, the patient ascribed to the boys his own role as a child, and assumed toward them the role of his mother. Only this assumption makes the contradictory features of his love-life understandable. The question is: what is the patient's motivation for assuming the role of his mother? This too found an ex-

---

121 Some aspects of the phenomena conceptualized by Schilder as appersonation have been treated by him (705) in relation to the body-image; others have since been treated in the psychoanalytic literature under the headings "ego-boundaries" and "ego-states." Cf. Federn (174, 175), and Brenman, Gill and Hacker (101).

122 See Schilder (696).

planation. His parents had always treated him coolly, and his mother withdrew even the usual small amount of tenderness when his older brother became a schizophrenic. It was then that the patient, 12–13 years old, must have decided to make himself independent of his mother by taking her role; thus he became the recipient of all the tenderness which he, when thrashed and shamed, felt toward her. The motivation that leads to identification is transparent: here too needs are the determiners. The identification is with a love-object: he identifies with the mother toward whom, according to the scene reported, his sexual impulses were directed.[123] But the moment identification took place, love disappeared. Complete identification destroys the love-object: one does not need it any more—one is it oneself.[124]

Identification is a process of such basic importance that we must discuss it further. Every lover identifies with his beloved. He heaps on her all the virtues, while he humbles himself deeply; he appears to himself small and insignificant. He becomes impoverished in ego-libido, because he lavishes it on the object. It seems that this loss is made up by identification with the beloved, which he expresses by acquiring her habits, her turns of speech, her love-play—revealing without knowing it that thereby he partakes in her, this supernatural being. In love identification does not become complete, otherwise the love-object grows superfluous. Similar relationships obtain in other areas of psychological life. We identify with all the people who inspire respect in us. The sergeant in *Wallensteins Lager* identifies with his war-lord, and expresses this in his hawking and spitting. The follower identifies with his leader, the hypnotized person with the hypnotist, the believer with his god.[125]

Our example is particularly important because it shows that identification driven to completion destroys the love-object. When the believer identifies with the god, he himself becomes the god; it is thus that mysticism is so close to heresy, and the church always distrusts mystics. Angelus Silesius wrote:

---

123 This formulation by-passes the role played here by the aggressive drive (being thrashed—thrashing); cf. Anna Freud (200, Chapter 9), on "identification with the aggressor."

124 Cf. Freud (239, pp. 36–37), for the background of this formulation.

125 Cf. Freud (237).

"I know that without me the Lord cannot live a moment,
If I become naught, he must needs give up the ghost."

We have already seen that broad realms of life are ruled by identification; actually they are even broader. The growing child continuously identifies with the people who are raising him; indeed, his ego-ideal is altogether a sediment of his identifications with the people who have raised him. We also see that this ego-ideal has a relative independence within the ego.[126]

Now formal peculiarities of identification attract our attention. The question arises, is it identical with the experiences of role-playing? In role-playing the actor knows that he has taken on a role; in identification, role-taking occurs without an explicit wish, and its course abides by different formal rules. He who identifies has to deny much of his usual ego: he must repress much.[127] By now it is clear that projection too is but a form of repression. Torturing, painful, and undesirable experiences are made to appear, not as belonging to one's own person, but as parts of the external world. This too is a return of the repressed in a distorted form, except that here the distortion manifests itself in a, so to speak, formal way.[128] We see that our patient expels many of his own characteristics and displaces them onto the boys: they are beaten, they are shamed, and they are at the age when he was strongly attracted to the mother (the woman). We are justified in speaking here of an ego- or personality-projection. We might add that by his erection the patient expresses toward these boys the tender-sexual excitement his mother experienced while thrashing him.

In dreams too identification plays a great role, though this is often difficult to demonstrate. Freud[129] reports the following:

126 Cf. Freud (239, III), and (245, 3).

127 "Repression" here again is used in the sense of "defense." In a sense, Schilder's is the reverse of the generally accepted psychoanalytic formulation, that identification may serve as a defense-mechanism: cf. Fenichel (180, pp. 220–223).

128 The stress upon the distinction between form (function) and content is characteristic, and in some respects unique to Schilder. It is a distinction as yet little appreciated, but to my mind most important. Silberer earlier (781, 782) had a firm if partial grasp of it. My own studies (654, 650, 658) have brought home to me its importance, and for my first encounter with it I am in debt both to Schilder and Silberer.

129 See Freud (204, pp. 225 ff.).

"You always say that the dream is a fulfilled wish," begins a jocular woman patient; "now I will tell you a dream, the content of which is that a wish of mine is not fulfilled. How do you reconcile this with your theory?" This is the dream: "I want to give a dinner; but I have no supplies except some smoked salmon. I intend to go shopping; but I remember that it is Sunday afternoon, and all the shops are closed. I want to telephone to a caterer, but the telephone is out of order. I must give up my wish to give a dinner."

Analysis of the dream brings the following associations. The patient's husband is afraid of getting too fat, and has decided not to accept any dinner invitations. Her husband thinks a lot of one of her woman friends, and holds her up as an example to his wife; luckily this other woman is thin and dry, and the dreamer's husband likes full bodies. On the day before the dream the patient had visited this friend, who spoke of her wish to put on weight. These associations yield the following dream-thought: the patient does not want to give this dinner at all, since it might help her friend to put on weight and be liked even more by her husband. This interpretation obtained a surprising corroboration by the following association: the favorite dish of the friend is smoked salmon. The dreamer, whose wish the dream apparently denies, is anyway prone to forego innocent pleasures—such as caviar, which she particularly likes. Not only in the dream, but in reality too she has the tendency to deny herself things. Fundamentally it is not herself, but her friend whom she does not want to get fat. She identifies with the friend, but this dream does not clarify why. The identification must express a deep similarity.

When one hysteric imitates the seizure of another, it is not simple imitation; rather the patient assumes that she too, like the one with the seizure, is disappointed in love and from that derives the right to have such seizures. According to Freud (237), identification is "acquisition on the basis of identical etiological claims." It expresses an equation based on a common element that remains unconscious. Though identification occurs usually on the grounds of sexuality, this is by no means the only possibility.

Freud complements the interpretation of the dream of the cancelled dinner as follows: the dreamer puts herself into her friend's place in the dream because she wants the place her friend has in the husband's appreciation. At any rate, identification makes it possible to acquire the experiences of many people simultaneously. Thus one becomes the figures of one's environment, and it is the very unawareness of identification that makes it possible to store up a wealth of such experiences.[130]

The question arises: since in identification we incorporate experiences of others, are we approaching here an understanding of the nature of our knowledge of the psychological experiences of others? But such incorporation in itself presupposes the knowledge of the experiences and egos of others. Therefore one cannot explain in this way the apprehension of other individualities. Above we said that identification is paralleled by projection, which displaces our own experiences into others; clearly, projection is no way to gain knowledge of the psychological life of others, because it permits us to see in them only what we need to. Rather, we must assume that just as there is perception which is independent of our wishes, so there is a perception of the psychological life of others which is independent of affectivity.[131] Even if one were to engage in phylogenetic psychological speculations, one would always have to postulate the existence of psychological impulses in others, and the possibility of direct apprehension of them. Naturally, projection and identification will always cogwheel into these acts of apprehension. Knowledge will increase only when projection follows the lines of reality, but then the concept of projection no longer covers the experience. It becomes necessary to assume that it is possible for us to apprehend, and to empathize with, the psychic structures of others.

Apprehending and empathizing must be sharply distinguished. Our own experience is not the prerequisite of apprehending the experience of others, rather the reverse: to apprehend others makes empathic experience, that is, appersonation and identification, possible. This is my stand on the important

---

[130] Concerning the role of identification in socialization, cf. Rapaport (658, Part 7, XXIII).

[131] This again is one of Schilder's basic views, and one which appears to be the predecessor of Hartmann's concept of "primary autonomy." Cf. Schilder (752, e.g., p. 519); also Appendix, pp. 345 ff., infra; Hartmann (321), Rapaport (656).—Schilder's specific point here has the same implications as Erikson's (166) "mutuality" concept.

problem of empathy, a concept originated by Lipps (513), implying that the psychic life of others is grasped by our putting ourselves into it. But even simple description shows that on seeing someone in anger, I do not myself experience anger, but rather fear or anxiety. Indeed, even the embitterment experienced on seeing a friend embittered by injustice done to him has only a very indirect relation to my knowledge of my friend's psychic state. There is a direct apprehending of the gestures and postures of others, which, though experience partakes in it, in final analysis presupposes a primary apprehending prior to all experience. These problems we will encounter again in the discussion of ego-psychology.

The dream discussed last shows that when we say dreams are wish-fulfillments, we refer not to the manifest dream-content, but to the latent dream-thought. The latent thought of this dream may be formulated thus: "I do not want my friend to put on weight and be even more attractive to my husband." Now it would be a mistake to assume that this latent thought occurs anywhere in this complete form. It is rather a germinal thought, the form of existence of which will have to be considered in detail later. Since our analysis of this dream was quite incomplete, the dream appears simpler than it is, and we have not shown that this germinal thought is closely related to other germinal thoughts originating in childhood. According to our previous discussion, such germinal thoughts are drive-objects, and thus body-close and symbol-like.[132] It is precisely this that makes possible transformation into images apparently so different, which express not only the drive-orientation in question but also its opposite. Yet, in such formations, it is nearly always possible to decide which is the driving-wish and which attitude serves as a brake.

What was said here about dreams applies to neurotic symptoms also:[133] they are expressions of wishes to which other attitudes apply brakes. Indeed, this formulation holds not only for dream-formations, parapraxes, and neurotic and psychotic symptoms, but for every emerging image and thought.[134] At this

[132] A more precise formulation would probably replace "drive-objects" by "drive-representations."

[133] For the current psychoanalytic view of symptom-formation, see Freud (244).

[134] Cf. Schilder (751, pp. 508–509).

point we again connect with the theory of Ach and Kuelpe.

Concerning identification, cf. my paper by this title (696) and, first of all, Freud (237).

c) Dream mechanisms.[135] Role of childhood experiences in dreams[136]

Condensation of contents. Distortion of feelings. Examples of the role of infantile experiences in the dream. Infantile wishes. Relation of recent and infantile experiences. Somatic stimuli and day-residues. Displacement. The unimportant comes to the foreground. Omissions. Logical functions in dreams. Dream-form often represents content. Condensation and symbolism. Universality of symbols. Penis and vagina symbols. Other typical symbols. Common origins of everything psychological. Marbe's uniformity of psychic happening. Typical dreams. Confused and sensible dreams. Secondary elaboration. Representation by opposite. Sequence of manifest contents.

The theory of dreams leads us into yet deeper psychological layers. Again an example from Freud:[137]

"First: my friend R. appears as an uncle to me, I feel great tenderness towards him. Second: I see his face somewhat changed before me, it is—as it were—pulled into length, and the yellow beard surrounding it stands out particularly." The uncle to whom the associations lead was punished by the law for an action motivated by greed for profits. The dreamer's father had said of him that he was never bad, but just a fool. By this equation, the dream labels friend R. a fool. The next association is that R.'s beard, which unlike the uncle's was originally black, has begun to turn reddish-brown. Further associations lead to a conversation with a colleague N., a few days before, about the dreamer's having been recommended for professorship. N. congratulates him. F., the dreamer, refuses the congratulation: N. too was recommended but not appointed, and knows that the recommendation has no significance. F.'s religion is too much of an obstacle. But N. relates that accusations a woman once made against him in court may have been the obstacle in his case. Thus the uncle represents the dreamer's two colleagues, R. and N., neither of whom was

[135] See Freud (204, Chapters 6 and 7, particularly pp. 485 ff. and pp. 530–532).

[136] See Freud (204, p. 500).

[137] See Freud (204, p. 220); for background material for the understanding of this dream, see Erikson (167) and Gross (306). For a recent discussion of this dream, see Fromm (258 a, pp. 57 ff.).

appointed professor, and characterizes one of them as a fool and the other as a criminal. But the dreamer is neither and may hope to become a professor, since it was not because of their religion that the other two were not appointed.

The work of censorship can be well studied in this dream: it prevents the appearance of egotistical ideas. Not only are the images products of repression, but so is the feeling in the dream: it is ungenuine,[138] and merely an overcompensation of hostile and derogatory thoughts against both colleagues. We note that repression and distortion pertain not only to intellectual contents but also to feelings, which we are accustomed to regard as the most reliable indicators of drive-attitudes. Here hatred is turned into love. This is the less frequent case; turning love into hate is the more frequent result of drive-repression. Finally, for completeness' sake, let us mention the most frequent solution of drive-repression, already implied in our preceding discussions: the drive is turned to another object. That love and hate can represent each other derives from the ambivalence of sexuality, already discussed. This dream has yet another essential component. The dreamer judges his two friends as professorial hopefuls, as though he were the Minister of Education. This leads back to infantile wishes of the dreamer, who as a child, hearing from his father about Secretaries who came from the middle class, had fantasied himself into the role of a Secretary. Thus a grandiose dream of childhood, dating from the 11th and 12th years of life, emerges. The dreamer identifies with the Secretary.

Now we can penetrate more deeply into the structure of the dream. This dream has a recent stimulus, namely the conversation about the nomination. This recent stimulus would not suffice to arouse a dream: but the play of its ambitious ideas arouses infantile attitudes, and it is these that give the wish the energy to penetrate to consciousness in the form of the dream. This is a typical process, demonstrable by thorough analysis of any dream. We must assume that a great many deeply repressed childhood wishes are waiting for an occasion to penetrate. If a recent

---

138 "Ungenuine" translates *unecht*. The feeling in the first part of the dream—though by itself genuine enough, since it is rooted in the dreamer's actual feelings toward friend and uncle—is in contrast to the feelings to which the second part of the dream points, which are suppressed and not experienced by the dreamer.

experience arouses a wish, this wish secures the support of those deeply repressed wishes, which then strive to penetrate in the form of a dream but, being inhibited by censorship, appear in distorted form.[139]

A dream of an anxiety-neurotic patient may help to clarify this relationship.

"I see a wagon covered with gray cloth. Under the cloth something is fidgeting: exotic animals, similar to sheep. They have a wound towards the end of their backs. I think: I would not like to eat these animals." Associations: the cloth on the wagon reminds him of his mother's gray shawl, "but it has no relation to that." He thinks that something was cut off these animals. The edges are very red, it reminds him of a wound. Then the association: at the age of seven he saw his sister's genitals, which were like a red blood-spot. Later on he always thought women had male genitals, and dreamt of female figures with penis only. He dreamt this about his mother too. The recent stimulus for this dream was the patient's anxiety-attack on seeing a high-loaded wagon on the street: he was afraid it would keel over and fall on him. It may be assumed that this anxiety revived his infantile interest in the mother's body, which was pronounced in his dreams and fantasies. Simultaneously, his strong, scoptophilic inclination, which originally referred to the genitals of his sister, but pertains to those of the mother too, is also aroused.

We are dealing here with deeply repressed wishes. Several other motivations also play a role in this dream. The disadvantageous position of the female genital has preoccupied the patient: he is afraid that he might injure his penis in intercourse, and repeatedly has the idea of how much better it would be if the female genital were on another part of the body. In this respect too the dream brings a wish-fulfillment: it gratifies his incestuous wishes, his voyeurism, and takes care of his castration-anxiety by considering only women as castrated. These comments do not complete the interpretation; a full dream-interpretation presupposes insight into the structure of the neurosis. Neither are we sufficiently informed about the recent stimulus arousing the dream. What we know is that he is in love, but has doubts as to the success of his courting; both are probably among the

[139] Cf. Freud (204, pp. 505–509).

sources of the dream, in that they revive his wild infantile wishes.

In every thorough dream-analysis we encounter such un-controlled infantile wishes, the contents of which for the most part we have already discussed. In this dream, for instance, we encounter voyeuristic and incestuous wishes, with which we have become acquainted in discussing infantile sexuality. The cardinal complex of life, the Oedipus-complex, presents itself in ever new varieties. Dreams imply return, regression, to previous drive-stages; and fundamentally the transition from image to percept is also a regression.[140] Examples could be easily massed, but I will add only one easily surveyed dream from my own observations.

The patient, a 35-year-old virgin, has a repetitive dream. She is in the anteroom of an apartment. Two burglars are pushing themselves through the half-open door, and the dreamer prevents their entrance only with great difficulty; one is short, the other tall. Associations: around her 13th or 14th year of life, there was a burglary in her home and valuable silver was taken. The son of the janitor was strongly suspected of having taken part. One of the dream burglars, the taller, resembled both this man and the patient's brother. Further material came only in the next session, in which the patient reported that on the previous day she had been tortured by a vision of a little naked girl lying on her stomach. This report was followed, after vehement resistance, by the confession that the son of the janitor had made an assault on her when she was eight years old: he pulled up her skirts and attempted unsuccessfully to insert his penis. "Nothing happened," said the patient, and proceeded to her later love-relationships, in which nothing happened either. For a long time the patient has been maintaining a relationship with a dentist, which has led to far-reaching intimacies, but not to sexual intercourse. While relating this, the patient had the feeling that someone had spat on her arm. It was not difficult to infer that, both in the assault and in later intimacies, the men had ejaculations. Later in the analysis it became clear that the infantile erotic impulses were directed toward the brother, and that they had engaged in sexual activities. The dentist's repeated attempts to overcome the virginity of the dreamer may be regarded as the recent dream-stimulus, since the short man reminds the patient of the dentist. Clearly, the dream represents the entire love-life of the patient,

140 Cf. Freud (204, Chapter 7, B, particularly pp. 496–497).

and it is seen that the recent stimulus arouses repressed childhood experiences; these, in Freud's simile, may be compared to capitalists, who supply the capital for entrepreneurs, while recent stimuli are comparable to the entrepreneurs.

Somatic stimuli have no greater role in dream-formation than do day-residues. Somatic stimuli may arouse infantile impulses, but mostly they serve merely as material used in representing the infantile wishes aroused by day-residues.

Concerning the preceding dream, it should be added that it represents the scene characteristic of the dreamer's love-life. On the one hand, she wishes always for the repetition of these scenes; on the other, the longed-for consummation never takes place, and anxiety develops. The men represent partly the patient's love-objects, and partly their genitals; the anteroom is to be regarded as the dreamer's genital.

A striking characteristic of dreams is that they represent so much in a few pictures. In the uncle-dream, the picture of the man, which is itself a composite of two persons, and therefore fuzzy, includes the blond beard as an emphasized feature; this beard alludes also to the father of the dreamer, and to himself, since he is beginning to turn gray. In the last reported dream, the figures of the brother and the caretaker's son are merged into one. Such condensations[141] are indeed very frequent, and so are neologisms formed according to similar principles. These neologisms were noted even by such formalistic investigators as Kraepelin (445), but they failed to recognize that they have a definite meaning. Condensation-processes play a role not only in dreams, but in slips of the tongue, and in the neologisms of dementia praecox patients—as the studies of Stransky (811, 813), who calls them contaminations, show. Stransky made an interesting contribution to the theory of these phenomena. He observed such contaminations when he had his experimental subjects, in a state of relaxed attention, speak rapidly into a gramaphone. Relaxation of attention can produce such mixed formations.[142]

Besides condensation, displacement also plays an essential role in dreams.[143] What is important in the latent dream-thought need not appear at all in its manifest content. In the dream about

141 Cf. Freud (204, pp. 320–336).
142 Cf. Bleuler (89).
143 Cf. Freud (204, pp. 336–339).

the broken bed, the bed is not important and yet is the exclusive manifest dream-content; what was really intended, sexual intercourse, is omitted. Omission is an important means of dream-representation. Other forms of displacement are also clearly seen: in the burglary dream, the dreamer is not really concerned with the burglary as such, but it is almost the exclusive content. The techniques of omission and displacement play a role in waking thinking also, as well as in the symptom-formation of neuroses and psychoses. The complicated relationships of the latent dream-thought are not represented as such in the dream: the dream can represent only visually-pictorially; it cannot formulate in thought.[144] Thus, the thought, "The janitor's son behaves just like my brother," is expressed in the burglar-dream by a figure which stands for both of them. The same holds for the composite figure in the uncle-dream. Other logical relations too are expressed by the dream in the form of images. Causal relation may be expressed by the cause preceding the effect in the image-sequence.

Formal characteristics of the dream-content, such as vagueness, very frequently refer to the latent dream-thought. The form of dream or dreaming is used surprisingly often to represent the latent thought: in one of Freud's examples, an obscure point of the dream refers to the female genital. The awareness that "it is just a dream" usually hides a tendency to devaluate the drives underlying the dream. Senselessness of the dream often expresses scorn. Even judgments about the dream after awakening belong to its manifest content, and must be treated accordingly. Judgments in dreams should not be regarded as a product of dream-work; they belong to the latent dream-thought, and have been lifted as completed formations into the manifest dream-content. I stress again that affects too may undergo alterations in dreams: they may be inhibited, turned into their opposite, or displaced.[145] But these mechanisms are also general, and not limited to dreams.

The above discussion indicates that condensation is very closely related to symbol-formation:[146] it is often doubtful

[144] Concerning this "regard for representability," cf. Freud (204, pp. 361–368).

[145] But note Freud (204, pp. 434 ff.).

[146] Cf. Freud (204, pp. 368–397); see also Silberer (782), and Jones (388).

whether something is a condensation or a symbol. It is characteristic for symbols that they be typical.[147] There is a typical
young girls' dream in which they are pursued by men with knives,
sticks, etc., which are typical penis-symbols. The multitude of
symbols for sex-organs is immense. Box, room, container, are
symbols for female genitals. Fish, snail, cat, mouse . . . snake,
necktie, aeroplane, are male genital symbols. Wood is often a
female, hat and key often a male, genital symbol. Symbols are
equally valid in dreams, psychoses, neuroses, and myths. Loaded
carriages, tunnels, are frequent symbols of the mother's body
which plays a great role in dreams. Birth-symbols are frequent.
Body parts too are often symbolized; for instance, breasts are represented as sisters and buttocks as brothers.

Nothing met with as much opposition as the theory of symbolism, although it may be regarded as absolutely proven.[148]
Psychoanalytic experience demonstrates that the universality
of symbols is also uncontestable; we have reason to assume that
it is only one of the broad layers of psychological life common
to all people. Just as body-structures and body-functions are
universal, so too are certain psychological functions. These must
be phylogenetically our oldest possessions, and therefore it is
probably no accident that symbolism plays a particular role in
the regressive phenomena of psychological life. Even earlier,
Nietzsche thought the dream to be a revival of primeval man; and
we must expect that the deeper the regression, the more psychological functions common to all men come to the fore. Experimental psychological methods lead to similar conclusions. Marbe
(532) spoke of a law of uniformity of psychological happening:
if many people are asked to name a color, the answer of greatest
frequency is red; there are number preferences too. In view of
our theory of symbols and their universality, we can only agree
with E. Stern (802) that the uniformity of psychological happening rests on affective attitudes.

Now we may turn to the typical dreams. Dreams of nakedness represent infantile exhibitionism; those of flying and falling,
erotic wishes; those of water, either birth or urinary urges, both

147 For a review of the differences of opinion as to the nature and universality of symbolism, see Nachmansohn (575, footnote 81).
148 Cf. Schroetter (760), Roffenstein (676), Nachmansohn (575).

of which use partly the same kind of symbols. Flying dreams require closer discussion, since they seem to admit of a reduction to bodily stimuli. It is certain that vestibular and cerebellar afflictions are often accompanied by dreams of flying; but this fact does not invalidate the view here presented. For instance, we know that vertigo is a frequent conversion-symptom for inhibited impulses, particularly sexual. We have every reason to consider this conversion as something organic. Bauer and I (693), as well as Leidler (483) and Loewy (519), have demonstrated that the vestibulo-cerebellar equilibrium-apparatus can be influenced psychologically.[149] Thus, inhibited sexual impulses may cause vertigo as well as flying-dreams. Dreams of past examinations, which in spite of great anxiety were successfully passed, serve as encouragements in the face of sexual tasks to be mastered. Tooth-dreams are masturbation- and birth-dreams. I cannot go into details here.

A few formal problems should be discussed. As already mentioned, formal characteristics of dream-content, such as obscurity, often have a material[150] meaning. The patient's doubt as to whether or not a dream-representation is correct, proves in analysis to be not factual but rather an expression of repressive forces; therefore, when beginning a dream-interpretation, we must make ourselves independent of the dreamer's feelings of certainty or uncertainty about the dream. I have already said that the dreamer's judgments about the dream belong to the manifest dream-content.[151]

There are two kinds of dreams: the confused, and the logically ordered. Of the two, the confused dreams give us a more correct picture of the dream-thought. The smoothing over and tying together of the logical jumps and gaps of the dream, in keeping with the demands of logical thinking, is called secondary elaboration; and it often serves censorship by making the dream less transparent, and the repressed less discernible.[152]

---

[149] See also Schilder (719, 722, 723, 728, 736), and (750, Chapter 8).

[150] Schilder here uses the term "material" in contrast to "formal" in the sense of content vs. form, just as Silberer (781, 782) used it in contrast to "functional."

[151] See Freud (204, Chapter VII, A, particularly pp. 473 ff.); however, note again Schilder's emphasis on the distinction of form vs. content.

[152] See Freud (204, pp. 455–467).

A few important dream-mechanisms should still be discussed. The relatedness of opposites has already been mentioned: in the dream, objects are often represented by their opposites—for instance, a secret by a mass of people. The sequence of manifest dream-content proves nothing about the sequence of latent dream-thought: here, as in hysterias, we see inversions. Freud, for instance, reports a girl's hysterical seizure, in which pathetic indications of love-scenes are followed by her eagerly gazing at her toes: she thereby represented a love-scene which began in a street-car with a man watching the cap of the shoe on her crossed leg.

Finally: every dream-interpretation must face the question of whether a dream-element is a historical reminiscence or is to be regarded as symbolic.

d) Sleep[153]

The sleep-wish. Splitting of the ego in sleep. Sleep-ego and sleep-vigil. Sleep apparatus. Behavior on arousal from sleep. Dream as guardian of sleep.

A psychology of dreams presupposes a psychology of sleep, the foundations of which were laid by the studies of Liebault (497), Bernheim (65), and Forel (196). These authors have pointed out that going to sleep presupposes a sleep-wish. The neurotic renounces this sleep-wish because of his drive-dynamics.[154] The volitional wish to sleep is not identical with the drive-wish to sleep, which alone is decisive in going to sleep.

It will be worth while to discuss some further factors important for the psychology and physiology of sleep. In the moment of going to sleep, a splitting of the ego takes place: part of the ego turns away from the external world, but another part maintains vigil toward it.[155] This waking ego, Landauer's (474) sleep-vigil, guards the sleeper lest anything happen to him: it arouses the ego from its sleep when there is a threat. It is oriented toward the environment with an active attention. The mother awakens on hearing her children cry, but not at other loud noises; the miller awakens when the mill stops. The assumption that only

---

[153] For recent information as to the somatic aspects of sleep, cf. Kleitman (423, 424), Fulton (260, pp. 225, 258).

[154] Cf. "Symposium on Neurotic Disturbances of Sleep" (179).

[155] Cf. Rapaport (659) for a discussion of the variations in ego-functions with varying depth of sleep.

change in stimulation is perceived is incorrect: at the front can-non-blasts did not awake one, but the noise of a mouse did. We are dealing here with a particular distribution of attention.

Obviously, the drive-wish to sleep, in order to become effective, must have at its disposal an intact sleep-apparatus. We know that enforced morphine-abstinence results in extreme sleepless-ness, and, from experience with epidemic encephalitis, that lesions in the neighborhood of the third ventricle cause severe disturb-ances of sleep (Economo, 156). Mauthner (544) considered the gray-matter of the third and fourth ventricles essential for sleep.

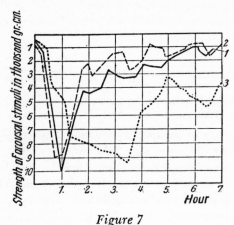

Figure 7

Normal sleep-depth curve, after Michelson

Troemner (836) ascribes such a special role to the thalamus. Im-portant evidence is that with changes in this region in epidemic encephalitis, we observe both excessive sleep and stubborn sleep-lessness, and occasionally reversal of the sleep-cycle, so that the patients sleep in the day and become alert at night.

So far, we cannot differentiate in the individual case the role of the sleep-wish from that of the sleep-apparatus, since the sleep-wish has an organic aspect also.[156] Thorough investigation of how various soporifics work may help here. It is probable that bromides, in so far as they are soporifics, work by eliminating in-hibitions of the sleep-wish. Neurotic sleeplessness is undoubtedly different from that of epidemic encephalitis, though the common

---

156 Cf. Schilder (698, 734) and (750, Chapter 20).

executive organ makes for some similarities. From a different side, psychoanalysis demonstrates the effect of the sleep-wish: dreams of convenience cannot be understood without assuming such a wish. After all, the behavior of people aroused from sleep demonstrates that they do not consider it a favor to be awakened: they thrash about and fend off the person awakening them, amidst all signs of unwillingness.

The dream is not a disturber of sleep: dreams of convenience demonstrate particularly that, by representing the pressing wish as fulfilled, they attempt to prolong sleep. We must keep in mind that there are always many things left unsettled from the day; these, reinforced by repressed infantile wishes, would not let the individual rest at all, were they not represented by the dream as fulfilled. The dream is the guardian of sleep, and only when wishes and needs become too urgent does the dreamer awake.[157] The study of sleep again demonstrates that it would be quite unjustified to separate organic from psychological: physiological chemistry has succeeded in discovering some somatic determinants of sleep. Also, study of the sleep-curve, measuring the depth of sleep by the intensity of the stimuli necessary for arousal, has brought results which cannot be explained simply on psychological grounds (Figure 7). By noting that certain animals, e.g. dogs, have a particularly shallow sleep, we may gain a new perspective: it may prove possible to derive the sleep-curve from biological needs.[158]

e) Freud's theory of the dream[159]

Pcpt-system and Mem-system. Preconscious and censorships. Image-character of dreams. Topographic and historical regression. The character of dreamwork. Primary process. Forgetting of dreams.

Now we are equipped to state Freud's theory of the dream. Freud assumes that, in the work of the psychological systems, excitations in general flow from the perceptual (Pcpt) to the motor (Mot) systems. Interpolated between these two, memory

[157] For a detailed and more precise discussion, see Freud (204, pp. 512–514, also pp. 209–211, 287).

[158] Cf. Troemner (836).

[159] For the source of this discussion, see Freud (204, Chapter VII), also (232) and (245, Chapter 1).

(Mem) systems progressively develop. Memories can attain access to the motor system only by becoming conscious.[160] Access to consciousness is guarded by two censorships: one prevents entrance of unconscious material into consciousness; the other separates the preconscious from consciousness.[161] When an excitation is prevented from entering consciousness and finding motor discharge, then a backflow toward the other end of the psychic system occurs, and memories are regressively transformed into percepts. Therefore, the image-character of the dream. Since the dream has at its disposal only images and not thoughts, it represents thoughts in the fashion of picture-puzzles. An example: Freud reports that a dreamer represented the concept "superfluous" by the image of standing in a room in which everything drips with water . . .

Through regression, the thought-content is dissolved into individual images of a picture-puzzle. Together with this regression, which Freud termed topographic, historical regression takes place: material derived from childhood is used by the dream.[162] As already indicated, there is an objective relation between topographic and historical regression.

We conceive of dream-genesis as follows: events of the day arouse thoughts and strivings which are not turned into actions, but remain unsettled, preconscious. A part of these trickles away its energy diffusely. Another part is spared this fate, by virtue of support from the unconscious. We conceive of drives as held back, but always on the watch for the opportunity to break forward. The wish originating in the unconscious is, however, held up on the boundary between unconscious and preconscious; it reaches the latter, and then consciousness, only in distorted and censored form. The peculiarities of the dream are, unquestionably, due to the processes of dream-work: to the ready displacement of energy from one image to another, that is, to the mobility of cathexes; to the particular potency of these energies, due to their not having been settled by action; to their indestructibility and timelessness. Freud terms these the primary process.[163] The

---

[160] For a discussion of the control of motility, see Freud (204, pp. 485–497).
[161] For a full discussion of this point, see Freud (229, pp. 122–127).
[162] Cf. Freud (204, p. 497).
[163] For the definition of the primary process, see Freud (204, pp. 529–533).

preconscious does not have these peculiarities, and its method of
work resembles closely that of consciousness. Dream-regression
revives not only infantile primeval life, but also phylogenetic
past: the dream is an avenue to the ancient history of man and
his psychic impulses.

The conspicuously fast forgetting of dreams used to be explained by their confusion and lack of order. Indeed, the state
of consciousness of the dreamer is an unusual one. In recall,
dream-experiences are paler, less rich, than those of waking.
Buehler (121) has shown that memory of thoughts is, in general,
infinitely better than that of images. It may be said, therefore,
that the pallor of dream-remembering is closely related to organically determined, essential characteristics of human thinking.
This does not contradict psychoanalytic theory, which explains
dream-forgetting by repression: the isolated images of a dream
correspond to unintegrated drive-impulses, and the chaotic infantile confusion of drives corresponds to conceptually uncen-
tered thinking.[164] We may assume that waking thinking takes
a stand against this chaos, and against the drives which express
themselves in it.

f) Infantile amnesia, and the genesis of neuroses and perversions[165]

Infantile amnesia as result of repression. Screen memories. Remembering
as a façade. More about the meaning of the infantile. More about regression.
Day-residue and infantile wish in dreams. The precipitation of neurosis. Primal
scene. The earlier theory of infantile trauma in hysteria. Sex-dreams of children as fantasies and as results of seduction-attempts in childhood. Conclusions about regression. The regression principle in disorders of brain-function
and in regeneration. Identical laws in organic structure, organic function, and
psychological processes.

In the foregoing we gained important new insight into the
theory of forgetting, and want to use it to fill the gaps in our
presentation. Man's continuous memory usually begins at the
fifth year of life; from before that only a few fragments are available. In general, investigators explain this infantile amnesia by
the difference between the child's and the adult's thinking. Freud
explains it as a product of repression: the third to fifth years of

164 Cf. Freud (204, pp. 470–485).
165 For sources, see Freud (205, IV), and (206, II).

life are the period of most intensive sexual activity, which ends only when the latency-period sets in.

These two explanations are not mutually exclusive. In any case, the turning away from proscribed impulses plays a role in forgetting this period. But from it a few memories stand out, which pertain to apparently unimportant events. It is demonstrable by the psychoanalytic method that these irrelevant memories hide something relevant which has been repressed. We call these screen-memories. They are not exclusive to childhood, though those of childhood may claim greatest interest. People's first memories are particularly significant. An anxiety-neurotic whom I observed reports as his first memory: he is lying on the floor and tries to peek under the skirt of his nurse-maid. He is a man with strong voyeuristic impulses. He places this memory at the age of one-and-a-half! Conceivably it is truly reproduced, but just as conceivably it was formed only later under the influence of reawakened sexuality. In any case, a core must have existed, around which the present form of the memory crystallized. The drive that manifests itself in the image is clear, but the origin of the image-content is uncertain. The earliest memory of another patient is his mother's threat to stab herself to death when his drunken father brought home a pick-up. He places this memory at the age of three. Analysis showed that an identification underlay this earliest memory—a feminine attitude toward the father. The scene expresses the patient's crucial drive-attitude.[166] Freud analyzed a childhood memory of Leonardo da Vinci: a vulture's tail pushes repeatedly into the mouth of the year-and-a-half-old child. Freud demonstrated that the vulture-tail represents the male genital, and that fellatio fantasies lay hidden behind this image. Here a symbolic distortion took place.

These examples illustrate the three main forms of screen-memories. Generally, every emerging memory must be tested as to whether or not it is but a front, and has a deeper layering. Later on we will show that basically every memory-image can be assumed to have such layering. But the relation of the individual layers to each other varies. Layer-formation and recall-possibility are intimately related; I need not go into the details of this. What

---

[166] Concerning the nature of such early memories, see Freud (205), and Fenichel (182).

will be the foreground, and what the background of experience, depends only on drives. Fundamentally, the theory of remembering is a segment of the theory of drives.[167]

In discussing dream-experiences, we ascribed a special role to experiences of early childhood. This needs further discussion. The same impingement on the fertilized egg has a much more far-reaching effect[168*] in the eight-cell-stage of division than in later stages of embryonic development; similarly, encroachments and experiences at an earlier and more plastic age must have a different effect than those which encounter a solidified psychic system. The accepted view that education must begin with the young individual is in line with this. We may ascribe to the experiences of youth, and particularly to those of infancy, much greater significance than to those of a later age.[169]

The child's drive-attitudes toward the parents are decisive for its later development. Its environment consists mainly of parents, siblings, maids, and toys; reactions to these depend partly on the environment itself and partly on the organic inheritance of the child.[170] Certain kinds of experiences at this stage may well influence the drives. Experience and congenital drive are factors of equal potency. It stands to reason that the period of most vivid drives, the third to fifth years of life, should be most susceptible to the influence of experiences. Drives must manifest themselves in experiences, so we must assume that the quality of the individual's drives manifests itself clearly for the first time in the infantile experiences of this stage. Because the quality of drives is decisive for later life also, it is urgent to explore this period. With the onset of the latency-period, whatever has already manifested itself succumbs to repression and is again forgotten. However, the forgotten retains its effect-value, as indicated by the readiness of the drives of this stage to reappear. Repressed energy strives to break through, and does so according to rules already

167 For reservations as to this point, cf. footnote 27, p. 162.

168* Nevertheless, damage suffered at an early stage is, under certain circumstances, more easily compensated for.

169 This is one of the fundamental facts learning-theories have been quite generally oblivious of. Cf. Hilgard (348). Hebb (328) did develop a learning-theory which takes account of this fact.

170 Cf. Freud (246) on constitutional drive intensity; also Hartmann (321) on ego apparatuses.

discussed. If in the course of later sexual development inhibition is encountered, and discharge becomes insufficient, the repressed energies, reinforced by the unused remainder, may stage a break-through at a fixation-point and result in a perversion.[171] Fixation-points are those points of sexual development which have attained particular significance due to constitution or experience. The concept of regression now attains further meaning: the back-flow of psychic energy goes into those channels which have been deepened most by experience.

Therefore, those partial drives are revived which have been already tagged, by experiences of the third to fifth year, as most essential ones. Clearly, the relationship is like that between day-residues and latent dream-thought; the latter also originates in childhood, and seeks gratification in the dream. These matters are important, because they contribute to the understanding not only of neuroses and psychoses, but of man's love-life in general. Neuroses are precipitated by an acute conflict, and usually one re-lated to sexuality. The patients feel unable to digest a certain ex-perience, and this leads to the revival of previous pleasurable im-pressions. Since all of the past cannot be settled by actions, it attains a value of its own; and if a higher-level action is not pos-sible, then at least a lower-level one is executed. For instance, homosexual activity is frequent in people who, having already at-tained a normal sex-life, suffer an infection or lose a love-object. It happens also that a man who is attracted to women proves impotent with them, and so turns to homosexual activity. But in this way only perversions would arise, not neuroses. Neurosis comes about only when outlet for the revived primitive drive is also barred, and it must find symbolic substitute-gratification. Whether a perversion or a neurosis will be the outcome depends essentially on whether or not the repression of infantile sexuality by the total personality, by the ego-ideal, is sufficiently energetic. According to Freud (206), neurosis is the negative of perversion.[172] Jung (391, 394) has put the main emphasis on the acute conflict,

171 Contrary to Freud's (206) early assumption, perversion is not the ex-clusive consequence; formation of other symptoms may be an alternative con-sequence.

172 This discussion oversimplifies the relation between perversions and neuroses, and draws a line between them which is altogether too sharp. Cf. Fenichel (180, Chapter 16).

and stressed that regression begins only upon failure in the face
of current tasks. This agrees with Freud's views, except that Freud,
whom we follow, considers the fantasies arising in connection with
conflict not accidental, but determined by previous experiences.

With Freud, we distinguish a variety of precipitating factors
in neuroses and psychoses. The most frequent of these is frustration: the individual becomes neurotic when cut off from any love-
life. The individual can become neurotic not only because of a
change in the environment, but because of an inner effort to gain
gratification available in reality—that is, in an attempt to adapt to
reality. In such an attempt he may give up a drive-gratification
which no longer suits his needs, but be unable to attain a deeper
drive-gratification.[173] There are also people who have never abandoned their infantile relationships, and in the attempt to overcome their childhood-fixations succumb to neurosis. But we also
see healthy people become sick, on whom no new experiences have
impinged; in these, an increase of libido in psychic economy due
to biological processes (such as puberty or menopause) has taken
place. The ungratified and dammed-up libido may open the way
to regression, and feed the same conflicts present in cases of absolutely external frustration. An onset of neurosis after a long-
worked-for success is also frequent.[174]

The intensity of acute conflict required to force regression
varies with the individual: some will regress on a minor conflict,
and others only after the most severe psychological strain. In general, neuroses require an acute precipitating experience for regression, but the character of the regression will be determined by
previous experiences, especially infantile ones. Basically, if we may
put it thus, a double trauma is required. The infantile trauma
may be an expression of a certain constitution, though psychoanalysis is recently inclined to regard a single experience, the
primal scene, as having the decisive determining role.[175]

In an early phase of the development of psychoanalysis, it was
the prevalent view that hysterias originate in certain sexual

173 For Freud's later views see (244).
174 For a detailed discussion, see Freud (221).
175 At the time of Schilder's writing this was actually no longer the case.
Rank's (648) "trauma of birth" theory made one more attempt to re-establish
the single-experience theory of neurosis. Subsequently this view fast became an
anachronism. Cf. Freud (244).

traumata of childhood, and specifically in later ones (after the sixth year of life). But it soon turned out that part of these traumatic experiences (seduction by those caring for the child) were products of fantasy, and that persons who actually had such experiences did not necessarily become hysterics. Clearly, fantasies may have the same effects as experiences; at any rate, they indicate the individual's particular sexual attitude. The origin of some childhood traumata is not assault on or seduction of the child, but rather his seducing others. Abraham (2) asserted that to experience sexual traumata is a specific form of childhood sexual activity. Be this as it may, we can regard neither the fantasies nor the traumata of later childhood as decisive for the subsequent neurosis, though drive-attitudes may come to a clear expression in them. The latter appear much earlier also: we use the term fixation-point to indicate those groups of experiences which have given sexuality a fixed form, on either constitutional or experiential grounds. Later on we will show that these fixation-points correspond to quite specific points of sexual development, which are particularly receptive to a back-flow of libido. It may be formulated that the back-flow of libido breaks through at fixation-points; and since the drive cannot be separated from the experiences in which it manifests itself, the experiences pertinent to the fixation are also revived.

This gives a view of the psychoanalytic theory of regression, to which we must add that regression too has its organic correlates. I have already pointed out that after brain-lesions, onto- and phylogenetic predecessors of the functions involved are revived.[176] According to Foerster (192) and Gierlich (274, 275), phylogenetically old forms of function are revived in hemiplegia. This may be considered as established in principle, even though there are differences of opinion between the two investigators: Foerster sees in hemiplegia a revival of the process of climbing, Gierlich a revival of a starting-off and jumping mechanisms. We have also mentioned the relation between children's speech and aphasia. The conception that choreatic movements correspond to those of infants and should be considered atavistic originates

---

176 Cf. Schilder (751, 752). Schilder appears to imply here that those organic lesions which bring about repression do so because they unleash processes which are the organic correlates of repression in functional cases also.

from Meynert; Anton has put forth evidence for it. Wagner-Jauregg has demonstrated that a primitive eating-movement, the Atz-reflex or infant-reflex, reappears in high-grade organic dementia; it is interesting that this reflex was also observed in a case of mouth-apraxia (Betlheim). What holds for the function of the brain holds for organic structure as well. If a five-toed salamander's leg is amputated, it regenerates a four-toed phylogenetically older, form. Thus the same laws hold for the psyche, for brain-function, and for organic structure. Apparently the lower mechanisms are included in the higher ones, but are submerged in them as long as these are not inhibited or destroyed.

For the development of the psychoanalytic theory of sexual traumata, see Freud (206). According to him, the primal scene (for details, see his study of an infantile neurosis, 235) is a single scene of early childhood. He describes a child who, at the age of one-and-a-half, observed the intercourse (dog fashion) of the parents. The primal scene cannot be directly remembered; it appears in various degrees of concealment and distortion with increasing frequency in dreams and associations, but only after a long period of analysis. To me, this is not the final word. According to Freud, this primal scene succumbs to primal repression, and it is primal repression that leads to repression proper.[177] Naturally, the dynamic effect of the primal scene depends on constitution.

10. THINKING[178]

Image- and imageless-elements of thinking. Awarenesses, thoughts. Connection of image- and imageless-material. Accompanying symbolic images. Silberer's autosymbolic phenomena. Examples. Fusions of partial contents. Affective transformation of image-material. The concept of accompanying images. Function of concepts. Concept as basis of possible actions. Meaning and will-act. Logical categories. Cognition of relations. Percept and image in relation of action. Pleasure-principle. Cognition as consequence of delayed gratification. Two memory-systems: personal and objective logical. Action as unification of

[177] This appears to be a misapprehension of the concept of primal repression. Cf. Freud (227).

[178] Schilder's depth of insight, breadth of understanding, and foresight, become perhaps clearest in his conception of thinking. A perusal of Vinacke's (849) most recent textbook on thinking shows that only now has academic psychology slowly approached the program laid out by Schilder. Humphrey's (360) recent volume on the experimental psychology of thinking, as well as his recent popular volume (359), bear out the importance Schilder attached to the work of the Wuerzburg School. The commentary and tentative theory of thinking in my source-book (658) is in debt to Schilder's writings in more ways than I can easily state. To my knowledge, Schilder's treatment of thinking, here and in (750), however unsystematic, is the only serious attempt to explore the bearing of psychoanalytic observation and theory on the problem of thought. Cf. Appendix, pp. 341 ff., infra; also Rapaport (655, 658, Part VII).

memories. Forces and counter-forces in thinking. Sphere as totality of memories pertaining to the object. Sphere-consciousness. Processes in remembering forgotten names. The schema of thought-process. On inhibition of thought-processes in the sphere. Symbol-like images lie àt intersections of two spheres. Sphere as locus of drive-transactions. Delay of impulses as source of the richness of thought. Organic-morphological analogies. Representation of concepts in series of pictures. Fringe and sphere. Hyperlogical and hypological thinking. Sphere and logical thinking. Schemata. Proprioception and sphere. Effect-value of spheric experiences. Sphere and organism. On apparatuses of thought. Actualization of knowledge. Correction. Effects of tasks in thinking. Predecessors of thought in the sphere. Instead of the specific the general, or instead of a total complex only one of its parts, determines action. Relations to animal psychology. Volkelt's spider. The ant. Relations to the psychology of dreams. The identity of preparatory phases of normal thought, schizophrenic thought-products, thinking of primitives, and that of children. The thought-process recapitulates phylo- and ontogenetic developmental phases of thought. Attributes of preparatory phases of thought. Omnipotence of thought, magic. Projection- and identification-mechanisms. Absence of opposition between active and passive. Attributes of some particularly important spheres. Godfather-power. Excess of meaning in the world of primitives. The unification of tendencies in the completed thought-act (Lipps). Degrees of unification. Self-evident judgment as the integrate of object-directed tendencies. Feeling theory of self-evidence rejected. Assumptions. The psychological manifold. Abstraction as consequence of attitudes. Final comment on the structure of concepts. The past in concepts: love-life, castration, as examples for concept-formation. Varieties of incomplete concepts: fantasy and productive thought.

Only now can we hope to penetrate into the mechanisms of thinking. Though we treat thinking under the heading of drive-theory, we must be aware that there are structures related to thinking which cannot be explained by genetic constructions. The very existence of images, thoughts, judgments, is in point.[179] Moreover, though affects and drives do play a most significant role even in perception, there *are* aspects of perception which are totally independent of any drive.[180] In every psychological event we can distinguish between an affective aspect, the intending, and an intellectual one, that which we intend. In other words, we are back at our basic distinction: act and object. So far, we have traced only the somatic conditions of object-formation; now we will be concerned with its psychological aspect.

Thought has imageless as well as image elements.[181] Recognition of this is to the credit of Ach (9), who spoke of "awarenesses,"

[179] Cf. Hartmann (321), on ego-apparatuses.

[180] Only recently do we have experiments which are rooted in the drive-theory and yet arrive at this conclusion, thus showing both these aspects of perception. See Klein (417, 418).

[181] Cf. Humphrey (360, Chapters 1–5, particularly p. 149).

and of Buehler (121), who spoke of "thoughts." In the distinction
between act and object, both "awarenesses" and "thoughts" are on
the object side: they are means of apprehending objects. An
earlier form of these concepts is Marbe (531) and Orth's (593) "position of consciousness." It is undoubtedly difficult to demonstrate
"awarenesses" in isolation; F. E. O. Schultz also has stressed this,
saying that a part or shred of image is always demonstrable, even if
merely of a pale and colorless verbal image. In contrast to the inconstancy, unreliability, and paleness of these images, the
"thought" is clear: it intends something quite definite. Even
superficial consideration shows that feeling-experiences cannot be
the essence of these clear "awarenesses." If there are total impressions, in H. Gomperz's (294) sense, which convey the certainty of
that which is intended (and I am convinced that his assumption is
correct) then these total impressions cannot be reduced to feelings.

The question is: how do image and imageless material connect? The two are not independent, and both pictorial and verbal
images often appear as symbols of that which is "thought." G. E.
Mueller (569) has pointed out that images often appear in the
course of the thought-process, partly before and partly together
with the goal of thought, and represent it symbolically. For instance, in learning experiments where a group of three numbers is
to appear, the middle number to be greater than the others, an
image arises of an acute triangle pointing upward.

There is an intrinsic relationship between the image and what
is intended. This is particularly clear in the autosymbolic phenomena of Silberer (781, 782): when he was sleepy but struggling
with a thought, an image appeared to him which represented the
thought symbolically. "*Example 1*: I am to improve a halting passage in an essay. *Symbol:* I see myself planing a piece of wood.
Example 5: I am trying to think of the purpose of the metaphysical studies I am about to undertake; that purpose is, I reflect, to
work my way through ever higher forms of consciousness—that is,
levels of existence—in my quest after the basis of existence. *Symbol:*
I run a long knife under a cake as though to take a slice out of it.
Interpretation: My movement with the knife represents 'working
my way through.' To clarify this apparently silly symbol, I must
give a detailed explanation. The symbol-basis, that is, the relationship which makes the picture here chosen usable for autosymbolic

representation, is the following. At the dining-table, it is at times my chore to cut and distribute the cake. I do this with a long and flexible knife, which necessitates considerable care. It is particularly difficult to lift the slices; the knife must be carefully pushed *under* the slice (this is the slow 'working my way through' to arrive at the 'basis'). There is further symbolism in the picture: the symbol is a layer-cake, so that the knife cutting it penetrates several layers (levels of consciousness and existence)."

In the course of thinking it is not always symbolic images that come about. According to G. E. Mueller (569), a fusion of part-contents of images often accompanies thinking; for instance, the image may appear in a strange color. G. E. Mueller also speaks of an affective transformation of the image-material: for example, the first of a series of digits to be recalled may, in the image, appear larger than the others. These transformations are not irrelevant rarities; every investigator of thinking has observed them (Michotte and Ransy, 557; Lindworsky, 505; Selz, 771). Allers (18) is mistaken when he asserts that thoughts and these symbolic images are unrelated.[182]

From the formal point of view, concepts may be regarded as the most primitive elements of thought.[183] How should we understand concepts? In logic, concepts are constant, unchangeable, and generally valid. This has already been mentioned. Psychologically, a concept may be represented *either* by a particularly clear example of the class, which is usually very incompletely imaged so that only its color and a few lines of its contour or perhaps a certain posture appear before the inner eye; *or* it may be represented by a series of such sketchy images; *or,* finally, by a fusion of such single images—such as a composite of many horse images, which may be not images of real horses but memories of pictures seen. Be this as it may, the image never exhausts the concept. The concept itself always has an imageless, yet object-like, core.

The formal attributes of concepts cannot be understood without clarifying the use of concepts. In the concept *horse,* a definite and clearly circumscribed part of the object-world lies before me. In it I have an occasion for and guarantee of an action, which are just as reliable as those afforded by a percept. Concepts are ideal

---

182 Cf. Schilder (751).
183 Cf. Schilder (707) and (752); cf. also Hebb (328).

jumping-off points for actions; their nature cannot be understood without realizing that they are bases for possible actions.[184] Meaning-experiences too must have a particularly close relation to action. The prerequisite of action is a circumscribed, clear, and definite setting. The experience of meaning is a preparation for the experiences of willing and doing; but this view does not call into question the phenomenological independence of these forms of experience.[185] What has been said of concepts applies to propositions also. I have already expressed the view that the content of the proposition is always a predicative relation. It represents some of the structure of relationships obtaining between objects.

Indeed, all logical categories point to the real external world; the category of existence and object, as well as that of doing and effecting, apprehends something that exists in reality.[186] In the category of inherence, I apprehend that this or that attribute belongs to an object. In judgments I express predicative relationships. The percept "blue sky" is something different from the judgment which is based on this percept: the sky is blue. The latter expresses something that goes beyond the former. The conjunction of two images, the simultaneous imaging of sky and blue, cannot explain the predicative relationship. The predicative relationship too is accompanied by images and their fragments, but neither explains its nature. Judgment too is a preparation for action. Judgments establish the existence, and show us the wealth, of relationships. Deductions, as Lindworsky's (505) experimental investigations show, are merely the continued establishing of relationships. From the formal point of view we have not only concepts, but we also cognize relations and state these in judgments. Since the kernel of judgment is a predicative relationship, the goal of thinking is to establish continuously the attributes of objects and thereby make it possible to cope with them in action. It should be noted that the concept attribute is used here in the broadest sense: there are also objective relationships between ob-

184 Cf. Schilder (752, pp. 529–530).

185 This is the issue of the autonomy of emergent psychological structures; cf. Allport (25, 26), also Rapaport (656, 657).

186 Schilder is consistently bothered by the apparent solipsistic implications of psychoanalysis, and is at pains to establish the existence and role of objective reality. This becomes particularly complicated because of his consistent rejection of the Kantian view (see particularly Schilder, 749). Here, however, the Kantian view comes in, as it were, through the back door.

jects, but for simplicity's sake we subsume them here as attributes.

What is the origin of concepts and judgments? We assume that the individual relates to the perceptual world in terms of his drives; seeing is a result of wanting to see, of intending an object; and we have noted that each percept contains the kernel of an action.

I see in order to reach the objects of my hunger and sex-drive; there is no dispassionate perceiving.[187] I turn to the percept when I need it, and barely has the act of perceiving taken place when the percept becomes the motive for further action. The act of perceiving, though it has its own existence, lies on the border of two drive-attitudes. Images always arise from drive-attitudes. The man images naked women when he is aroused sexually; the mourner images the dead beloved when he is longing for her. Images are expressions of drive-attitudes: I can image only that for which I have a drive-wish. But it appears that imaging does not result in the same drive-gratification as perceiving. We have reason to assume, with Freud, that on primitive levels imaging is hallucinatory: the hungry infant hallucinates milk.[188] Freud speaks of the pleasure-principle which finds expression in these uncontrolled hallucinatory images, where the drive is directed not toward the pleasure as such, but rather toward the pleasure-bringing object. When the drive is directed toward an action, rather than an image, the action leads to drive-gratification.

We have a simple schema before us: need leads us to the search for and finding of the drive-object (percept), and so to gratification through it. If the real object is not found, then the image that directed the search is either reinforced to hallucinatory intensity (provided that sufficient psychological energy is available), or is dropped and the energy so saved is turned toward other goals. These goals can pertain only to the real external world: in final analysis their content is the attainment of the drive-object, which requires insight into the structure of the external world. But such insight comes about only when there is need for it.

187 Schilder does not succeed here in synthesizing his insight into "dispassionate" structures and apparatuses, with his insight into the basic determining role of drives. No wonder; even today the "new look" trend in perception has run afoul on this very difficulty of synthesis. Cf., however, the solutions proposed by psychoanalytic ego-psychology (656, 657), and in the field of perception by Klein (417, 418), also Klein et al. (413–416).

188 See Freud (204, Chapter VII) and (216).

If drive-gratification could come about without cognition, cognition would not have arisen to begin with: there would be no energy available for it.[189] Due to lack of drive-gratification a welter of cognitive impressions arises, by means of which an ever greater part of the external world becomes amenable to us. We must assume that these impressions are at our disposal, organized in two systems. The first is the sequence in which they occurred, since our memory delivers not only the facts but also their sequence of occurrence and their arrangement; we may refer to this as the personal-system of remembering. The second is an objective system, in which memories and experiences are arranged according to their logical relations of similarity, difference, contrast, subordination, superordination; this was mentioned in connection with the so-called associations, and is a hierarchically strict, architectonic articulation.[190] How are concepts formed out of this memory material? It must be kept in mind that the possibility of mastering a horse is given only in previous experience with it: when one is to break a horse, this wish arouses all images acquired concerning horses, everything that has either a personal or objective relation to this goal. It is as though the new decision revives previous experience, as though the present were built upon the entire past. Not all of the past emerges in full detail, yet it enters into the action. Action is a tremendous unification of memories.

The experience of meaning also must be regarded, in this respect, as a preparation for action. So far we have considered only the simple case, when the intending of an image or object has an uninhibited course. This hardly ever occurs in reality, except in the most primitive and reflex-like actions. Usually we have many varied impulses. This is so even in perception: the object which I see demands that I attend to it as a whole, but its parts demand that I regard them particularly. Besides, many external impressions also demand to be attended. Thus there is a chaos of impulses, and my intending an image or a thought is opposed by other impulses. These contrary impulses may best be studied in symbols and symbol-like structures.

If the two systems into which psychological experience rela-

189 For a review of the pertinent psychoanalytic conceptions, see Rapaport (655, 657).

190 Cf. Bartlett (46), Bleuler (89, particularly pp. 591–592, pp. 629–631, footnotes 115, 122); also Rapaport (658, Part 7, IX).

tive to an object is organized are designated as the *sphere* of the object, then we may conceive of every thought, image, and percept as embedded in such a sphere. When the image "horse" emerges, its entire sphere reverberates.[191] The studies of Buehler (121) indicate that there is a sphere-consciousness, that the sphere is not just a logically inferred abstraction, but something psychologically real.[192] In other words, with each experience its logical as well as subjective locus is given. Indeed, the process of remembering forgotten names suggests that their place is given not as a mere void, but together with an inkling of what is actually sought. We may know that the name begins with an R, that it resembles another name, and differs from it by such-and-such (see pp. 158 ff., above).

In general, when a concept, a thought, a proposition, or a judgment emerges, first its sphere appears: that is, the logically superordinate always arises first: thinking begins with general "concepts." Within this broad realm, the already familiar formations take place: due to counter-impulses, fusions (condensations, contaminations) bring forth symbol-like images, particularly when the way to the goal is obstructed. When the intended concept is not reached because of an affective distraction, the thought-process does not emerge from the sphere—that is, does not go beyond the general concept.[193] This is the case when, at an examination, a candidate, asked about a certain species of animals, does not get past whether it is warm- or cold-blooded: he reaches only a superordinate concept.[194] But he may also mistake one order for another, and classify carnivores as rodents; that is, he may get derailed within the sphere and substitute a coordinate concept for the one meant. In his confusion, the examinee will be prone to mix trains of thought, particularly when the memory-material is not well anchored. The answers Rodenwaldt (674) obtained from healthy recruits are interesting from this point of view: Luther invented the Bible, he wanted to throw over Christianity, he didn't believe in Christianity; the war of 1870 was that of the Great Elector against Napoleon, that of Emperor Frederick the Great against Russia; a Catholic said Luther was the Pope, etc.

---

[191] Cf. Hebb (328), on the formation of assemblies.
[192] Cf. p. 124, supra.
[193] Cf. Schilder (751) and (707).
[194] Cf. Rapaport et al. (650, Vol. II, Part 4, Chapter II).

In these examples, the pressure to give an answer replaces the spontaneous impulse to think, and it is under this pressure that the fusions come about.[195]

Derailments like these may take place in personal-experience material also, and something heard within the hour may slip into the answer even though it has no objective relation to the theme. If acts of thought corresponded only to our wishes, they would approximate reality as little as a hysterical wish-delirium or a delusion. If other impulses which do not follow the structure of reality become effective in thinking, for instance, excessive repression, then the thought-act will again miss its actual goal, even though it has taken up new elements and has become enriched thereby.[196]

Every object is the center of a sphere, of a drive-attitude: objects are coordinated to attitudes. Concepts too correspond to definite attitudes. There is always a multitude of such drive-attitudes; if in a schematically simplified case we postulate only two drive-attitudes, then the point reached by the thought-process is one which belongs to the spheres of both drive-attitudes. Expressed differently: symbol-like formations, condensations, fusions, lie at the crossing-points of two spheres, two drive-attitudes. The image itself never represents the drive-attitude completely: the complete fulfillment of a drive-attitude is the action. This can be most neatly studied in relation to the sex-drive: the less the gratification the drive reaches, the more the images become massed.

Accordingly, the very presence of images in thinking should be regarded as an indication of inhibition. Indeed, it was demonstrable in experiments, for instance, Martin's (535, 537), that when difficulties are encountered, the frequency of images in thinking increases. We stress again that verbal images, and these are the most suitable for thinking, have a relatively non-sensory character; as Stricker (818) already knew, they have an extraordinarily close relation to the motor-system, so that fundamentally every word-image carries with it the corresponding innervation.

No psychology of thinking is possible without the premise that there are real object-structures, a reality, which we apprehend

195 Cf. Rapaport et al. (650, Vol. I, Part 2, Chapter II, b).
196 Here Schilder makes an attempt to solve the problem by-passed above: cf. footnote 27, p. 162. A hierarchic distinction between drives and the various attitudes deriving from them is one of the possible solutions.

by thinking. This reality comprises first objects, second the relations of objects to each other, and finally values (still to be discussed). It depends on our organization how much of these structures becomes amenable to us. We regard drives as the fluid part
of our organization, and the organism as drives structuralized into
forms. Objects demand that we regard them as they really are and
according to their real value. On the one hand, objects demand
our recognition, thereby continuously checking our drive-strivings; on the other hand, these strivings reach out after objects, continuously drawing new ones into the circle of attention. The very
existence of such a multitude of partial drives brings broad
segments of reality into relation with each other; the locus of these
transactions is the sphere.

As already stressed, the essential core of thinking is a continuous establishment of relationships. The various parts of the
sphere are continuously put into relation with each other, and
these newly created relations are continuously tested as to whether
or not they correspond to the requirements of objects. The sphere
is where ever new relation-experiences emerge; in it, drives directed toward objects are continuously checked[197] by counter-
drives, bringing forth ever new images; and these images are again
put into relation with the others. It is this checking[198] which makes
the richness of thought possible: this psychological proposition is
well supported by what we know about the development of the
nervous system. The brain may be considered simply as that organ
which makes it possible to delay response to a stimulus; and it may
be said that one of the characteristics distinguishing man from animals is his ability to delay his drive-gratifications longer. Here, as
always, study of organic development must lead to the same laws
as study of psychological structures.

Now we can understand why a concept is so often represented
by a whole series of images: these represent repeated sallies of an attitude, each of which may have been differently checked. Individual images differ according to the quality of the checking attitude. Now we understand symbolic images also: they emerge and

197 "Checked" translates *gebremst*; this concept in essence served Schilder
as the concept of "delay" served Freud (216). But in Schilder's conception,
various drive-impulses check each other; in Freud's conception, ego-structure
performs the function of delay. Cf. Rapaport (658, Part VII).

198 Ibid.

may persist as the "slag" of thought-development. We understand also why sometimes concepts appear which are in part too general, in part too specific, and in part coordinate, instead of the ones we seek.

There is a type of psychological experience, that of schizophrenia, in which these preparatory phases of thinking may be readily studied. In schizophrenic thinking, preparatory phases of thought appear instead of completed thoughts, and interchanges within a range of concepts, displacements, and condensations are continuously observed. Symbolism and allegories appear in ever new images.[199] It is only since the advent of psychoanalysis that we have gained a deeper insight into these problems. It is true, James (373) had ingeniously shown that in every psychological experience we must distinguish between a sharply circumscribed core and an unsharp periphery or *fringe*, and that the fringe-area has a decisive role in psychological life; but his discoveries and those of experimental psychology have taught us nothing about the structure of this fringe-area. The schema produced by such investigations was filled with life only by psychoanalysis.

Every thought begins in the sphere as a generality: Erdmann (164) has stressed that general concepts precede specific ones, and Buehler's (122) observations on children corroborate it. True, it takes a specific impetus to arrive at such generality, but this is like the relation of day-residue to dream, or of acute conflict to neurosis. Every thought begins in the sphere, where the transactions between attitudes, indispensable to fruitful thinking, take place: the greater the manifold of attitudes and impulses, and the wealth of transactions, the more of reality will be represented there. The transactions within the sphere are the prerequisites of productive thinking; only in spheric thinking is it possible to survey the whole of the world without words. The sphere is the locus of Erdmann's hyperlogical thinking, the products of which—without being dressed into words—are more valuable than verbally formulated thought. Only in terms of the sphere can we explain Schopenhauer's assertion that *The World as Will and Idea* arose in him as a single thought. In the sphere lie the prerequisites of artistic creation, of all creative activity in general. The wealth of the sphere must be controlled, however, by being brought in

199 Cf. Schilder (691, 692, 707, 751, 752).

touch with actuality, to attain a form that makes action in the external world possible. Unifications must take place, because without them thinking in the sphere remains worthless: hyperlogical thinking is intimately related to hypological. Hyperlogical thinking becomes hypological if it does not finally differentiate out of the sphere. On the other hand, the sphere is the matrix, the not-frozen, the essentially live part of thought, capable of development.[200] The deep shudder of awe which the unprejudiced person feels when faced with certain utterances of the mentally ill is a consequence of the sphere's appearing, as it were, naked; the primeval ground of our psychological life is unveiled. As remote as strict logical thinking may seem from the experiences of the sphere, there is a deep similarity between the two: logical thinking too, in final analysis, rests on cognition of relations, and continual setting-into-relations is characteristic of the sphere.[201]

We must once more raise the question: how is the sphere represented psychologically? It coincides with what Buehler (121) called thought-nuclei or sphere-consciousness. In it we encounter both images and imageless elements. We must single out one kind of image, the schemata, since these seem particularly suited to represent broad realms of psychological experience in image-form. We must assume that there is a great multitude of such schematic image-systems, and that they are used by every thought. We regard these schemata as technical aids which make it possible to survey quickly an abundance of material (cf. Lindworsky, 505; and G. E. Mueller, 569).

Fundamentally, the sphere has the same elements as completely developed thought. Feelings too exist in the sphere. We have become accustomed to regarding them as reflections of intendings. We must assume that there is an extraordinary abundance of coenesthetic elements in the sphere. I have repeatedly stressed that as the corporeal aspect in thinking increases, the less possibility there is for discharge in action. An experience remains spheric only so long as it does not lead to clearly circumscribed concepts, which in turn are preparations for action.

Spheric experiences are dammed-up, body-close, and have a

200 Cf. Kris (460, 461) for the expression of similar conceptions in the terminology of psychoanalytic ego-psychology.

201 But note the failure to take cognizance of this in psychologists studying thought; for example, Wertheimer (877).

greater share of coenesthesias (and feelings). Spheric experiences, unlike clearly conscious ones, belong less to the external world than to the body. But the sphere must not be equated with co-enesthesias, because that would disregard the structure of the sphere. The effect-value of spheric experiences must be extraordinarily great, since they are dammed-up and have no outflow. Nor should one ascribe effect-value solely to spheric experiences: everything psychic rests on the sphere, which in turn rests on drives, on the organic.[202] In final analysis, it is the drives which are effective: they are fed by the organic, and provide all psychological experiences with energy originating in the depth of the organism.

Besides schemata, there are other apparatuses of thought, the structure of which must be regarded as a given, and which cannot be reduced to affectivity. For instance, under certain circumstances, even complicated problems are answered simply by an actualization of knowledge: without mediation a complex of knowledge comes to consciousness, parts of it elicit its appearance as a whole (complex-completions), and the material so arisen is also continuously corrected (Selz).[203] These are facts which do not admit of further reduction. Furthermore, tasks are always present and active in the directed thought-process; they may put already known means to use in reaching a goal of thought, or find the means if they are not yet known. The less obvious the means used for the end in question, the more ingenious the idea seems. If the means cannot be found by memorial reproduction, success must wait on a favorable accident. The conscious task-settings are always with us, lurking in us; and when a usable means presents itself, it is seized and used in a new connection. While set to a certain goal, we may encounter a means suitable for other tasks already set. These are the results Selz obtained by the method of introspection. Obviously, they obtain their full vitality only by psychoanalytic considerations.

Now we can formulate our findings more generally. Drives

[202] Schilder's discussion here—and his "sphere" concept in general—point up the continuous transition between the primary and the secondary processes (Freud 204, Chapter VII), which as a rule have been treated in the psychoanalytic literature as a sharp dichotomy.

[203] See Selz (771), and Humphrey (360), on Selz. Cf. also Rapaport (655) and (658, Part 7, XVIII).—Here again Schilder clearly sees the relation between energy and apparatus.

and thinking in the preparatory phase center on the sphere, and there are two major alternatives: first, the intending is directed toward something general, and only a broad outline of what is sought is reached; second, only a part of the goal is reached, and it takes the place of the whole. Both cases shed light on the structure of neurosis, on the thinking of the child, on the thinking of primitives, and on animal psychology: the formations of the sphere are similar to these evolutionary predecessors of thought.

To illustrate: Volkelt (856) describes spiders who, when the situation changes in the least, do not throw themselves on the fly; the slightest change in the total-complex suffices to bring about an entirely different action. Conversely, according to Henning (337), it is sufficient to give an ant the odor of another breed of ants to expose it to the attacks of its own breed, who mercilessly kill it. One signal, irrespective of others, decides action; all other objective factors are suppressed. Uexkuell (841) reports: "I have found that hungry *eledone moschata* (a cephalopode) like to attack hermit crabs. But if the crab-shell bears an actinia which burns the eledone, it will soon give up its futile attempts; then it ceases eating altogether, will not accept even this favorite crab, and perishes. This experiment shows that the plasticity, so-called, of the eledone's brain is little: new experience does not create new habit, but breaks up their world of objects." Here rejection based on experience spreads unwarrantedly from the single experience to behavior in general; indeed, this reminds us of undeveloped thinking. Similarly, primitive man, who is well adapted to his environment, fails immediately as soon as even one factor in it is changed.[204] On the one hand, only total situations elicit corresponding attitudes on primitive levels; on the other, a single signal, regardless of everything else, decides action. Attitudes are also displaced to other objects without objective justification. Let us remember that dreams too disregard broad segments of material—that for instance in the uncle-dream all attributes of friend R., excepting those which stamp him as a fool, are abstracted away. Apparently the dream takes the single thing it needs, and cares

[204] While Schilder's formulation is entirely too sweeping and lacks amplification, it touches on a crucial issue of comparative and developmental psychology. For more recent systematic surveys of pertinent material, see H. Werner (870), and Thorpe (832); for particularly important studies, see Lorenz (522), and Tinbergen (833), as well as Piaget's studies (611, 612, 613, etc.).

nothing about the rest. In neuroses, the possibility of loving exists only when a complex infantile situation recurs.

We have every reason to assume that the conditions of dream, neurosis, and primitive evolutionary stages are the same.[205] The same symbolic and symbol-like formations which populate the dream are encountered in the psychological life of primitives and in myths also: all these are manifestations of primitive sexuality. For instance, in those puberty-rites in which the chieftain urinates into the mouth of the boy initiated, the underlying idea undoubtedly is that of impregnation, urine replacing the sperm and mouth the genital opening; but the whole activity represents the initiated being reborn by this impregnation and becoming a full man. (For the psychoanalytic view on puberty-rites, see Reik.[206]) It is also easily demonstrable in magic experience that the magic view of the world depends on the lack of sharp definition of the boundary between body and world, and the shading of images into percepts. There is no doubt that magic belief is the most primitive and primeval religion: Preuss (637) and Vierkant (846) have convincingly demonstrated this. The investigations of Freud (220), Jung (395), this author (692, 707), and Storch (810), have irrefutably shown that phenomena of this sort in schizophrenia coincide with those of primitive experience. In both, preparatory phases of thought appear instead of completed thought. Though no watertight proof is feasible at this time, the demonstrated identity of some of the stages permits the inference that the thought-process recapitulates the phylogenetic and ontogenetic development of thought. Each thought is first thought in the ancestral fashion; from this nucleus, clear judgment arises in the same way that the multicellular organism developed from the unicellular in phylogenesis, and as man develops from the fertilized egg-cell. According to this conception, every act of thought has a long prehistory, part of which rests on the individual past and part on the kind of the organism it is [Driesch's (150) organic reaction basis].[207]

How do the preparatory phases differ from the final form of

205 For reservations concerning this sweeping statement, cf. footnote 204, p. 248.

206 See Reik (667, pp. 91 ff.).

207 Cf. Schilder (751, particularly p. 517). Surely this formulation throws every caution aside.

thought? In the preparatory phases, the full directedness toward reality is lacking: thinking acquires its factualness in the last phase of its development. First come the stages of affective transformation and symbolization; if cognition were determined only by these, the world would seem to be subject to the wish [Freud's (220) omnipotence of thought]. If the wish exerts its effect without mediation, then it is plausible to surmise that all effects are those of wishes (magic-belief); and the belief that the effective forces are psychological in nature is supported by the closeness of world and body which obtains on this level. The dominance of drives brings mechanisms of acquisition and repulsion (projection, identification, appersonation) to bear on the undeveloped thought-material; as a consequence, the possession-relation between subject and object, between body and world, shows affectively rooted fluctuations. Personality and world are quite differently related to each other under these conditions than they are usually.[208]

Due to the mechanisms of projection and identification, there is no sharp division between one's own personality and that of others; active and passive thus cease to be opposites, and acting and suffering are experienced as identical. Since the total situation may be represented by any single part of it, the concept of effectiveness pertains equally to whole and part; and somatic as well as psychological effects are, in accord with magical conception, thought of as the psychic will. When development goes from the schema to the specific, there must be a phase in which only the general is relevant and differentiation within the sphere is in abeyance: for instance, the sphere God-father-power-authority remains an undifferentiated and affectively founded general concept. The same goes for the sphere, effect-nature-sexuality-will.[209] Ambivalence of the dominant affects, together with the prevalence of schemata, orders concepts into pairs of opposites: they are divided into the great realms of good and bad. Spatial relations like right-left, close-far, above-below, are also subsumed into these great realms of good and bad, in keeping with the inclination to spatial symbolization observed by both Lindworsky (505) and Selz (771). Finally, due to the tendency to interchange concepts belonging to

<hr/>

208 Cf. Schilder (751, particularly pp. 515–516).
209 Cf. Schilder (751, particularly pp. 513–515).

the same sphere, masculine comes to stand for right and good, and feminine for left and bad. These conclusions are borne out by the extensive experience of psychoanalysis with normals and neurotics, and by direct observations of schizophrenics.[210]

The world of primitives appears to us richer in meanings and relationships than that of people on a higher level of development; in psychoses too an excess of images, at first surprising, is encountered. Undeveloped thought appears more rich and many-faceted than completed thought. Completed thought is simpler than its preparatory phases: in the course of thinking, a unification of opposed tendencies takes place. The insight into this unification we owe to the studies of Lipps (512). We cannot understand thought-development if we overlook the fact that it implies the unification, control, and ordering of the manifold of partial impulses, and their integration into the completed decision or thought. The theory of personality too must take into consideration that unification has various degrees, and there are personality-types in whom unification in a decision is never complete. Every percept, image, thought, and decision develops from a multitude of spheric impulses, which in the end become the fringe, periphery, background of experience; they are never completely lost, but only to a greater or less extent unified.[211]

Now we come to the formal character of thoughts and judgments. Here two factors must be considered. If *everything* about an object that requires attention has entered into thought-development, and if *all* the object-directed tendencies which are amenable to me are satisfied by a judgment, then it is a self-evident judgment . . .[212] Thus, self-evidence has nothing to do with feeling-experiences, which attach themselves only later to the act of insight. Self-evidence is insight into object-relations based on demands raised by objects. When we are not completely sure that we have done justice to these demands, then judgment is more or less uncertain. We can experience many qualitative shadings in degree of certainty of judgments, including opining, believing,

210 On the concept of space, see Schilder (750, Chapters 12 and 22), and Werner (870, Chapter 5). Cf. also Erikson (166).

211 The "unification" Schilder discusses here he refers to elsewhere as "synthesis"; apparently it refers to the same processes as the psychoanalytic concept of "synthetic function of the ego" (cf. Nunberg, 582).

212 Cf. Schilder (752, pp. 532–535); see also Freud (216, 243).

assuming. We have good reasons to explain these differences by degrees of unification and kind of drives involved. No doubt the character of intendings varies with the degree of certainty and self-evidence.

Assumption—which Meinong (547, 548) studied with particular penetration—is an especially important variant of these acts. In it, a state of affairs is marked as undecided: nothing is stated about its correctness. We must separate our knowledge that assumptions arise out of opposed drive-tendencies, from our query as to their psychological consistency. In general, we must not be seduced by genetic psychological studies into overlooking the infinite qualitative variety of psychic forms. We are indebted to Scheler (688, 689) for extraordinarily subtle descriptions of such varieties. In pursuing genetic psychology, we reduce varieties to gain insight into dynamics; but this must not lead us to interpret them away.[213]

Yet another realm of formal characters requires clarification: the realm of abstractions. To abstract means to disregard; it is, to begin with, negative abstraction—that is, more or less clear, conscious neglect of existing parts of objects and of partial impulses. Basically it makes no difference whether one abstracts from entire units or only from parts. Alongside negative abstraction, there is always a positive: one aspect is particularly emphasized. Our preceding considerations make it easy to infer that positive abstraction arises from needs, and that negative abstraction is only a special case of repression.[214] Abstraction arises from the need to discard, from the manifold of givens, all that is unnecessary for the action at hand. To begin with, the question is always one of establishing what is identical, what is similar, and what is different [cf. Seifert's (770) study and see his bibliography].

Only now can we clarify the psychological structure of concepts.[215] They are rooted in the sphere and arise from it. The sphere contains all of the person's past, all those experiences by which a drive-attitude ever became satiated; the past belongs to

[213] Cf. Rapaport (659, 661), on the relation between the psychoanalytic and the phenomenological view of judgments and varieties of conscious experience.

[214] So far, there is no justification for this challenging generalization. Concerning the process of abstraction, cf. Ach (9), Hebb (328), also Rapaport (658, pp. 706–707).

[215] Cf. Bleuler (89, pp. 641 ff.); and Rapaport et al. (650, Vol. I, Part 3). See also Hebb (328).

the fringe of every experience. Every concept rests on all the pertinent experiences from the child's first opening its eyes.

I want to illustrate this in some detail with respect to one concept. Psychoanalysis—particularly Freud (206) and Jung (391)—has demonstrated the role of the father in the fate of every human being. The attitude of the child toward the father determines how as a grown-up he will relate himself to people whom he respects, is subordinate to, or loves. The father revives in every superior. Man's attitude to authority in general, which reaches far into his attitude to life as such, is preformed by infantile experiences. In-fantile-homosexual ties play into this constellation also. In the woman's love-life, her love for her father revives again and again; she will seek in her lover the father, or at least the father-ideal. In neurotic and normal persons these relations become unveiled in long drawn-out analyses; in schizophrenics they often lie on the surface, and the father-figure is frequently represented in the form of God. One of my patients believes that she will become the heavenly mother, and marry first the Saviour and then God the father; the Holy Ghost has impregnated her, and she has given birth to a dove amidst great pain; the heavenly mother moves into a still higher heaven. Another case I observed: a patient—other-wise lucid—choked to death his office-chief, in the belief that his own father had put the man up to not letting him advance. He cannot stand it anywhere, believing that his father is working against him. He is struggling against the idea that, since his father has moved away from his mother to another woman, he is now supposed to take his father's place by his mother. He is also hurt that the family does not trust him to replace the father. The father disturbs the son's sexual pleasures also, he squeezed the son out of his first affair.

This sketch is of a quite typical concept of father, which may be considered simply the behavior-rules for relating to an au-thority both beloved and hated: it pre-forms the position toward God, emperor, superior, and authority in general. Freud (214, 218, 234) was able to demonstrate that the choice of love-object too is connected with the child's relation to his parents. Thus there are men who can find pleasure only with a humiliated love-object, be-cause in sexual relations with respected women they experience a revival of the incest that they are trying to avoid.

Every bodily injury arouses anxiety about the genitals, that is, castration anxiety. Anxiety about the integrity of the body, as is present before every operation, arouses ancient fears; the concept operation carries a mood which demonstrably implies those first threats to the child's body.

The concept of money reaches to those depths in which gold and feces are equated, and feces regarded as a part of the body endowed with magical power. But every time the concept cuts out of all this manifold only what it needs for a certain action. The same holds for propositions.

Now for a closing formal comment. There are two kinds of undeveloped concepts. The first of these is incomplete as regards form as well as content: the many individual meaning-experiences remain unconnectedly side by side, and once dropped, reappear now here, now there. This lack of completion we see in normals in the course of thinking, before they have reached their goal, but it is seen particularly clearly in acute phases of schizophrenia. The second type is complete as regards form, but its content is dominated by symbol-like images and lack of directedness towards reality. Such are the errors and prejudices of normals, and the consolidated delusions of schizophrenics and paraphrenics. We may assume that concept-formation has two phases: one elaborates the concept-basis, the other unifies the meaning. The concept-basis represents that part of the world which is necessary for the action in question; the final meaning is a further preparation for action.[216]

In chronic schizophrenia the concept-basis loses its firm delimitation, and threatens to include the whole world in a chaotic inarticulate fashion; in acute cases also we see a chaotic manifold of meaning-experiences. In objectively correct concepts, the concept-basis is narrow and the meaning unified. Still, every concept is based on the individual's entire experience, and even factually correct concepts arouse everything, though in final analysis they subordinate it all to the goal. This completes the theory of conceptual thinking and thinking in general.

Now a few questions can be answered rather easily. Produc-

216 Cf. Schilder (707, 752); also Bleuler (87, 88). The distinction made here is one between those incomplete thought-products which are not synthesized by the secondary process, and those which though incomplete are synthesized.

tive mental activity and creative fantasy are part of the whole picture I have presented here. From the formal point of view, the basis of every fantasy is this attitude: it does not matter whether what is fantasied is or is not real. These fantasy acts in turn are built on drive-acts, which mean or wish that which is fantasied to be reality. Accordingly the drive-attitude, which regards as reality that which is fantasied, is the more fundamental. We know the child's fantasies, and know that he merges fantasy and reality. In the daydreams of hysterics these fantasies revive, and the daydreams come close to being hallucinations. Fantasy-formations in general do not depart too much from the structure of reality; in psychoanalytic terms, they display the structure of the preconscious.[217] Any other formulation of the concept of fantasy leads to contradictions. For instance, to consider fantasy as the prerequisite of creative mental activity is to mistake the relatively highly differentiated formations of fantasy for the more primitive ones of the sphere, within which those transactions that lead to creative synthesis take place. One more factor should be mentioned: the basic tendency is to take what is fantasied for what is real, and only by-and-by does fantasy lose this character. Tales place the products of fantasy into far-off lands and long-past times, and in this form the child continues to believe in them for a long time, though he has renounced his wish to encounter them in present reality.

Creative mental activity is thus a special case of reality-adapted thinking. In final analysis, it is connected with the goals of the total personality, which we will discuss later when we have become familiar with the structure of personality.

This presentation is based on the studies of Kuelpe's[218] school, which however attain their full meaning only through psychoanalysis. I have attempted to show this in a study on thought-development, and in my volume *Seele und Leben* (707).

On the thinking of primitives, see Levy-Bruehl (488) and Frazer (199); on child psychology, Stern (800) and Buehler (122). Storch (810) deals with the relation between the thinking of primitives and schizophrenics. For related psychoanalytic literature see Jung (395), Freud (220), Rank (646). I cannot enter here into such details as the relations between archaic inheritance, dream, neurosis and schizophrenia.[219]

[217] Cf. Bleuler (87, 88), and Kris (460, 461).
[218] Cf. Kuelpe (470), also Humphrey (360).
[219] Cf. also Schilder (692), and H. Werner (870).

11. Hypnosis[220]

Somatic effects of hypnosis. Hypnosis and affect. Somatic apparatuses which are influenced by hypnosis. State of consciousness in hypnosis. Sleep-vigil in hypnosis. Hypnosis and hysteria. Infantile-erotic attitude in hypnosis. Hypnosis as masochistic attitude. Magic world-view. Transformation of magic world-view. Hypnosis as an achievement of the hypnotic subject. The reservations of the hypnotic subject. Playful aspect of hypnosis. Hypnosis and crime. The hypnotic subject turns away from the external world and from his memories. Post-hypnotic amnesia. Post-hypnotic suggestion. Amnesia not always prerequisite for execution of post-hypnotic suggestion. Hypnosis and suggestion. Hypnotic sleep as suggestion-effect. Suggestion as interpersonal relationship. Contrary views.

We turn now to a particular form of experience and drive-attitude: hypnosis. The hypnotized subject's perceptual world is altered: he sees things others do not, and he does not see things others do. On the command of the hypnotist there arises before him a new colorful world, and changes take place in his body too. The hypnotist can induce, by suggestion, alterations even of somatic functions which the subject otherwise cannot alter by his will. I speak here of the theoretically most important form of hypnosis, somnambulism. The number of people who develop hypnotic somnambulism is not large; according to Troemner (837), it is 25 per cent.

I will start with the somatic effects of hypnosis. We may consider hypnosis a sleep-state; and though this view is contested by many authors, the behavior of a person in deep hypnosis corresponds in every detail to that of the sleeper.[221] He quivers as he goes to sleep, he rubs his eyes as he awakens, and like one awakening from deep sleep he is giddy for a short while. His pulse shows occasional changes, though different authors cannot agree on whether it accelerates or decelerates. The somatic changes attainable in hypnosis are important. One might say summarily that the entire vaso-vegetative system is amenable to hypnotic influence. The somatic influence of hypnosis is identical with that of affects: all affects are accompanied by changes of blood-distribution, heart-action, gastro-intestinal secretion, and motility. (We shall discuss these further below.) The somatic effect of *strong* affects will have

220 Cf. Schilder (703, 712, 724), and particularly (718); for a recent survey of the field see Brenman and Gill (102), and for a recent general discussion of hypnosis, Brenman (103).

221 Concerning the relation of sleep and hypnosis, see Darrow et al. (139), and Gill (279).

to be discussed in detail below; corresponding observations in hypnosis are not easy to make, for obvious reasons. Yet unquestionably hypnosis can elicit burn-blisters (Forel, 196; Schultz and Heller; Alrutz, 29), influence menstruation, and cause far-reaching changes in the gastro-intestinal tract. No doubt, hypnosis has effects considerably exceeding those on the vaso-vegetative system. First of all, it can influence the musculature: hypnosis as such, without any suggestion, elicits muscle-rigidity or muscle-flaccidity; either can easily be changed, by appropriate suggestions, into the other. The hypnotized subject's ability to hallucinate points to an influence on cortical apparatuses. Experiments by Bauer and myself (693) show that instinctive (cerebellar?) movement-reactions can also be hypnotically influenced.[222]

It is hard not to relate the somatic effects of hypnosis to particular brain-apparatuses. Hypnotic sleep, just as natural sleep, must be related to the sleep-apparatus in the neighborhood of the third ventricle. There are also important vaso-vegetative centers in this area: I refer to the sympathicus-center of Karplus and Kreidl (403), which is probably in the *Corpus Luysi;* and to the *dystrophia adiposogenitalis,* which is usually assumed to be related to a lesion in the floor of the third ventricle. In the close-by *lenticular-nuclei* there are centers of muscle-innervation, probably subserving primitive static motility. The catalepsy and rigidity of hypnosis reminds one of motor-disorders connected with lesions of these apparatuses. We may assume that the responsiveness of these varies from individual to individual; so that of two persons with identical attitudes towards the hypnotist, one will not achieve hypnotic sleep because his sleep-apparatus is less responsive, and the other will not get blisters because his vasomotor-apparatus is less labile. Primary differences in the behavior of musculature also refer to organic differences. Thus, the influence of hypnosis on somatic conditions depends on the quality of individual apparatuses, and the influenceability of each of these is quite independent of that of the others—though apparatuses influenced by hypnosis may have a mutual secondary influence on each other.[223]

222 Concerning the somatic effects of hypnosis, cf. P. C. Young (902).

223 Schilder's discussion of apparatuses and of their individual differences here achieves a clarity which was reached only much later by psychoanalytic ego-psychology (321), and the "new look" trend in perception research (417, 418).

For instance, we know that the excitability of vaso-vegetative apparatuses is changed by sleep, and that with sleep a different state of consciousness sets in. In general, the somatic effects of hypnosis show that hypnosis and affectivity are most closely related. Both are related to phylogenetically old parts of the brain. Though the increased ability to hallucinate relates to the cortex, it shows a primitive mode of its functioning (see above).

The state of consciousness of the hypnotized subject shows a broad range of fluctuations: particularly good subjects—those who carry out all the commands of the hypnotist without contradiction, and readily understand even complex setups—are in a state of consciousness not very different from that of the waking person. Even in these one occasionally sees a striking dream-like forlornness. In less experienced and trained subjects, the dream-like quality of experiencing is paramount, and condensations like those in dreams are demonstrable. More or less all shades of transition between dreaming and waking consciousness are encountered.[224] In formal respects, the state of consciousness of the hypnotized subject differs from that of the sleeper in that the former maintains his contact, rapport, with the hypnotist. In final analysis this is merely a particular form of sleep-vigil.

The differentiation from hysteria, and from the hysterical special state, is not difficult either.[225] In the hysterical special state, the patient transforms his fantasies into reality, and it is his wishes that are fulfilled; in hypnosis, the subject's relationship to the hypnotist dominates the picture. Otherwise, there are many common characteristics. In hypnosis too, infantile erotic attitudes are revived.[226] The hypnotist becomes the archetype of the father; he both arouses love and demands unquestioning submission—precisely the father's attitude toward the child. If hysteria is a breakthrough of infantile erotic attitudes, then the boundary-line between hysteria and hypnosis cannot be sharp; indeed, at times we see hypnotic somnambulism change into a hysterical twilight state, and hysterical symptoms of other sorts appear in hypnosis, for instance, hysterical seizures. The transition is entirely fluid from

224 For discussion of these transitions see Brenman (103, 103a).

225 Cf. Brenman (103), and Rapaport (659).

226 Cf. Ferenczi (184), Brenman and Gill (102, pp. 103–113); also Rapaport (654, Chapter 6); for a different view see Brenman et al. (101).

normal hypnotic somnambulism, in which the hypnotized subject's relation to the hypnotist dominates the picture, to pathological somnambulism. For instance, the individual's wanting not
to give up the comforts of hypnotic sleep, and remaining asleep
in defiance of the hypnotist, is already a severance of the relation
to him, though usually the hypnotist's renewed energetic command suffices to induce awakening.

Pathological phenomena in hypnosis are clearly due to hypnosis tapping the drive-layers underlying hysteria, arousing but
not controlling them. The following observation is particularly instructive: a young man was admitted to a clinic because in hypnosis he suddenly began to rage and attack the hypnotist. In a
newly induced hypnosis at the clinic, it was learned that the young
man had been repeatedly hypnotized by lay-hypnotists. Some of
these occasionally gave him the suggestion to act insane: a fly is
coming closer and closer, becomes bigger, etc. In the hypnosis
which ended in the rage-attack, suddenly the earlier hypnotist had
appeared to the patient, suggesting that he act insane. He carried out the instruction; naturally his present hypnotist knew
nothing of what had occurred, and was helpless. Here the effect of
the "command" of the earlier hypnotist was effected in hysteria by
the "command" of the person's own wishes. It is also instructive
that the present hypnosis could arouse the memory of the previous
one. Experiences—as we have shown—tend to arouse first of all experiences from identical layers, that is, those of identical drive-
attitudes.[227]

The evidence for the infantile erotic nature of hypnosis
(Ferenczi, 184) is extensive. To the trained observer, the gestures
and facial expressions of a woman entering into and emerging
from hypnosis are unquestionably erotic. In the analysis of patients who have been hypnotized, one obtains clear statements
that they were sexually excited while in hypnosis. Such excite-
ments at times condense into the accusation that the hypnotist has
misused the subject sexually.

The sexual constitution of the hypnotized subject is remarkably mirrored in his relationship to the hypnotist. Hysterics, with
their strong tendency to devotion, to object-cathexis, most easily
reach the stage of somnambulism. In compulsion-neurotics, spite

[227] For an example, cf. Gill (277).

is dominant; and sadistic as well as anal fantasies break through.[228] Hypnosis is pleasurable submission, and thus has infantile characteristics. It cannot be understood without an understanding of the psychology of masochism and sadism. In every sadist there are masochistic, and in every masochist sadistic, trends. I want to refer in brief to the analysis of the homosexual whom I cited earlier to facilitate the understanding of identification. He had sadistic impulses which arose from his identification with his mother, while his original attitude toward her was masochistic. It bespeaks the completeness of identification in this case that apparently all of his masochistic role was allotted to the boys. We note that these boys represent, in final analysis, his previous ego. In other cases, identification is not this complete, and we can demonstrate with greater certitude the co-existence of sadistic and masochistic attitudes. Acting and suffering do not appear here as opposites: the basic attitude of the sadist is that he wants to cause the other pain not for pain's sake, but rather to ascertain his unconditional power over him; in turn, the masochist endures pains as the supreme expression of his submission. The sadist vicariously enjoys the submission of the other, and the masochist the greatness of his torturer. The hypnotized person too partakes in the greatness of the hypnotist: for him the hypnotist has the power of creator, he can create new things in the external world by his word.

The belief in the creative power of the word, which finds its clearest expression in the initial words of the Gospel according to St. John, "In the beginning was the Word," is the core of every primitive magic world-view. Here the word is identical with the wish, with the magic wishes which in turn are equated with deeds. All magic procedures rest on the transformation of image into percept, on the change of thought and wish into reality, and on the blurring of the boundary between subject and object.[229] In

228 Concerning hypnosis of compulsive personalities and compulsion-neurotics, see Schafer (685), and Ehrenreich (158, 159, 160).

229 While engaged in explaining hypnosis in terms of drive-dynamics and transference, Schilder here advances a formulation which puts the burden on an alteration of judgment and consciousness. He uses the same terms which he applied in discussing thought-processes in the preceding chapter. Indeed, the emphasis in recent theorizing about hypnosis has shifted from drive-attitudes to the understanding of the ego-functions and their changes in hypnosis: cf. Brenman et al. (101, 105), Gill (277), Brenman (103), Gill and Brenman (278).

other words, magic is a world-view connected with the most primitive sexual attitudes. It belongs to the stage Freud (220) labeled as that of omnipotence of thought, where the sense of reality has not yet interposed its corrections. According to Ferenczi (183) several such stages may be distinguished: that of absolute omnipotence, which may be ascribed to the satisfied, wish-free embryo, all of whose wishes are satisfied in advance; that of the infant who hallucinatorily creates for himself everything he wishes; and finally, that at which wish-fulfillment can be enforced only by crying. All these stages have in common that changes in the external world come about solely by the wish, without action: wish and thought are equivalent to action. The child must learn by-and-by that it does not have such omnipotence after all; but when he does renounce it for himself, he ascribes it to the people of his environment, whereby the mechanism of identification intervenes. At a further stage, not the parents themselves but their imagos (God, king, etc.) are invested with this power. Finally, even this last belief is given up, after a final attempt to save it by projecting it into bygone times, and only the belief in an omnipotent, but no longer human, God remains. The wish for such a creating power is never completely given up; it is alive in all of us, and in one way or another we try to escape harsh reality.

In hypnosis this infantile wish breaks through; but the hypnotized subject, being too cowardly to ascribe the creative power to himself, attributes it to the hypnotist. The hypnotized subject's attitude is comparable to that of a child who still ascribes to his parents the powers of creator; and by way of identification, both the child and the hypnotized subject partake in them. This lays bare the roots of the hypnotized person's attitude toward the hypnotist. Clearly, hypnosis is merely the fulfillment of the hypnotized person's own wishes, and the hypnotist's personality plays no significant role in it.[230] Indeed, anyone who has the necessary self-confidence can hypnotize.

It must be added, however, that the hypnotized person does not completely submit to the will of the hypnotist; a part of the right of disposition he always reserves for himself. He interrupts the hypnotic state when he wants to. If something improper is

---

[230] For the interpersonal aspect of hypnosis, here disregarded, see Brenman et al. (105), also Brenman (103, 106).

asked of the subject in hypnosis, he either rejects it while in hypnosis or awakens.[231] This is the final reason that hypnosis always bears a somewhat playful character, which distinguishes it so much from the manifestations of real devotion, great love, deep ecstasy. In many respects, the hypnotized subject acts like the dreamer who, when the dream begins to become painful, says to himself, "It is just a dream," and may even awaken from his sleep. Clearly, inherent to hypnosis as such is a reservation like that of the actor playing King Lear, who even in the moments of deepest immersion in his role is aware that he is only acting, that he is actually Mr. X.Y., etc. This should not be taken as a contradiction of what we have said about the somatic effects of hypnosis: the actor too sheds genuine tears, and if studied his limbs would show plethysmographic fluctuations of volume.

The layering of experience in hypnosis is accordingly complex: one part of the personality sleeps, or rather dreams; another is turned toward the hypnotist in the fashion of sleep-vigil; still another watches lest the person undertake something, for the sake of the hypnotist, which is against his own total interest. Now, it is conceivable that the hypnotist will convince the total individual that he must entirely submit to him; but then hypnosis turns into serfdom or devotion, which has nothing to do with hypnosis as such. This settles the question: is it possible by means of hypnosis to make a person a criminal against his will? It is possible only if the total personality can be induced to consent; without the will of his total personality, without his own inclination, the hypnotized person will not carry out criminal actions. Experience bears out this theoretical inference. There are no unquestionable instances in which hypnotically suggested crimes have been actually carried out. Laboratory experiments are *a priori* unsuited to decide the issue, since, as we have seen, the hypnotized subject does not lose his awareness of the total situation: he knows what is happening with him, and is justified in assuming that Professor X or Y will not mislead him into murder. Interestingly enough, experimental subjects prefer to commit even their sham-crimes on subjects whom they dislike anyway.[232]

[231] For evidence, see Brenman et al. (105).
[232] For reviews of the literature on the pertinent experiments, see Young (902), and Weitzenhoffer (866).

This brings us back to the state of consciousness of the hypnotized person. A hypnotized subject who is transported by suggestion from the auditorium into a forest and made to pick wild flowers, moves securely on the steps of the rising auditorium and does not bump into the benches; so it must be assumed that he has somehow perceived the auditorium and the people in it. It is noteworthy that subjects in deep hypnosis, acting on the suggestion not to see certain persons who are present, will avoid looking at these "negatively hallucinated" persons: they must perceive somehow what they profess not to perceive. This can be easily demonstrated: if anesthesia is suggested, the subject does not feel pinprick and touch; but in a renewed hypnosis, in answer to appropriate questions he can readily state where he was touched or pricked. So some kind of perception took place, but it is apparently denied by that part of the personality which presides over the whole situation. We say that, for the sake of the hypnotist, the subject turns away from, represses,[233] the external world which he actually does perceive.

Similarly the hypnotist can induce him to renounce many of his experiences, to forget his name, the experiences of his youth, etc. On awakening, the experiences of hypnosis succumb to forgetting; but it can be demonstrated that this forgetting is only apparent, and is really repression. By renewed hypnosis it can be restored to consciousness; even simple suggestive maneuvers can restore it; it may emerge spontaneously, or appear in a subsequent dream, or be perceived in a mirror held up. Affectively toned experiences of hypnosis, which are apparently forgotten upon awakening, reveal themselves by complex-reactions in association experiments. All these phenomena urgently raise the question: why then do experiences of deep hypnosis succumb to amnesia? The first assumption may be that the hypnotized subject tries to emulate a dreamless sleep, to please the hypnotist. Secondly, he is probably ashamed of the infantile-erotic attitude, the submission, he displayed toward the hypnotist. Thirdly, differences between the formal characteristics of experiences in hypnotic and waking

---

[233] Technically it would perhaps be more correct to term this "denial," but the phenomenon has not been subjected to a thorough empirical examination to show whether either of the terms is applicable in the specific sense in which psychoanalysis defines them.

states also play a role; but these formal differences are merely expressions of changed drive-attitudes.[234]

One can give hypnotic suggestions that are slavishly carried out by the subject after the termination of hypnosis, in spite of the amnesia. Occasionally it is observed that eliminating the amnesia cancels the post-hypnotic suggestion: the suggestion that, after awakening, the subject should respond to a certain question by clapping his hands, is carried out until the amnesia is lifted, either by renewed hypnosis or some other means. This fact was the foundation of Breuer and Freud's (108) original theory, according to which post-hypnotic command is effective only as long as it is not amenable to the criticism of waking consciousness, being hidden behind amnesia, and the individual is helplessly at its mercy. The effect of repressed, painful experiences is similar; such experiences are pathogenic only so long as they are not remembered. Indeed, Breuer's original formulation even assumed that only those experiences which take place in a hypnoid state bring about hysteria. But instances are not rare in which there is no amnesia even for experiences of deepest hypnosis, and yet post-hypnotic commands are promptly carried out; therefore, amnesia cannot be the decisive factor for the effectiveness of hypnotic experiences. Probably those attitudes of the subject toward the hypnotist, discussed above, are decisive. Correspondingly, the genesis of hysteria must also be different from that of Breuer and Freud's original conception.

We have discussed the effect-value of experiences, and have shown how closely it is tied up with drive-constitution and prior drive-experiences. This is just the point at which hypnosis and suggestion shade into each other; it is crucial that the phenomena attainable by hypnosis can be attained by mere waking-suggestion also. Indeed, hypnotic sleep is but an effect of suggestion; this view is shared by most authors, for instance by Bernheim (65), Lehmann (481), Wundt (894). At this point, however, the problems of hyp-

---

[234] This amnesia is by no means as ubiquitous as it might seem from Schilder's discussion. For a survey of information concerning it, see Rapaport (654, Chapter 6). Here Schilder again succeeds in bringing together the drive-dynamics (points 1 and 2) and the ego aspect (point 3) of the phenomenon; he does not bring to bear on the latter his insights concerning "autonomy of emergent products," and considers the states of consciousness "expressions of changed drive-attitudes."

nosis and suggestion shade into the basic problems of inter-personal relations, of leader and follower, of persuasion, and of adopting convictions from others.[235] The crucial feature of suggestion is, clearly, that we can be led by it to beliefs, actions, and indeed percepts, for which we do not have sufficient objective evidence. In this respect too, the subject submitting to hypnosis or suggestion is like a child; his behavior may be briefly described as a regression to infantile drive-attitudes, a view in good accord with the physiological facts. The playful character of suggestive and hypnotic experiments must be kept in mind, however; in this respect they differ from the suggestibility of everyday life, which in general does not disregard reality-factors to the same extent, and only rarely regresses to hallucinations.

In accord with Bernheim (65) and Janet (376, 377), as well as with the prevailing views, we trace the effects of hypnosis and suggestion to the psychological processes obtaining between the hypnotist and the hypnotized subject. Recently Alrutz (29) has championed the old view of an "influence" emanating from the hypnotist. He based this view on his observation that passes of his hand at some distance from the hypnotized subject's body caused changes in the sensibility of the subject which varied with the direction of the passes, and could not be explained by the usual sensory perceptions of the subject. If this view were correct, then a part of hypnotic phenomena would have to be explained by non-psychological effects. Though I do not have a final judgment in this matter, lacking appropriate data of my own, I consider it improbable that Alrutz's assumptions are correct.

Hypnosis makes it possible to penetrate deeper into the psychological structure of interpersonal relations. Freud (237) considered this matter extensively, but we will defer our discussion of it until we have clarified our view of the structure of personality.

Forel's (196) well-known volume gives the best orientation about hypnosis. Of Janet's (376) older writings, *L'automatisme psychologique* is the most notable. The psychoanalytic view of hypnosis, which I have followed here, rests on a study by Ferenczi (185). Concerning the somatic effects of hypnosis, see among others my paper "Wesen der Hypnose" (703). On hypnosis and crime, see Kogerer's (440) summary.

[235] At this point, Schilder, despite his disregarding of the interpersonal aspect of hypnosis above, is again ahead of his time and expresses a view that Sullivan (825) and White (880) were still groping for two decades later. Cf. also Brenman (103, 105, 106), and Rapaport (658, Part 7, XXIII–XXIV). Note, however, the roots of this development in Freud (237).

12. The Unconscious[236]

Helmholtz's unconscious inferences. The Unconscious and act-experience. The object-function is extra-conscious. Repression in sense-perception. A synthetic function in perception, inferred from agnosia. The act as experience. Effect-value. Hypnonarcosis. Levels of consciousness. Automatisms. To be aware and to reflect. Formular abbreviation and its relation to consciousness. Hypnosis and the Unconscious. The system Unconscious and the spheric experiences. The systematically repressed and the system Unconscious. The difference between inhibition of spheric development and repression. Relations between various phenomena called unconscious. Effect-value and the system Unconscious. Two forms of past experience. Relations between synthetic function and spheric experiences. Consciousness as a perceptual organ. The Unconscious and the psychologically real.

Various issues discussed above point to the important problem of the Unconscious, and we will now turn to it.

Helmholtz (333) thought that simultaneous contrast resulted from unconscious inferences, but it turned out to be a process in the visual organ which had nothing to do either with inferences of any sort or with the psyche . . .

In perceiving objects, we see them built of a manifold of mutually contradictory details; yet through this welter of sensations a function points to the object. This function lies outside of consciousness, and may be labeled the object-function.[237] We have to dwell on this point. We have taken an act-psychological point of view throughout, the essence of which is the distinction between the contents of which an object is built and the object itself. We intend objects, and they appear. They are not sums of our sensations, but simply objects which are before us. Our perceiving or imaging of objects is not psychological work, not a result of psychic activity; it is rather an entirely extra-conscious mechanism, which is not represented in experience, even if we also take into consideration our background experiences, though it can perhaps be brought into relation to psychic activity by means of phylogenetic, or generally genetic, considerations. The object-function is extra-conscious. When we observe and perceive parts of a landscape, we simultaneously suppress many sensations, such as after-images and contrast phenomena, which never come fully to the consciousness

236 For sources see Schilder (704), Freud (229, also 204, Chapter VII, F). For the revision of Freud's views in light of his structural theory of the psyche, see (239), and (247); also Kris (460). Cf. also Rapaport (659).

237 Cf. footnote 12, p. 44, and footnote 35, p. 56, supra.

of the untrained observer. This is probably because the neglected sensations are irrelevant to action. This neglect apparently issues from biological tendencies, goals, which correspond to those encountered in the process of repression.[238] These tendencies become most obvious in the fate of double images due to eye-muscle lesions: one of the images is suppressed, so that in older lesions of eye-muscles double images are no longer demonstrable. We have no reason to consider these neglected sensations unconscious.

In agnosias there appear peculiar perceptual impairments.[239] The optic agnosia patient registers individual parts of the percept, but is unable to make a whole out of them. These unintegrated parts undergo spatial displacements and fusions (condensations). This synthetic function of perception is not demonstrable at all in consciousness; it is undoubtedly somatic, probably has several stages, and probably is related to the object-function, but all of its details are as yet not known. The same, naturally, holds for all the senses. Though there is a deep and essential homology of a formal character between the structure of percepts and that of concepts, and even though the structure of concepts is amenable to psychological understanding, nevertheless the synthetic function cannot be considered to be psychological.[240]

There is otherwise much more in perception that is not apprehended directly, though it is, in some form or other, extant psychologically. I am referring again to Poetzl's (631) repeatedly mentioned dream-experiments: there, what is not directly apprehended undoubtedly exists somehow psychologically, and therefore cannot be regarded as unconscious. We distinguish between *objects*, which appear, and *acts*, which are experienced. Many psychologists do not recognize this directedness[241] of experience. Nevertheless, for us the act is an experience, this directedness is experienced, and our own experience we can objectivate, hold up before ourselves, and reflect on at any time. Therefore,

238 Schilder here hypothesizes a close relation between physiological processes of selectivity and those referred to by the concept repression. Poetzl's (631) experiments, as well as Betlheim and Hartmann's (69) studies, are his points of reference. Compare again Hebb (328).

239 "Impairments" is an unsatisfactory translation of *Abbauerscheinungen;* the latter implies that the impairment brings primitive factors to the fore.

240 Compare again Hebb (328) for strikingly similar assumptions.

241 "This directedness" refers to the intending implied in acts.

every drive must be amenable to consciousness, regardless of what happens with its representations.[242]

It could be argued that the experience of directedness is not the real essential but its effect. We have already discussed the effect-value of psychological experience and have seen that we mean it by something not psychological, but rather physiological that fits into our causal formula concerning nature. For instance, we saw that the effect-value of the hypnotic command, "Sleep!" depends on the condition of the sleep-apparatus also. The whole issue is best characterized by Friedlaender's (250) finding that a preceding hypnotic suggestion makes narcosis possible with smaller amounts of drugs than would be otherwise needed (hypnonarcosis). This procedure saves chloroform, and it may be said that the psychological effect of hypnosis can be equated with a certain amount of chloroform.[243] A part of the effect-value will manifest itself in the depth of hypnosis; another part, namely that pertaining to the condition of the sleep-apparatus, will not be psychologically represented at all. These considerations can be most clearly illustrated in apraxia: here, though the sub-goal images and intentions are intact, the investing of them with innervations is so altered as to suggest that a synthetic function is disrupted. Besides motor-apparatuses, there are also thought-apparatuses.[244] We have no right to consider the extra-psychological factors of the effect-value of an intention as psychological and unconscious; rather we must consider them as not psychological. The intention, however, which in part mirrors the effect-value, is amenable to consciousness. The problem of the effect-value of experiences is only indirectly related to the problem of the Un-

---

242 Schilder, impressed by the continuous transition of primary and secondary processes (the former predominant in unconscious, the latter in conscious thought), sought to unite the two by considering them simply different stages of the evaluation of thoughts as they evolve from the "sphere." Thus he considered all thoughts as conscious, differing from each other only in the degree of evolution. What he could not so subsume he considered "not psychological," i.e., physiological.—In final analysis this appears to be a purely terminological difference, once the continuous transition between primary- and secondary-process thought—to express which Schilder developed his terminology—is accepted as a fact of observation. It is at present so accepted, and expressible in the usual concepts of psychoanalysis also: cf. Kris (460), Rapaport (655).

243 This is an undue simplification of the issues. On "Narcohypnosis," cf. Brenman and Gill (102), and Horsley (357).

244 Cf. Appendix, pp. 341 ff., infra.

conscious. Some investigators, having insufficiently apprehended the problem of effect-value, conclude that the unconscious is the psychologically real. The problem of the psychologically real will be discussed further below.[245]

Before turning to those phenomena which are generally considered unconscious, I want to examine the problems of levels of consciousness and of automatisms. The child must learn first every innervation necessary to walking, and must carry out partial-acts one at a time with full awareness; but the adult need only give the impetus to walking and the partial-acts proceed, as it were, automatically. Nevertheless, when I advance my foot in walking, even if I am not clearly aware of what I am doing, I put forth a more or less conscious intention. The whole act of walking remains in the ego-field, in the field of consciousness, and intentions of a low level of consciousness are being put forth. Such processes play a significant role in our psychological life: consider, for instance, writing. Single partial-acts which earlier have been clearly conscious are now on a lower level of consciousness; others seem to have disappeared altogether. Kretschmer (450, 453, 454) speaks tellingly of a law of formular abbreviation (see the section above on action).[246]

What has happened with these disappeared parts? How far are they retained on a lower level of consciousness? Apparently they have become somatized, structuralized.[247] The biceps of the athlete become powerful; and we may assume that the brain-apparatus, as well as the biceps, undergoes such a permanent change. What becomes organic in the course of a formular abbreviation has become extra-psychic, and apparently irreversibly so: I cannot distill anything psychological from the biceps. Probably there are such formular abbreviations, such transformations into the organic, in the realm of thought in the narrower sense; Selz's (771) investigations point to such. We see that there are various levels of consciousness; Westphal (878) extensively studied them.

Certain other experiences are *a priori* on a low level of con-

[245] Schilder is wrestling here with the issue—generally by-passed in the literature—that not all of what is not conscious is unconscious in the dynamic sense; some of it is organic to begin with, and some of it is structuralized, even in an irreversible way, and as such is not amenable to psychological analysis.
[246] Cf. footnote 8, pp. 104–105; and p. 12.
[247] Cf., e.g., footnote 72, p. 74.

sciousness. In reading a book I attend to the main idea I am after, while much of the detail never comes alive. When I lecture, some formulations appear to me more difficult and I make myself more sharply aware of them; others remain, even while I speak them, on a lower level of consciousness. There is a long way from dim awareness to clear reflection; and not only images, percepts, and thoughts can be on various levels of consciousness, but feelings, drives, will-acts, and actions also, though the latter four can be observed only by an act of internal perception, on whatever level of consciousness they may be.[248] Levels of consciousness have nothing to do with holding up past experience before oneself. Partial phases of every thought and action occur at various levels of consciousness.

Level of consciousness, however, is by no means a criterion of the value of the thought. Acts of thought in which all details appear at full height of consciousness are certainly uneconomical; and we know that well-habituated sequences, which are partly on a lower level of consciousness, disintegrate when too much of them is brought to a high level of consciousness.[249] In turn, thinking on a low level of consciousness can also be unpurposive, as when an act of thought automatically repeats previous mistakes. We can distinguish between experiences which are *a priori* on a low level of consciousness and remain there, and those which reach a low level of consciousness by the process of formular abbreviation. Whether or not there are descriptive differences between these two genetically different forms is an open question.

In general, the issues we have brought up so far do not play a role in discussions about the Unconscious; rather, the assumption of an unconscious psychic life is usually supported by reference to hypnosis and psychoanalysis. According to Freud, even before the advent of psychoanalysis the existence and mode of functioning of the psychological Unconscious were plainly demonstrated by hypnotic experiments, and particularly by posthypnotic suggestion. I have demonstrated above that what is repressed by hypnosis must be psychologically present in some

248 For a discussion of levels of consciousness and varieties of experience on them, see Rapaport (659).

249 For examples see Rapaport (658, pp. 589, 622 ff.), and (650, pp. 111 ff.), on the judgment-difficulties of obsessionals and schizophrenics.

form. This holds both for perceptions suppressed by hypnosis, and for experiences in hypnosis which after awakening are not remembered. If by post-hypnotic suggestion I make a *grande dame* out of a servant-maid, the background awareness of not-being-a-*grande-dame* will not be silenced thereby; the hypnotized person intentionally disregards this experience. Here we speak of repression in the narrower sense. We must stress, however, that these background-experiences in hypnosis do not differ, as regards structure, from everyday experiences. Only occasionally in hypnosis do we see dream-like fusions and condensation. These mechanisms we have already discussed in detail; and supported by the findings of psychoanalysis, we searched for and found them in the preparatory phases of the thought-process also.

Freud discovered these mechanisms and described them as those of the system Unconscious, to which he ascribes the following characteristics: absence of contradiction,[250] primary process, mobility of cathexes, timelessness, substitution of psychological reality for external reality. Or in more detail: the drive-impulses of the unconscious stand side by side, and do not contradict each other; it is thus that there are no relations between them, no doubt, no degree of certitude; by a process of displacement images may transfer their cathexes to others, and by a process of condensation they may attract additional cathexes. The processes are neither ordered according to time nor changed by elapsing time.

According to Freud also, affects and feelings are not unconscious in the same sense that drive-representations are.[251] This assertion is empirically correct: feelings and affects have a greater tendency to break out of the sphere than do images and thoughts belonging to the sphere. But affects are subject to the same kind of displacement as are images: Freud has pointed to the reversal of love into hate.[252] It is also certain that affects demand to be noticed more urgently than do image-elements pertaining to them.

[250] "Absence of contradiction" translates *Wiederspruchlosigkeit;* that is, the logical rule of the excluded third does not hold here.

[251] See Freud (229, III). Schilder here restricts "drive representations" to "ideas," while Freud considers both "ideas" and "affect charge" to be "drive representations."

[252] See Freud (226, 230), but cf. (229, III, and 204, pp. 434–435), concerning the unchanging character of affects.

Somatic effects connected with affects are unlike the effects of those connected with clearly conscious images; they must be the more effective because they do not lead to drive-gratification by action. Expressive movements are intense because they belong to the sphere. It follows that spheric experiences may be apprehended by other people: there is a direct "unconscious" communication between people without the aid of consciousness. The somatic effect of affects need not be a passing one, but may be lasting; in this case it is capable of molding the body.[253] Both clearly conscious and spheric experiences have a propensity to be lasting in time. We have anyway assumed an indestructibility of psychic experiences. It should be conceded, however, that in general the unintegrated drives retain their dynamic value better than the integrated ones, since the latter find outlet in action.

In the system Unconscious—the sphere, in our terminology—all thoughts and impulses remain on a low level of development. Thus, the thinking of children and primitives (and probably of animals) has a greater share of spheric constituents; but in adults too the thought-act may remain within the sphere. Here we have conceived of the ability to think as a live function. Schizophrenia effects an inhibition of the development of thought, and in hysteria and dreams a similar effect, though one of lesser extent, is occasionally observed. The counter-impulses set in while the thought is still in the process of development. The acts of turning-away, in hypnosis and in repression in the narrower sense, also correspond to biological attitudes, but are directed at already fully developed thoughts. I have stressed that experiences in hypnosis are equivalent to those of the waking state. The systematically repressed belongs to the realm of Freud's Preconscious (Pcs). These are thought-processes very similar to everyday ones; they correspond to day-residues of dreams, which also belong to the system Preconscious. It is very important not to equate the repressed with the sphere. There are individual instances in which the essential differences between systematic repression and inhibition of spheric development may be readily studied.[254]

[253] For a summary of the psychoanalytic theory on affects and their chronic forms, see Rapaport (654, Chapter 2), also (660, 657).

[254] Schilder here endeavors to cope with complex problems of thought-organization which were not faced at all by the topographic trichotomy (Unconscious, Preconscious, Consciousness) of psychoanalysis, and which only re-

A schizophrenic woman, when still capable of setting herself concrete goals, accomplished a complete repression of her pre-psychotic personality.[255] She asserted that a certain Miss Pol (her own name) competed with her, tried to suppress her, and was a lewd and dangerous person. Mr. Pol, her father, wanted to put Miss Pol in her (the patient's) place. The patient herself indulged in luxuriant fantasies in which she was a duchess, an empress, a detective. She asserted that her father, whom she did not acknowledge as such, came to her at night and had sexual intercourse with her. As the schizophrenia progressed, the systematic repression disintegrated; instead, spheric products came increasingly into the foreground of the clinical picture. Freud (239) himself has stressed that the quality of consciousness need not be in abeyance when unconscious mechanisms become effective; he has advised that no excessive importance be attributed to the symptom "consciousness." According to the views I have presented here, a psychological unconscious does not exist at all: everything psychological is extant in the background of experiences.[256]

Nevertheless, we must now examine whether there are not relationships between those varieties of experiences which are subsumed under the concept Unconscious. The act of turning-away has no direct connection with the sphere, though occasionally it facilitates spheric fusions. Nor has repression any direct connection with experiences of a low level of consciousness, though there are certain relationships between the two phenomena. There are transitions between not-noticing, neglecting, and turning-

---

cently have been tackled by the new conceptual means of psychoanalytic ego-psychology. Cf., for instance, Kris (460). Schilder's disinclination for sharp conceptual delineation, and the consequent fuzziness of his "sphere" concept, keep us from seeing clearly, on casual reading, how broadly he observed and how deeply he thought through the limitations of the framework of psychoanalytic theory of thinking as he knew it at the time. His observational evidence is scattered throughout his writing, and his theoretical solutions are intimated and nowhere focussed.

255 It is unclear what "repression of . . . personality" means systematically. The observation which follows poses a complex ego-psychological problem of schizophrenia so far hardly touched. But compare Federn (176, 177), Wexler (879), Eissler (161), Bak (42), and Knight (431).

256 The quest to establish the continuity between primary and secondary process seems to carry Schilder too far here. The conception thus arrived at is reminiscent of Goldstein's (291) view of the unconscious.

away.[257] But levels of consciousness are in no lawful relationship with spheric fusions; what is experienced at a lower level of consciousness need not undergo spheric fusion. For instance, those parts of a book which interest us little need not always become subject to spheric condensation. In this respect it is irrelevant whether the experiences in question are *a priori* on a lower level of consciousness, or came there in the course of formular abbreviation. Indeed, it does seem that a high degree of schematization particularly protects us against spheric fusion; I have mentioned previously that a low level of consciousness occasionally favors spheric fusion.[258]

Every decision and every thought must pass through the fringe, must develop in the sphere, which contains the individual past. Clearly, the effect-value of every experience is co-determined by the past. Past as well as present experience derives its effect-value from biologically grounded drive-attitudes. In every clearly conscious decision there is still a trace of the fringe, of the background from which it was born. We would arbitrarily sever the unity of experience by ascribing effect-value only to the sphere, though it partakes even in the clearest experiences. The fact that decisions must mature out of the sphere does not mean that they are effectless: it would be incorrect to ascribe effect-value only to those experiences which remain within the sphere. But it must be stressed, in harmony with Freud, that every condensation and displacement is accompanied by important changes in dynamic values.[259] Again: the evolution of every conscious decision also passes through the sphere, and its dynamic value is determined by this evolution.

Only now can we take up the problem of memory. Past experiences must be present in their original, unchanged form, as the surprising emergence of apparently long-forgotten experiences in psychoanalysis indicates. The question is: does this past exist

[257] This is the problem of the relation between various mechanisms of defense which has been so little explored or understood. Cf. A. Freud (200), Fenichel (180), also Brenman (104).

[258] Here the weakness of the concept "sphere," and the lack of systematic coordination of it with the concepts of "level of consciousness" and "formular abbreviation," become clear. It is only possible that the concepts of recent psychoanalytic ego-psychology can obviate these difficulties; cf. Kris (460), Rapaport (659), Hartmann (321).

[259] For detailed discussion see Freud (204, Chapter VII, B).

only in the form of dispositions? The conscious awareness that we all have that our past is in an immediate way with us speaks against this. Experiences do not depart from consciousness after a certain time; and even when something like that happens, as in repression, we experience it as a rejection of things that *are* present.

Therefore, I believe that nothing once experienced ever leaves consciousness; everything past persists on a lower level of consciousness, though in a specific form, namely, that of something past. All experiences are indestructible and they are present not in a spheric, but rather in a preconscious, form. This memory-material is subject to ever new condensations and displacements, so that every experience is represented twice: once in its own form on a low level of conscious (in the preconscious), and once in the form of spheric fusions (in the unconscious).[260] We can thus distinguish a foreground and a background of experience. The background consists of experiences at a low level of consciousness, of systematically repressed experiences, and of formations of the sphere. The spheric formations, however, can emerge from this background. The terms background-experience and fringe-experience are interchangeable; they refer to conscious experiences, though of a particular quality. The dynamics of experiences is extra-conscious in so far as it is not reflected in the act, the conscious character of which is, to my mind, beyond doubt.

We have searched in vain for the psychological unconscious in:

1) the function of the sense-organs,
2) the object-function,
3) the synthetic function,
4) the effect-value of experiences,
5) the automatisms which have turned into somatic forms.

We have come to the recognition that in these we find something not psychological but rather somatic, which moreover cannot become psychological.

Furthermore, we sought the unconscious in:

260 Neither this proposition itself, nor its context, makes clear what Schilder refers to by this "double representation" or why he seems to need it; cf. Freud's (229) treatment of a similar problem.

1) act-experiences,
2) experiences of low levels of consciousness (whether primary or secondary),[261]
3) systematically repressed experiences,
4) the sphere (Freud's Unconscious),
5) the forgotten past.

When reviewing this whole body of data in quest of the psychological unconscious, it became striking how similar the phenomena of impairment in cortical lesions, as in aphasia and agnosia, are to those encountered in inhibitions within the sphere. Both show fusions and condensations. In agnosia there is an inhibition which prevents the final integration of images and is readily comparable with neurotic inhibition. All this warrants the inference that organic happenings may be considered identical in nature with drive-mechanisms.

Here again we come to the conclusion that the body is a structuralized[262] psychological process, and that this structure expresses an intrinsic unity with the psyche. The clearest expression of this unity is seen in the organization of the brain.

There is a widespread psychological view according to which consciousness is merely a perceptual organ which makes certain aspects of the psyche proper amenable to our observation. To my knowledge, this view was first put forth by Nietzsche. Freud thought that consciousness was the organ of perception, while the unconscious was the psychologically real: the unconscious process was the object perceived by consciousness.[263] If following Freud we regard drive-representations as the core of the Unconscious, then clearly they are also contents which we apprehend as objects. They belong to the realm of internal perception, which no more mediates to us a "thing-in-itself" than does external perception. Psychological energy (libido, etc.—the source of the effect-value of experiences) is a concept of natural science which mediates the coordination of psychological knowledge with the events of the inanimate world: it is to be fully equated with somatic energy.[264] But these concepts have no epistemological

261 I.e., whether originally such, or having become such by automatization (formular abbreviation).
262 "Structuralized" translates *Form geworden.*
263 Freud (204, Chapter VII, F).
264 "Psychic energy" as a heuristic concept may be said to have proven

value, since our descriptive discoveries do not teach us about epistemology.[265] Lipps (512) too considered the Unconscious the psychologically real, and in my opinion his formulations also rest on an insufficient apprehension of facts.

Since Lipp's (512, 513) and Freud's (204, 229) work, the problem of the psychologically real is in the foreground of interest. The views presented here I have elaborated in a minor study (704). The literature of the problem is enormous. The Bleuler (83)-Kretschmer (453, 454)-Bumke (125) controversy is instructive. Though I deny the existence of a psychological unconscious, I consider Freud's discovery of the system Unconscious a great psychological advance.

13. PATHOLOGY OF THE THOUGHT-PROCESS[266]

Flight of ideas, a disturbance of relatively developed thought-formations. The developed thought must be integrated into a hierarchic order. Liepmann's superordinate images. Structures of thought. Affectivity and thought. Association experiment in mania. Wealth of thought in mania. Depressive thought-inhibition. Dementia. Congenital and acquired forms of dementia. Toward a theory of dementia. Dementia as obstruction of the psyche.

The basic distinction between undeveloped and developed thought also opens an avenue to a better understanding of the pathology of thought-processes. In schizophrenia, undeveloped thought is predominant. Undeveloped formations appear in hysteria and compulsion-neurosis also; yet in compulsion-neurosis the total personality combats these formations, and in hysteria the overwhelming part of thought is fully developed and only recedes into the background. I have in mind our discussion of the ego of the sleeper and of the hypnotized person. We are warned here again that, without a psychology of the total personality, we cannot consider the psychology of thinking complete—and that it is by no means irrelevant which aspect of the personality is expressed in the undeveloped thought.

---

valuable. As an explanatory concept it has the strength that we have not discovered a way to get along without it; but it has the weakness that it is a quantitative concept which is so far not amenable to measurement. Surely this state of affairs does not justify Schilder's peremptory assertion.

265 Here Brentano and Husserl, who have so enriched Schilder's psychological tool-chest and insight, get in his way epistomologically, as they did earlier in his appraisal of Kant. Piaget's (611, 612, 616) work has shown that descriptive discoveries may teach us about epistemology.

266 See Schilder (691, 692, 707, 750, 751, 752); cf. also Bleuler (89) and Buerger-Prinz and Kaila (123) and their annotations, for references to recent work in this field.

But there are also thought-disorders which involve fully developed thought: here belongs, first of all, repression. Parts of the thought which pertain to something are suppressed, do not emerge at all; this is a mechanism frequently encountered in everyday life. Once I have reached a thought I can either objectively develop it further, or I can drop it and turn to new goals. In flights of ideas, we see thoughts once reached immediately dropped in favor of any newly arisen idea, image, or impression. This particular intending of new stimuli of the external world is called hyperprosexy, but it does not occur before the previous idea has fully matured: we are not dealing here with pre-stages of thought. It is astounding how much of the material offered by the external world is taken in by such manic patients. In describing flights of ideas, the main emphasis must be placed on the enormous interest in, the greedy intending of, everything new. The patient with flight of ideas does not stick to the thought reached; his interest is fleeting, he changes his goals quickly and they show no organization; interests and goals are leveled.[267] We note that the ordered thought-process organizes the fully developed constituents of thought into whole-structures, and we have good reason to assume that such whole-structures presuppose hierarchically organized interests in the external world. At any rate, it becomes clear that thought-development must be assumed to take place in stages, and that every developed idea is subject to a further system of adaptations. According to Liepmann (500), there is in mania a loss of superordinate images;[268] while recognizing the factual correctness of Liepmann's study, we consider the loss to be one of thought-structures. Flight of ideas is typically connected with elation, and it is probable that the relation to the external world depends on our affective life. In mania we see a preponderance of external and clang-associations, while internal associations recede. Remarkably enough, we find partially similar reactions in normals, when their internal preoccupations are shielded by a superstructure of external associations. Similarly, we have good reason to assume that mania is a compensation for painful experiences. Yet the connection between elation and a rich stream of

267 I.e., they have no hierarchic organization; cf. Rapaport (658, p. 625).
268 "Superordinate images" translates *Obervorstellungen;* cf. Bleuler (89).

ideas must be considered as not further reducible.[269] While the association-experiment shows no acceleration of ideas, it is certain that in mania there is a particular richness of thoughts and experiences. The association-experiment is a particular task in the face of which the manic proves relatively ineffectual.

In depression, the individual is chained to sad ideas from which he cannot escape; the content of ideas becomes uniform, and the psychological processes, particularly those of thinking, are slowed: we speak of an inhibition. Such patients are "set" to sadness, they show interest for nothing else, and do not want to part with their sorrow. Even in them, as a result of compensation, external fleeting associations are occasionally observed. Some authors refer to this, perhaps not quite justifiably, as a flighty inhibition of thought (Schroeder, 759). Sorrow and anxiety are occasionally linked to each other, and there is a form of anxiety which compels vehement motor-discharges and is connected with a flighty pressure of speech. But all these deviations of the thought-process encroach on relatively completed acts of thought.[270]

The thought-disorders subsumed under the concept of dementia are especially important.[271] The most striking aspect of dementias is that they disregard parts of reality which must be taken into consideration. For instance, a paretic sees an acquaintance on the other side of the river and without a second thought goes into the river to meet him; or drops an object from a window and jumps after it on the spur of the moment. There are many object-structures which demand to be taken into consideration but are ignored by the paretic: for instance, if one is admitted to a hospital it is necessary to know the reason of admission; but the paretic, though he feels he is well, does not protest against admission, or if he does, has no idea how to make his protest effective. He figures poorly, because he is no longer able to apprehend the characteristics of numbers and number-series. The acquired dementias are distinguished by the uneven distribution of their disregard for object-structures over various areas: alongside most

269 Cf., however, Abraham (6, particularly pp. 150–151), B. D. Lewin (489, particularly pp. 60 ff.), and MacCurdy (524, Chapters 23–25).

270 Cf. MacCurdy (524).

271 Cf. Schilder (752, pp. 555–570). Schilder's concept of "dementia," rather closely following the general German usage, includes both feeble-mindedness (amentia in English) and functional, as well as organic, deterioration.

severe parapraxes, one can observe in them a consideration of object-structures the mastery of which demands considerable psychic
effort. In congenital dementias the mastery of object-structures is
insufficient to begin with, and though such patients may apprehend some realms of structure better than others, for instance,
idiots with excellent memory or very good figuring, the defect is
more even. But the thinking of idiots and imbeciles is closed; their
concepts are sharp, but show a dearth of characteristics; their
concept-basis is meager.

The problem of dementia is as yet unsolved; it may become
amenable to solution from the following vantage-points.[272] It has
been demonstrated that in schizophrenia, at least in the majority
of cases, the apparent dementia is an affective blocking, a turning-
away. That is, schizophrenic dementia is similar to those twilight
states of hysterics in which senseless answers are given in a fashion
which appears made-up and artificial, like those given by prisoners
who more or less consciously simulate a mental disorder (Ganser
syndrome). Only the motives for talking aside from the point differ in these various instances; what underlies all of them is the
affective turning-away from the question. In turn, we know that
an organic lesion of certain parts of the brain has an effect similar
to that of psychic inhibition; I refer to our discussion of psychic
blindness. It might be assumed that interest in partial-structures
is inhibited, and thus no total apprehension comes about. Clearly
this inhibition would exert its effect on fully developed thoughts
too. The acquired dementias, by the way, are mostly connected
with more or less pronounced memory-disorders; and we have conceived of such memory-disorders also as inhibitions. It is characteristic of all forms of dementia that the devaluation of an insufficient regard for object-structures are combined with a heightened estimate of the patient's own person—that is, with a narcissistic attitude. Their sexuality too is often, though not always, on
a primitive level.

A few words only about epileptic dementia. The thought-
processes of the epileptic are sticky, cumbersome, and perseverat-
ing; they do not get away from a goal once chosen. The strong
inclination to perseveration again raises the question, is it an ex-
aggeration of a factor which plays a role in normal thinking also?

272 Cf. the following with Schilder (752, pp. 577–580) and (720 a).

Indeed, we are already familiar with this factor. It is the perseverative tendency of Mueller and Pilzecker (571), and Freud's (236)[273]*
repetition compulsion. The psychological value of these factors is
thus far unclear, but it seems that a deeper penetration into the
problem of dementia may bring the next advancements in the
psychology of thinking.

Dementia is generally assumed to be as a rule directly related
to changes in brain-anatomy, clearly demonstrable in various
forms of dementia. It is also usually assumed to be a simple loss of
abilities and knowledge, directly related to the damaged part of
the brain. As against these views, I refer to our discussion in the
beginning of this volume, showing that disorders even in gross
brain-lesions are phenomena not of loss, but rather of functional
change. Brain-lesions have an inhibitory, obstructive effect; and
I believe that this point of view will be sustained by the study of
dementias. To my mind dementia is not a destruction but an obstruction of the ego, of the personality.[274]

The "functional view" of dementia is represented by Eliasberg and Feuchtwanger (162).

14. FEELINGS[275]

a) Phenomenology

The manifold of feelings. Wundt's classification. Polarity of feelings. Differences between acts of feeling and acts of sensation. James-Lange theory rejected. The object-component of feelings. Feelings are not core of the ego. The
body-close component of feelings. The object- and subject-component of feelings. The depth-dimension of feelings. Sentiments.

Thus far we have said little about feelings. According to
Wundt and his school, feelings are the dominant element in
psychic life. But this view could arise only because Wundt recognizes neither acts, nor thoughts,[276] nor spheric contents, and therefore considers as feeling everything psychological that is difficult
to analyze. He does not distinguish even the content-aspect of feeling from the feeling-intention or feeling-act. It is altogether im-

[273]* O. Gross also points to partly related facts in discussing the after-
effect of experiences, that is, the secondary function.

[274] For a related view cf. Shakow (774 a).

[275] Cf. III, 1. d., supra; also MacCurdy (525); for surveys of the more recent
literature see Rapaport (654, Chapter II) and (660).

[276] I.e., in Buehler's (121) sense.

possible to build a dynamic of psychic processes on such a vague psychology of feelings. Yet it is the merit of Wundt (895) and Lipps (512) to have recognized that the old schematic classification of feelings into pleasurable and unpleasurable is insufficient. They justly stress that the manifold of feelings has infinite qualitative shadings. Wundt classified feelings into three main groups: pleasure—displeasure, excitation—relaxation, tension—release. Feelings have polarity: to every positive feeling there is a negative counterpart, just as temperature sensations divide into those of warmth and cold. The content-components of feelings are closely related to certain sensations, and Stumpf (822) expresses this well when he speaks of feeling-sensations.

We must not fail to recognize that feeling-contents too are intended, and that feeling-intending and sensation-intending differ from each other. Sherrington's (778) experiments also speak against such a complete equating of feelings and coenesthetic sensations as was proposed by James and Lange (375). Sherrington transected a dog's cord, just behind the origin of the phrenic nerve; in a further operation he bilaterally transected the vagus. The drawing presented here indicates the parts of the body in which sensation was preserved. The dotted parts are insensitive; the continuous line indicates the boundary of the insensitive re-

Figure 8

The dotted parts have lost sensation, due to the operation. The curve represents the diaphragm, which was left sensitive. (After Sherrington.)

gion. The diaphragm is the only muscle posterior to the shoulders which retained its afferent nerves (Fig. 8).

In spite of the exclusion of such a tremendous mass of coenesthesias, this animal showed normal affective reactions. This finding must warn us against simply equating feelings and coenesthesias, even though close relations between them are unquestionable.[277] Feelings are a more central reaction, a reaction to the attitudes and stands taken by the personality. They mirror the intending of objects, and even their polarity is merely a reflection of the polarity of drives. But drives are directed at objects, and feelings appear as essential components of objects. We speak of a sad landscape, of cheerful sunshine, of gay colors. When I am angry, my anger attaches to an object and radiates to other objects I concern myself with. When I am melancholy, my melancholy clings to objects that are prone to arouse melancholy. It may be said in general that every feeling has an object-component.

We have brought feelings into psychological relationship with coenesthesias; this however implies that they, like sensations, must have somatic resonance. They are in the body, and their relation to it is more direct than that of visual perception, and just as direct as that of pain or sexual sensation. Lipps (512) thought that feelings are the core of the ego: this is factually correct only in that feeling-resonances are interwoven with the body, which is ego-close. Again like sensations, feelings are in part my reaction to objects. Nevertheless, feelings are not the core of the ego, which is fundamentally irreducible, being the total personality with all its strivings.[278]

A classification of feelings would have to take into consideration the relation of the object-aspect of feelings to their subject-aspect. Feelings connected with intake of nourishment and visual perception of objects, are definitely oriented more toward the object-aspect than are those of bliss and happiness, for instance.

[277] For reviews of the more recent work in this field, see Alpers (28), Rapaport (654, Chapter II), and Lindsley, in Stevens (808).

[278] This formulation shows how little explored and understood feelings were when Schilder wrote; the situation is not significantly better today. The role of feelings in ego-functioning seems to be the crucial unknown (cf. 660), and Schilder comes close to putting the matter thus, but the lack of clarity of his ego-concept prevents him. On the one hand, the autonomy of the ego ("irreducibility") appears to get into his way; on the other, the ego becomes for him "the total personality with all its strivings."

But Krueger (468) correctly stresses that the depth-dimension of feelings must also be considered: it makes a difference which component of my personality is involved in a certain striving. Feelings too, like drive-impulses, are directed; but what we might say about this point coincides in essence with what we said about drives, and no detailed discussion is necessary here.[279]

Pfaender (603) distinguishes sentiments from feelings. To my mind their similarities are far-reaching; sentiments, just like feelings, are reflections of attitudes . . . Nevertheless, Pfaender seems to be right that in sentiments there is an upward and downward dimension related to specific attitudes.[280]

Reviewing once more the phenomenology of feelings, it is clear that the feeling-reaction attaches only to an intending of an object. In the feeling-reaction itself, we distinguish its content and the feeling-intending; and in the content, we discriminate between object-component and subject-component. Besides the qualitative shadings of feelings in the plane, we note that feelings have a depth-dimension also.

b) Somatic expression of emotions[281]

Emotional effects are fundamentally effects of drive-attitudes. The effect of pleasure and displeasure on pulse, respiration, and blood-volume of organs. Weber's investigations. Tension-phenomena on the plethysmographic curve. Reversal of the plethysmographic curve. Changes in stomach-juice secretion and the psychogalvanic phenomenon. Involuntary movements. Respiratory symptoms of lying.

The many somatic changes accompanying emotions are due to the close connection of emotions with the body. Since we consider emotions as dependent phenomena, we may speak of them as somatic manifestations of drive-attitudes. The somatic changes concomitant with emotions are those of pulse, of respiration, of motility of the gastro-intestinal tract, of salivary, sweat, and digestive glands, indeed of the entire vaso-vegetative system.

The entire organism is directly dependent on the vaso-vegetative system. Furthermore, vaso-vegetative changes are not the only emotional effects: attitudes and affects also directly influence the

---

[279] For the details of a similar view, cf. Rapaport (657, 660).

[280] For literature concerning attitudes and sentiments, see Rapaport (654, p. 101).

[281] For a survey of the pertinent literature, see Dunbar (151).

musculature (cf. section on hypnosis above). Finally, expressive movements too are effects of attitudes, though in a somewhat extended sense, and of emotions arising from them, upon the body.[282] Every expressive movement announces an emotion also. In final analysis, the entire body appears to be an instrument of the total attitude, which finds expression both in volitional movements and in vaso-vegetative processes. For instance, even such a purely volitional action as writing may express the essential traits of the total personality (cf. Klages, 412).

But let us return to the somatic effects of emotions, in the narrower sense.

The effects of pleasure and displeasure on the body have been particularly well studied. According to Lehmann (480, 481), displeasure results in a passing breathlessness, followed by a few particularly deep breaths, and then for a while by more or less irregular breathing; the blood volume of the arm sinks considerably

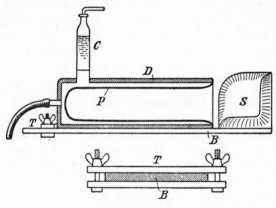

Figure 9

Mosso's Arm-Plethysmograph, improved according to A. Lehmann. (From Lehmann, 481, "Somatic Manifestations of Psychological Conditions," Vol. I.)

below the norm, the pulse becomes shallower and somewhat faster. When displeasure disappears, a reaction against the changes sets in for a while: arm-volume and pulse-intensity not only return to normal, but somewhat exceed it. With pleasurable impressions

282 Cf. Allport and Vernon (23), and Bull (124).

the somatic changes are more difficult to demonstrate, and less uniform. First, pleasurable stimuli suitable for laboratory conditions elicit only feelings that lack intensity. Second, the phenomena that accompany any arousal of attention, and resemble those of mild displeasure, interfere by covering up the effects of pleasure; so many observers could find no specific reaction to pleasure. According to Lehmann, it is the diametrical opposite of the displeasure-reaction: the pulse slows down and becomes stronger, the blood-volume of the arm drops momentarily at the beginning of stimulation, then rises rapidly above the original level. But these changes rarely, if ever, occur together: either pulse-intensification, or pulse slow-down, or volume-increase is usually missing. (This discussion derives from Ebbinghaus-Duerr, 153, Vol. I, pp. 565–566.)

Particularly detailed investigations of blood-volume displacements accompanying psychological processes were reported by Ernst Weber (861). He used mainly the Mosso-Lehmann plethysmograph for measuring arm-volume (cf. Fig. 9). The arm is encased in a rubber balloon (P), which in turn is enclosed in a cylinder (D). The space between cylinder and rubber balloon is filled with water (C), the volume-fluctuations of which are registered by a Marey-capsule. The arm is fixed in its position by an elbow-support (S). Weber determined simultaneously the brain and ear blood-volumes by means of simple airtight capsules, and the abdominal blood-volume, by means of Mosso's scale and a rubber balloon introduced into the rectum. Mosso's scale keeps the subject at first in equilibrium; but in the wake of affects, the foot or the head of the scale rises or sinks because of blood-volume displacements. The following table represents Weber's findings.

Of particular interest in this table is the fact that even the intention of movement (Weber's movement-image) suffices to increase the blood-volume of the limbs. This finding has, however, been questioned. The most important of Weber's physiological findings concerns the unusual innervation of the brain's blood vessels: it alone is independent of the vasomotor center of the medulla, and depends on a special vasomotor center above the medulla oblongata.

Weber's investigations have been called into question by more recent studies. According to DeJong (389), the plethysmogram shows the same reaction to all psychic stimulation, and any psychic activity, pleasure, displeasure, psychic effort, excitation, tension, will elicit it. In this normal curve of psychic stimulation, a brief increase in volume is followed by a drop. DeJong (389) explains

	Changes in the volume of the blood in:			
	Brain	External parts of head	Abdominal organs	Limbs and external parts of trunk
With movement-images, with or without execution of movement	+283*	—	—	+
With mental work	+	—	+	—
With fright	+	—	+	—
With displeasure feelings	—	—	+	—
In sleep	+		—	+

the first by increased heart-action, and the second by vessel-reaction. Kueppers (471) and Bickel (73) also assume that all psychic stimuli are followed by one kind of reaction only. According to Kueppers it is attention, and according to DeJong it is psychic activity as such, that results in a drop of the volume-curve.[284]

The normal curve does not appear when the tension of the vessels is excessive. Earlier Lehmann had reported that some subjects incline to tension. Kueppers has pointed emphatically to this narrowing of vessels due to tension, which makes further contraction upon psychic stimuli impossible. Distraction can eliminate this tension; but in catatonics we frequently find vessels rigid in their volume, which cannot be relaxed by distraction. DeJong infers that this is an organic tension-condition of the vessels. He distinguishes: hypospastic curves, of great pulse-intensity and strong normal reaction to stimuli; normal curves; semi-spastic

284* + means increase, — means decrease of the blood-volume of the body part in question.

284 The discordant results may be due to pronounced individual differences. This possibility has been overlooked by Schilder, and is still being overlooked in such studies. For an analogous state of affairs in perception, cf. Klein (417, 418).

curves, in which, due to tension, the initial rise is strong, while the vessel-reaction is small; spastic curves, in which there is no reaction to stimuli; hyperspastic curves, in which tension is so great that no pulse-changes come about.

Weber and Bickel describe a reversal of normal reaction in fatigue. Bickel speaks of a psychasthenic reaction, but this is called into question by DeJong, who suggests that it is an appearance referable to semi-spastic curves.

Survey of this material suggests that psychic tensions do express themselves in the plethysmographic curve; but only these tensions and psychic activity as such show on the curve, and no classification of feelings can come from these investigations.[285]

Bickel studied the changes of blood-pressure accompanying psychic activity, and found that in general it rose. However, this was not due to contraction of peripheral vessels, nor was the heart-rhythm dependent upon such contractions.

I can only refer briefly to Berger's (57) investigations of somatic manifestations of psychic conditions. He was concerned primarily with the brain blood-volume curve, and studied cases of skull injury; in another study (58) he dealt with the temperature of the brain in intellectual work, and found that it rose 1/20–1/100 C°, one to two minutes after the stimulation.

Pulse and blood-pressure phenomena are but a small part of affect-influences on the body. Let us be reminded of Pavlov's (597) brilliant studies showing that secretion of the digestive glands varies with the stimulus-object presented.

Schrottenbach (761) investigated in detail the changes of stomach-juice secretion under the influence of psychic experiences. According to him, secretion is increased by: chewing food, associatively aroused visual images of food, hungry feelings aroused by acoustic association, pleasurable affect without appetite. Secretion is inhibited by: passing unpleasant affect, chronic but fluctuating unpleasant affect, sleep. The latency after visual and acoustic stimulation is considerably longer than after chewing. This experimental demonstration, that every reactive change of stomach-secretion in man may be elicited by a variety of stimuli, is noteworthy. The relation of these stimuli to each other at any given time creates infinitely varying conditions for the increase and in-

285 Cf. P. T. Young (903).

hibition of stomach-juice secretion. The physiological conditions for increase and decrease of stomach-juice secretion also prove complex: on the one hand, changes of the blood-vessel apparatus due to psychological stimulation play a role; on the other, the stomach-glands are also directly influenced, as shown by the qualitative differences in secretion dependent upon the quality of stimulation.[286]

The so-called psychogalvanic phenomena have aroused special interest:[287] the electric current between two points of the human skin changes under the influence of affects, presumably because of changes in sweat-secretion (Tarchanoff, 826; Veraguth, 845; Gregor, 301).

We saw that affects manifest themselves in changes of the innervation of voluntary musculature in the discussion of expressive movements. Sommer (783) has described an apparatus which registers muscular movements in any direction.

It is quite possible to infer complicated psychological processes from expressive movements and recordable somatic manifestations. Benussi (55), for instance, succeeded in establishing a definite respiratory picture of lying.

c) Dynamics of emotions and psychic energy

Images and emotions as distributors of psychic energy. Dynamic effect of experience and somatic apparatus. Theoretical consideration concerning psychic energy. The economic point of view of psychoanalysis.

Even everyday experience indicates that affects find discharge in action: rage evaporates in an assault on an opponent.[288]

What of the dynamic value of emotions? Just like other experiences, such as perceptions and apprehendings, emotions have a dynamic value within the totality of experiencing, but only in so far as drive-forces are bound, manifested, or expressed in them.

286 For a survey of other work in this field, particularly Heyer's, see Dunbar (151).

287 For a survey of the present situation in this field, see McCleary (527).

288 Schilder, in this initial statement, brushes aside as self-evident a very complex and debatable matter. For his source, see Freud (229). Schilder, like Bleuler and many psychiatric and psychoanalytic writers, equates affect (emotion) and drive-cathexis. Psychoanalytic theory proper regards action, affect, and idea as various avenues for the deployment of drive-cathexis. See Freud (204, Chapter VII); also Rapaport (660 and 668).

It is unquestionable according to all the preceding considerations, that drives, not emotions[289] must be regarded as the source of energy, which may be discharged not only toward external psycho-energy; on the other, they require images in relation to which they can unfold. At the same time, these images are fused with emotions; image and emotion appear as distributors of psychic energy. Every emotionally toned image is invested with psychological energy, which may be discharged not only toward external psychological structures[290] but also into the organism; and this is where the somatic effects of emotions come in. As already stressed: emotions are secondary to drive-attitudes, which basically are the only dynamically effective factors in psychic life.

Activity and passivity in psychic life must not be mistaken for dynamic effectiveness: a passively accepted experience may have great dynamic effect.[291] Activity and passivity are act-modifications, while the concept of dynamic effectiveness refers to something extra-psychological.[292] We must assume that the way a happening will influence subsequent attitudes is already implicit in how it is experienced; the experience already indicates how much or how little energy will be discharged into the body. Besides attitudes and emotions, there is another determining factor of somatic effects; and this cannot be reflected psychologically. For instance, an affect of the same effect-value will not be deleterious in the young individual, but in an arteriosclerotic may cause apoplexy, lasting speech-disorder, etc. Here too, just as in regard to sleep, we must distinguish between first, the effect-value, which depends on the attitude and partly reflects the somatic process, and second, the apparatus on which the drive exerts its effect. But we have no direct knowledge of the condition of this apparatus.

Here a discussion of psychic and physical energy seems neces-

---

289 "Emotion" translates *Gefuehle*. Schilder's usage of the terms "affect" (German: *Affekt*) and "emotion" is not consistent and apparently interchangeable. His formulation reflects the common psychoanalytic assumption.

290 It is unclear whether this is a typographical error and should read "external physical structures," or whether it reflects the conception that the discharge takes place in the subject's "psychological space" in which the objects of the external world—one of which is the body of the subject—are represented by "psychological structures" (cf. Lewin, 493).

291 Cf. Lewin (495, pp. 91–94).

292 Cf. Freud (226), also Bibring (71), for the common psychoanalytic formulation.

sary. To begin with, we do not mean by psychic energy a specific form of energy, but merely that energy which is somehow coupled or connected with psychological experiences. I have already discussed how the transformations of psychic energy are similar to those of other organic-biological energies. It seems to be characteristic for psychological forms of energy, however, that they are related to images. I have not yet discussed this theoretically, though I did indicate that images become more pronounced when impulses are checked: then action, which aims directly at the object, changes into an image. It is plausible to assume that image-production is a transformation of checked energies.[293] According to this view, images arise when reality cannot be mastered simply by action; and the more richly reality unfolds, the richer in images we become. It is pertinent here that in cortical lesions there is an alteration of images; we may conjecture that the cortex is the locus of those structures that transform into images the energies of drives checked by the external world. The processes within the sphere appear from this vantage-point as changes in drive-transformations caused by cortical inhibitions. These speculations do not explain how an image of this or that construction appears as the result of drive-inhibition: in general, qualitative characteristics elude treatment in terms of energy. This limitation of treatment in terms of energy is a subject-matter for the philosophy of nature. Scientific psychology, however, cannot avoid using the concept of energy.[294]

Psychoanalysis speaks of an economic point of view, and means by it that the organism strives to attain a certain amount of pleasure and makes arrangements to this end.[295] In my view, the

[293] Cf. Schilder (751) and Freud (216).

[294] Cf. footnote 71, p. 192. While the use of a psychological "energy" concept—as indeterminate as it still is—seems to be so far indispensable for a dynamic psychology, Schilder's lack of awareness of the difficulties involved is disturbing.

[295] This is an inadequate, indeed a misleading, formulation. The economic point of view (concerned with the amounts of cathexes involved) is for psychoanalysis one of the three indispensable points of view in the study of psychological phenomena. It is concerned with the quantities of energy involved in the psychological processes, and with the psychic apparatuses' method of disposing of them. The two other points of view are: the dynamic point of view (concerned with the forces involved in the conflict) and the structural point of view (concerned with the role of the id-ego-superego in the phenomenon). An analysis of a psychological phenomenon taking all three points of view into consideration is termed a *metapsychological* analysis.

individual has goals and purposes, and it is these that he attempts
to realize.[296] Pleasure and pain do not seem to me by any means
the original goals and purposes. But Freud (236) is right in assert-
ing that pain is connected with an increase of stimulation in the
psychic apparatus, while pleasure is somehow linked with a decrease of it: the sexual act demonstrates this. Freud concludes from
this that the psychic apparatus subserves the purpose of mastering and settling the stimulations that impinge on it from the outside and the inside. The economic point of view takes into consideration the role of energic-quantities also. The problems Freud
treated under the economic point of view coincide in part with
those of effect-value. We have repeatedly raised the question, How
is effect-value reflected in experience? The question, Are emotions indicators orienting us about energy-displacements in psychic economy? is of the same order, significance, and difficulty.

For a concise presentation of the basic assumptions of psychoanalysis, see
Binswanger (74).

d) Body-build and character[297]

Generalities about conversion and somatic phenomena in neuroses. Limits
of psychological influence on the body. Sudden graying. Blood-glands and affect. Body-build and character. Pyknic build and pyknic temperament. Relation to circular psychoses. Asthenic-athletic build and special dysplastic types.
Schizothymic temperament. Relation between temperaments and completed
vs. incomplete thinking.

Drive-energies which do not attain their proper goals are
channeled to related ones, as indicated in our discussion of repression. The repressed, the incomplete, the spheric, must have
an especially strong influence on the body. We are back at the
problem of conversion, and the advance we have made is only
that we must unlearn to consider conversion into somatic symptoms as something only psychological.[298] Di Gaspero (262), for
instance, has demonstrated that hysterical paralysis may be accompanied by a vaso-vegetative paralysis which the patient cannot have directly willed. Recently, Parrisius (596) has been able

296 For further exposition of this view, see Schilder (749).
297 For a survey of the literature and a more recent attempt in this direction, see Sheldon (775, 776, 777); for its critique, Holt (354) and Adcock (10).
298 Cf. Alexander's (15) discussion of this point; for a survey of the literature pertaining to the following discussion, see Dunbar (151) and Weiss and
English (865).

to demonstrate changes in the capillaries of neurotics, that is, an organic effect of the psychological. The psychogenic diarrheas and the even more frequent psychogenic constipations are in point here; and so are the often psychologically determined disorders of menstruation. I must stress that the psychic influences on tension-states of the musculature can hardly be overstated; and in keeping with our discussion above, we must assume a psychic influence on the striate body in hypnotic catalepsy. In some diseases of the striate cortex, certain attitudes arouse severe organic tensions. Psychoanalysis (Groddeck, 302, 303) has asserted the psychogenic origin of a great many organic illnesses: such as goiter, bleeding of the lung, etc. Though Groddek's claims are excessive, psychological influences on the body have certainly been underestimated.[299*] To Felix Deutsch (144, 145) we are indebted for valuable investigations into the psychogenesis of Basedow's disease, but in some respects he also goes too far. Yet research must face seriously the question whether much of what we have been accustomed to regard as hereditary is not identification with parents and siblings.

Under the influence of affects, particularly those which break in suddenly, considerable somatic changes can come about. Thus, sudden graying has been reliably reported; and it is easily conceivable that fright and depression might cause a drop of blood-pressure sufficient to endanger life even with a normal heart (cf. Knauer and Billigheimer, 429). There are reports that primitives' fright over having transgressed a taboo caused their instant death. F. Braun (98) reports that newly captured birds often perish due solely to their nervous condition. That a diseased heart (Braun, 99) can react to an affect by stopping, and that a rigid vessel in the brain may be burst by increased blood-pressure due to affects, is well known. This brings into focus the crucial fact that somatic changes due to affects need not be reversible, but may be lasting.

The relation of affects to endocrine glands must be regarded as particularly important, because through these the entire regulation of metabolism may be influenced psychologically. Raimann's (644) finding of glycosuria in depressive psychoses is pertinent

---

[299*] On the relation of the nervous system and metabolism, see Allers's (16) survey. Naturally, much of this material is only preliminary to the problem of the relation of psyche and metabolism.

here. It must be assumed that, through the sympathetic and para-sympathetic systems, affects can influence the entire body. In turn, we know that affectivity is also co-determined by the conditions of internal secretion. I have in mind, for instance, the psychological changes following castration, as well as those observed in eunuchoidism, both of which take the form of infantilism, affective imbalance, unpredictability (cf. Fraenkel, 197); furthermore, there is the mood-lability of Basedow-patients. In final analysis, the endocrine formula of the individual is an essential factor of his total personality. Though a full understanding of these matters must take the total personality into consideration, nevertheless the quality of a man depends crucially on his affectivity, which in turn is related to his endocrine system.

The individual character of the endocrine system certainly expresses itself in the physique also. Kretschmer (456, 457) describes his pyknic type as of short limbs, well-nourished appearance, and inclination to fresh facial color; bony-frame rather delicate, musculature soft, abundant fat deposition on face, neck and trunk; portly head, chest, and belly, with shoulders rather narrow and pushed together, making for a barrel-like trunk: the head sitting somewhat forward on a short, thickset neck. In typical cases the skull is low, the crown flat with a well-shaped occiput; the face soft, broad and round, of medium harmonic proportions and well-formed details. The profile is soft, mildly raised, with a fleshy nose; the frontal outline of the face if slightly schematized has a flat pentagonal or broad shield form. The hands are short, broad, soft, but delicately built; the hair is, in the average, soft and thin, with an inclination to early and extensive baldpates. According to Kretschmer, there is a particular affinity between this form of body-build and circular psychoses, as well as those cyclothymic character-types that are small-scale copies of these psychoses. These are people whose mood swings between gay elation and depressed sadness, and whose psychological tempo is mobile and comfortable with rounded, natural, soft movements.

While in manic-depressives the pyknic body-build type predominates, in schizophrenics we find multiple crossings and mixtures of the characteristics of various body-build forms, the most frequent of which are the asthenic and athletic types. In addition, there are in schizophrenia several dysplastic special groups, which are in part closely related morphologically to the familiar dys-glandular body-forms (tall eunuchoids, certain eunuchoid or polyglandular obesities, and many infantile and hypoplastic forms). Athletic men are slender, rather long-limbed; their appearance is dominated by the broad, muscular shoulders, contrasting with the youthful lower part of the body, narrow pelvis, slender legs, forming a trapezoid-like frontal trunk-outline. The bony structure is powerful, particularly at the shoulders and at the ends of the extremities. The musculature is well developed and appears in plastic relief from under the taut, fatless skin. On their strong long neck sits a sharp tall head, with a high middle-face, strongly cut chin and solid bony relief. The frontal outline of the face is a steep egg-form.

Male asthenics have a cylindrical trunk, long narrow rib-cage, narrow shoulders; extremities and neck also have a longish effect. Throughout bones are gracile, muscles spare, and skin thin. The head is small, either tall or round. The long-drawn sloping nose contrasts with a sharp lower jaw, so that the jutting nose and the receding chin readily make for an angular profile—which, by the way, is frequent in schizophrenics of other body-builds also. The frontal outline of the face tends in typical cases toward a fore-shortened egg-form.

The skin of schizophrenics is frequently pale. The basic hair (head and brows) is stiff and rough, ingrown and long-lasting, though, in the average, weak terminally. In male schizophrenics, eunuchoid traits are often mixed into the body-build: excessive length of extremities, increased width of pelvis, etc.; there are femininities in males, masculinities and genital hypoplasia in females; and last but not least, hypoplastic traits, dwarfism, and stunting either of the whole or of parts of the body, particularly of the face, which may be low, receding, plainly inferior, and underdeveloped, with a pitiful stub-nose.

Psychopaths whose make-up and temperament are related to those of schizophrenics have similar body-builds. We call them schizothymic types and by that mean people who are now over-sensitive and irritable, now cold and unapproachable, whose psy-chological tempo is now jumpy, now obstinate, whose thinking and emotions are strongly ambivalent, and whose movements often do not correspond to the stimulation, being held back, stiff and peculiar.

Kretschmer no doubt succeeded in characterizing two particular types which we continuously meet in life.[300] To me it seems that the affective types Kretschmer outlined also have definite characteristics of thinking. The thoughts of cyclothymes are completed, fully-developed; those of schizothymes are predominantly spheric, un-unified. But it is questionable whether the rich manifold of normal life, the great variety of temperaments, permits of a division into only two groups. Though temperaments and body-builds are parallel in many cases, mixed forms are still the most frequent (Kretschmer speaks of alloy-forms). He enlists the aid of genetic studies also, and finds a great frequency of pyknic types in the kinship of cyclothymes. These investigations can by no means be considered definitive; nevertheless, the control studies so far seem to corroborate the basic position of Kretschmer's theory. Typical forms of body-build are more frequent in cycloids and cyclothymes than in schizophrenics and schizothymes.

In his life-cycle, every individual shows some change in body-type (Hoffman, 351, 352). At the age of 30 to 40 there is a greater inclination to pyknic body-forms, while youth tends to asthenic-athletic ones.[301] Correspondingly we find in youth incompleted thoughts, spheric formations; these, called in everyday life "idealism," recede in maturity. It is important that here again we see a close connection between body and psyche.[302*]

So far we have spoken primarily of that affectivity which is closely related to sexuality. But while we dealt in detail with the role of sexuality, we have scarcely spoken about the nature and role of ego-drives. This omission is of no consequence for many of our considerations, since we have assumed a broad common zone of ego and sexuality—a zone which may prove to be the matrix of all affectivity. The considerations on thought, on displacements and condensation, are independent of the classification

300 Cf. also Murphy (574, pp. 147–152). While the problem of constitution impresses itself increasingly on all dynamic psychology (246, 321), attempts at clarifying it so far seem to be unsatisfactory. As a consequence, Schilder's conjectures which follow appear altogether premature.

301 Compare Holt and Bellak's (353) findings with Sheldon's somatotypes.

302* Concerning the relation of body-build types to ethnic types, see Kretschmer's (456) recent statement.

of individual drives as ego-drives or sex-drives. Nevertheless, we must now turn to the role and nature of ego-drives, of the ego, of the personality in general.

My psychological views are in essence voluntaristic, those of a drive-psychology; and in this respect I stand completely on the grounds of psychoanalysis. I wish to call attention to Specht's (784) survey of the literature of attention, which also takes a voluntaristic view.

VI

EGO AND PERSONALITY

1. On the Phenomenology of Ego-Experience[1]

Ego as an irreducible entity. Ego and body. Body-consciousness. Ego-constancy. Uniqueness of the ego. Unity of the ego. Depth of experiences. Rich and meager experience. Negated experience and repression. On the dynamics of ego-experiences. Object-structures, values, and rich experience.

Association psychology builds the ego out of single elements: for Hume and Mach, the ego is a bundle of sensations. Wundt and Lipps ascribe a special role to emotions in the ego, but Lipps began to realize that in final analysis the ego is irreducible. The concept of sensation is meaningless if there is no ego which senses; emotion too presupposes an ego which feels. Transcendental idealism considers the ego, as it considers the thing, a postulate of thinking. Per contra, I must stress that the ego is directly experienced and is *a priori* inherent to every experience: it is not a postulated reference-point of thought, but an undeniable experience.[2] But why do not all thinkers recognize this experience? Apparently because it is on the act-side and not on the object-side of experience. To repeat: acts are experienced, objects appear. It takes an internal reorientation to perceive acts: they flee from perception. The ego is the source of acts: the intendings emanate from the ego. We need not always register the ego in the course of experience, but it is always our ego which experiences.

The question arises whether the ego relates in the same way to all experiences, and thus, first of all, what its relation to the body is. In any case, the body is ego-close, while the world is ego-

[1] Cf. Freud (239, 244) and A. Freud (200) for the general psychoanalytic view; see Hartmann (320, 321, 321 a), Allport (26), and Rapaport (656), for discussions of the specific problem of ego-autonomy which Schilder poses here.

[2] It seems that here Schilder deals with what is now referred to as the "self" rather than the ego. Cf. Introduction, footnote 11, *supra*.

distant. These are irreducible qualities, but empirical factors are added to this primary qualitative difference. I relate myself differently to my body than to the world; I can volitionally move it, it is in a particular way subjected, subordinated, to me. But in turn, I cannot escape the pain that comes from my body; I am subjected to it; there continuously arises something from my body without my contribution, even if only coenesthesias. These two opposing factors determine for me what my body is. For a creature which could not move, body and world would be completely identical. Under conditions in which the possibility of action is interdicted, we do observe some confluence of body and world.

Scheler (689) speaks of a specific bodily consciousness, which fills everyone. Indeed, it must be admitted that there is a unity between bodily sensation and the external image of the body, just as there undoubtedly exists a consciousness of specific mastery over, and specific belongingness with, the body. Although bodily consciousness must be presupposed to be a basic form, it by no means coincides with the anatomically given body: jewelry, walking-stick, tools also belong to it.[3] In schizophrenics we constantly observe how parts of the body get thrown in with the external world, while parts of the external world get thrown in with the body. But the opposition, body vs. world, is retained as basic scaffolding, even though a primeval condition in which body and world shade into one is conceivable. Even then, however, the ego would persist and confront its objects. The condition of one-ness of body and world differs from that seen in identification: identification recognizes other egos, it is directed toward other people.

The ego always confronts its objects, one of which is the body. In images, thoughts, feelings, percepts, I always intend an object. The ego is the precondition of all intendings of objects.

The term ego is meaningful only in so far as it refers to something constant and unchanging. If I say, "Yesterday I was a different man," I cannot possibly mean that my ego has changed: only the experiences of the ego and its modes of experiencing have changed. The ego is constant and unchanging in time; furthermore, we ascribe to every ego a particular uniqueness. *My* thinking, feeling, acting, are *a priori* completely different from

3 Cf. Schilder (725, 740, 747); see also Federn (117a) on "ego boundaries."

those of a *you*. Every act I execute has the signature, "my act"; and it would be wrong to assume that this "my" attains its coloring only through experiences. My experience in regard to this "my" would not be different had my real experiences been different. Kaspar Hauser's *my* is as full-ringing as that of someone who has grown up under normal conditions.[4] We may formulate: every ego is at the same time a person.

The ego thinks, feels, perceives, has a past and a present. One cannot say that experiences are attributes or parts of the ego, because every experience presupposes an ego; the ego lives in its acts, independent of their objects. The fact that the unity of the ego is preserved in spite of the multitude of its acts can only be described, not be further explained.[5] Even the simplest willed decision involves a multitude of obstructing counter-impulses, which are integrated into a final unity by the decision; but all these impulses imply the same ego, which remains self-same at every moment, even in mutually contradictory acts: it is the unity of experiencing. It is a singular unity, one in which all previous experience of the ego, the past as the background of experiencing, is always present. I have presented empirical evidence for this contention in the preceding. All previous experience is continuously in readiness; it is within the reach of the ego; it affects and colors the present.

At this point it becomes possible to distinguish several important kinds of experience, according to the relation of this past to the present, and according to the act involved. Ego-experiences vary in depth. When all my experiences unite in the focus of the present, when all the multitude of my tendencies enters into a particular decision, the experience is rich and unified. The acts of creative inspiration, in which the human being experiences himself as a whole, are of this kind. In these, the

---

4 The title and name of the hero—who grew up without contact with the world—of J. Wassermann's novel. Schilder's formulation of this important point appears at present—after some understanding of the issue of "ego autonomy" has been reached—extreme and excessive. Such excesses are common when so well entrenched a conception as that of "nurture" has to be tackled.

5 This is in curious contradiction to Schilder's pioneering insight into the necessity of hypothesizing "synthetic functions." The contradiction fades, however, if we assume that he is speaking here of the subjective self-experience rather than of the functions and structures underlying it. Schilder's phenomenology and his dynamic understanding are here at odds. The difficulty is still with us in the lack of clarity of the role of "self" in the ego-structure or amongst ego functions.

meaning of existence is condensed into the present experience, which, indeed, seems to contain the canon of future experiences also.[6] Such experiences are in contrast to others which are meager, contain only partial tendencies, and occur, as it were, on top of an untouched block of the past, though they do not depart from the main tendencies of the personality. Our everyday activities are such meager experiences: we carry them out, not reluctantly, yet without full involvement. Or the present experience may take place against the background of a past which strives toward entirely different goals. The past can rise in negation of what we are doing. Then we have a negated experience, such as we encounter when we act against our better judgment; or when occupied with essential matters—such as mourning over the loss of a beloved relative—we are necessitated to other thoughts or doings; or when other impulses than those that the day requires override everyday attitudes. The negation of experience has two major forms. In the first, negated experiences, the negation of what I experience at present is clear and explicit; in the second, repressed experiences, the negation is suppressed, and with a part of our personality we can turn, apparently undisturbed, to our everyday tasks.

Here our goal has been to represent the qualitative varieties of experiences as we actually encounter them: richness, meagerness, and negation are descriptively demonstrable varieties. All these kinds of experience do not contradict, but rather rest on, the unity of the ego.

It is clear that insight into the nature of ego-experiences is beyond the province of the dynamic point of view underlying the second major part[7] of this book. But a considerable part of even these matters is apprehensible by the scientific-dynamic approach, because the degree of richness and unification of experience depends on drive-attitudes.

Full personality-experience presupposes a total world struc-

---

[6] Concerning the nature of creative experience, cf. Kris (461), and Freud (229, p. 127), on the maximal economy and overdetermination of creative products. See also Schilder (692, 707), and his Chapters VI, VII, IX, XIX, in Lauretta Bender (50 a).

[7] I.e., Part V, which centers on psychoanalytic discoveries. Here Schilder bows to the phenomenological approach and takes a stand much like Allport's (26) more recent stand. And though he has anticipated much of its groundwork, he does not reach the solution of the autonomy problem which psychoanalytic ego-psychology arrived at recently. Cf. footnote 8, pp. 103–104.

tured in depth, the particulars of which I lovingly intend again and again. Full harmony, which I attempted to describe above, results from intendings and attitudes, and we may conceive of it as the resultant of biological interests. Meager experience implies interests which do not express our drive-structure fully. Negated experiences are resultants of contradictory drives.

I find it necessary to make here a brief remark which transcends the field of psychology. We must ask: what are the objects of strivings? Our answer is that strivings always aim at values. Some values adhere to things, and we speak then of goods; but there are values which do not turn directly into goods. The values which adhere to things are values of a low order and must be contrasted with those which pertain to thing-structures. The value of an object increases with its structure. According to the preceding section, structures are points of attack for the manifold of drive-attitudes, and to intend structured things means to order one's drives into a structured unity. The world of values naturally includes interpersonal relations, and here too there are structures.[8]

It may be said that the more penetrating his intendings of structures, the more articulated in depth is the person's drive-life; and what we have called rich experience presupposes not only the emergence of objects of the past, but also the structural articulation and absolute coordination of drives toward a definite goal. This leads to the conclusion that only a biologically rich organism with a wealth of drives can attain really full experiencing. The last proposition is corroborated by the observation that deep experiences of happiness, which as a rule accompany full experiencing, are encountered only where a richly articulated and structured external world and a world of values is mastered by thoughts or action.

The same holds for the experiences of the great mystics: they all had a moment in which they enjoyed full experience, the unity with God, the *unio mystica*. But they could not hold onto this without turning again and again to the external world with definite goals.[9] For instance, Saint Theresa found full happiness

---

[8] The problem of values has been neglected by psychoanalysis, and only recently has it aroused the interest of other psychoanalysts. See Schilder (749, Chapter 23) and (743). Cf. also Ginsburg (280) and Ginzberg et al. (281).

[9] For a very similar conception, cf. Kris (460, 461) particularly his concept

only in the active organizing work of her order (cf. Delacroix, 142).

It seems to be generally true that only the deed, the action, which takes its place purposefully and meaningfully in the world, permits full-valued utilization of the past. This is so because only the external world, and the world of values anchored in it, is sufficiently varied to give the drives ever new points of attack for unfolding life fully. These general principles are continuously corroborated by experience. Only the mastery of difficult tasks, which presupposes the overcoming of many partial strivings, gives full gratification. If we by-pass reality, which demands hierarchically articulated partial strivings, we attain only empty gratifications: such are the hallucinatory gratifications of hysterics, but also the gratification derived from banal conversation and works of art which merely please but do not force us to discover new object-structures.

We know that in schizophrenia there occur deep ecstasies that cannot be held onto, because the continuous touch with reality is lacking; and the bliss connected with such ecstasies is not lasting either.[10] The psychology of ecstasy can be understood only as the revival of the entire past, the mobilization of the whole sphere, the sighting of the entire previous experiential series in ever new relationships, and the readying anew of all these for decisive action. Thus, ecstasy appears as a revival of the past, as a passing regression—which, however, is a transition to a new progress, a new synthesis, by means of a new goal. The dynamic analysis of such conditions shows that regression takes place under the direction of drives and goal-settings, and that each more powerful drive must reorganize the entire personality in order to orient it toward the new goal. In speaking of drives here, we should realize that from the descriptive point of view the expression *goal-setting* would be more correct; but then *goal-setting* too must be taken as a concept of dynamic psychology. Otherwise we would have to exclude this area from the realm of scientific study, though it can and must be treated scientifically. If ecstasy, or full experiencing in general, does not somehow lead back to

---

of "regression in the service of the ego" as an indispensable phase of creativity, followed by a phase of "elaboration."

[10] Cf. Kris (461) on schizophrenic art, in which such a return to contact with reality is lacking; it therefore remains magic and is not elaborated into a social act of communication.

actuality—e.g., in the mystic to a life of grace, in the prophet to political action, in the artist to effective work, in the scientist to formulations of general validity—then impoverishment must set in, because the experience cannot retain its fullness. This psychological state of affairs is well characterized by the words of Ulrich Brendel, in Ibsen's *Rosmerholm:*

> *Brendel:* Just as I was ready to empty the horn of plenty, I made the painful discovery that I am bankrupt.
> *Rebekka:* And all your unwritten works?
> *Brendel:* For twenty-five years I sat here like the miser watching his locked money-box. And yesterday—as I opened it to take out the treasure—there was none.

Full experiencing shades into meager experiencing. We see extremes of the latter in idiots and imbeciles of various degrees, who do not even know the range of possibilities for happiness. It should also be stressed that not even sensuous pleasure can be the same for primitive as for highly developed organisms. It is absurd to assume that an idiot could have experiences like Tristan's. Gratification depends on the total structures that are mastered in order to reach it.

2. DEPERSONALIZATION[11]

Negation of various fields of experience. Concrete demonstration of the negating experience. Self-observation and internal negation. Estheticism. Hypochondriasis. Depersonalization as prodrome of neurosis. World-destruction fantasy. Dynamics of self-observation. On the quality of the foreground-experience in repression.

Negation of experiencing is most clearly seen in cases of depersonalization.[12] The person afflicted by depersonalization complains he is no longer the same, no longer himself. Indeed, in clear-cut cases the patients complain that they no longer have an ego, but are mechanisms, automatons, puppets; that what they do seems not done by them but happens mechanically; that they no longer feel joy or sorrow, hatred or love; that they are as though dead, not alive, not real; that they cannot image their body, it is

11 For the literature of depersonalization, see Schilder (690, 697, 749, pp. 188 ff.); see also Oberndorf (583–586) and Fenichel (180, pp. 418–420).

12 It is very questionable whether the term negation is used here by Schilder in the sense in which it is usually used in the psychoanalytic literature. Freud's (243) use of the term is of a later date than Schilder's.

feelingless, and they experience neither hunger, thirst, nor any other bodily needs; that they cannot image nor remember, or intuit how their relatives look. The world too appears to them changed, strange, unreal; to some, objects look like those on another planet. In a word, the perceptual world is estranged.

If one studies such patients with objective methods, it turns out that the raw material of their somatic sensations is unchanged. These patients have feelings, because they show clear-cut affective reactions and their expressive movements have nothing rigid about them. Their lack of memory-images is not a loss of imagery, but rather an inhibition of existing memories. Most instructive are those cases who assert emphatically that they neither see nor hear, though objective examination of them yields negative results. It becomes clear that such patients fight, defend themselves, against their perceptions; they negate them internally because they negate internally their entire experience, and prevent themselves from experiencing anything fully. It is noteworthy that many of these patients are nevertheless capable of complex achievements. It must be said that here negation does not essentially change the dynamics of psychic happening; yet the patients experience these achievements (which can be of high quality) as originating not in their center but on their periphery, and label them therefore automatic. This is not without justification, since what we usually call automatic action also occurs on the periphery of the ego; the ego is only partially involved in it. Automatized actions in general, in contrast to those in depersonalization, are not negated. When internal negation is far-reaching, it may lead to an alteration of the dynamics of psychic events. This can be most clearly seen in images: when we image something against an internal reluctance, the image will at first be paler, and perhaps finally will not appear at all, as a consequence of negative determination. Our discussion of the effect of attitudes on imaging is in point here.[13]

The change in percepts is due to the patients' refusal to accept their experiences: the percepts are negated. The perceptual substratum remains unchanged in so far as it is not altered by a change in the orientation and auxiliary apparatuses of attention. Flat, two-dimensional perceiving is a case in point.[14]

It is noteworthy that the negation of experience, descriptively

13 Cf. Schilder (737).
14 Cf. Schilder (750, Chapter 12).

established, can be traced by dynamic-genetic study to concrete and specific experiences, which bring about and maintain the negation of the experience in question. M. Loewy (518) reports such an observation, and some of Abraham's (3) and H. Hartmann's (316) observations are also pertinent. Just as the conflicts which lead to neuroses are mostly in the sexual realm—all of them, if sexuality is defined in the strictly psychoanalytic sense—so are those in depersonalization.[15] In one of my observations, depersonalization set in after a mother's incest-dream which represented her in intercourse with her son. The compulsive return of the memory of this dream regularly re-elicited the depersonalization.

The question is how these patients come to assert that their ego is destroyed, that they are no longer people. We must point out that all depersonalized patients observe themselves continuously and with great zeal; they compare their present dividedness-within-themselves with their previous oneness-with-themselves. Self-observation is compulsive in these patients. The tendency to self-observation continuously negates the tendency to live, and we may say it represents the internal negation of experience.

The problem of depersonalization is closely related to that of estheticism; the emptiness and ungenuineness of depersonalization as well as estheticism arises because the intention to experience never contains the total personality, and the tendency to self-observation (self-reflection) prevents the full development of experience. The depersonalized person continuously observes not only his experience but also his body, and the case-history of each of them reports hypochondriacal sensations; here too the negation of bodily-experience is the driving force. Such persons do not let their bodily-sensations come up freely; in psychoanalytic terms, the narcissistic attitudes are negated. In turn, however, the increased observation of their own organisms becomes a continuous source of stimulation, the genetic relation of which to sexuality in general and narcissism in particular is undeniable. Accordingly, psychoanalysis considers hypochondriasis a narcissistic neurosis. Finally, we must add here that what is ego-close, the body, the subject, becomes the center of things for anyone engaged in continuous self-observation; therefore depersonalization may be charac-

---

[15] This point by-passes the role of aggression in depersonalization, which according to clinical evidence is salient.

terized as the experiencing of everything in relation to one's own person, not in relation to the object.

Dynamically we express it thus: interest (i.e., libido) is withdrawn from the external world, and this is the cardinal symptom of the incipient neurosis. Every neurosis begins with such withdrawals, the final result of which is a concentration of libido on one's own person.[16] As this process progresses, the world becomes increasingly shadow-like and finally fuses into one with the body. In the depersonalized patient this process reaches only a certain point, so that he remains aware that the world has not changed, but only appears changed to him; the psychotic feels that the world has really changed. A fantasy or delusion of world-destruction comes about, and in the Schreber case Freud (217) first showed this to be a withdrawal of libidinal cathexes.

Occasionally one sees depersonalization-phenomena in the transition from the waking state to a hysterical twilight-state[17]: particularly frequent is the estrangement of the perceptual world, where only the cathexis of the immediate situation is withdrawn, while the cathexis of the world in general, even if only of a fantasy world, remains. Clearly, depersonalization is one of the nuclear problems of psychology and psychopathology. Basically, it ushers in every neurosis and psychosis; it serves as the key for the understanding of certain nihilistic delusions in depressives (remarkably enough, cases of anxious depression frequently complain of a loss of ability to image) and of the world-destruction fantasy in schizophrenics; for normal psychology, it elucidates the mode of experience of estheticism and the meaning of full and pure experiencing.[18]

It is noteworthy that self-observation, which represents negation, exerts in many cases no significant influence on the execution of actions, though Pick (624), in his study of movement, found that it can be disturbed by attention centered on it (see above). Repression, as seen in hysterics, is an extreme effect of those forces that negate experiences; delusions and hallucinations are their positive effects. The repression of an experience appears to leave the foreground of experience essentially unchanged; but to keep down the repressed continuously requires an expenditure of drive-

16 For a detailed discussion, see Freud (241, 242).
17 Cf. Brenman et al. (101).
18 Cf. Schilder (737).

energy, which must be withdrawn from foreground-experiences.[19] In the twilight-state it is reality that is repressed, so that twilight-experiences are meager. In both the twilight-state and its negative, the repression of hysterics, a significant amount of energy is withdrawn from foreground-experiences. Consequently, the foreground-experiences will imply a lesser part of the personality's interests; and this meager experience will also be unsteady, since it is in continuous danger of being over-run by negating tendencies.

We have become acquainted with the following kinds of personality-experience: 1) full experiencing; 2) meager experiencing; 3) negated experiencing; 4) experiencing impoverished by repression.

The theory of depersonalization presented here is based on an extensive investigation of my own. Oesterreich (588, 589), following Wundt's psychology, undertook to explain depersonalization by a lack of feelings, and failed to see that these feelings have succumbed to repression; they are negated or denied feelings. If, as Oesterreich assumes, there were a lack of feelings, the good objective achievements of many depersonalized patients could not be explained except by assuming that the feelings have lost all their dynamic value; and this assumption contradicts Wundt's theory of feelings, which Oesterreich has taken as his point of departure. Recently Schneider (756) devoted a study to the phenomenology, and Giese (276) to the clinical problem, of depersonalization. The theory presented here is in its phenomenological aspects related to Pfaender's (603) and Haas's (310) views, whose conception of the ungenuineness of feelings in depersonalization seems to me of fundamental importance. Nevertheless, this significant phenomenological insight must be supplemented by the insights of psychogenetic psychology,[20] which show in every actual case that negation does not come about or exist without cause, which in turn is always represented by definite drive-directions; or, to express it more correctly, negation arises always from definite and clearly circumscribed experiences.

Depersonalization is thus the resultant of contradictory experiences; when it occurs in conjunction with an epileptic twilight state, or with the inception of a schizophrenia, the effect of the

19 For a fuller discussion, see Freud (216, 227).
20 For a preliminary discussion of this point, see Rapaport (660).

organic disorder is merely to bring more into the foreground the experiences in question and their drive-directions. Indeed, one of the crucial propositions of our psychological theory is that an organic brain-lesion never destroys anything psychological; it only causes psychological processes to alter their course, and existing attitudes to change their form of appearance. Psychoanalysis has taught us to see that a commonsense psychology, which is familiar with single experiences and their effects, represents the state of affairs more truly than a psychology which is built of sensations, images, and feelings, instead of experiences and drives.

The syndrome of depersonalization is encountered in various neuroses and psychoses; thus, we have no right to assume that specific mental symptoms should be ascribed to specific psychological changes. It often appears in normal persons also in conjunction with déjà vu (cf. Heymans, 344, 345; in the section on déjà vu above). In general, all the phenomena of psychoses may be encountered in normal persons, but the stand the total personality takes toward them is different. We must ask ourselves about every psychopathological phenomenon: what part of the individual's personality is expressed in this?

3. THE EXPERIENCE OF TIME[21]

Physical and psychological time. Feeling-processes, sensation-processes, and time-experience. Relation of time-experience and rhythm. Complication experiments. The present is not a physical concept. Meaning of rhythm.

Only now, after our glimpse into the nature of the ego, can we approach the problem of time-experience. To understand "psychological time," one must free oneself from the physical concept of time. Bergson (61) was right in pointing out that infinite acceleration or slow-down of time would not alter the equations of science, but would radically alter the mode of experience. The flow of time is intimately related to the course of life and psychic processes. The present is a concept which has meaning only in relation to experiencing personalities. The inanimate has no past, present, or future.

Wundt (897) stresses that the experience of time is attended by characteristic feeling processes, which are connected with internal touch-sensations, usually accompanying both rhythmic and arhyth-

21 For literature concerning the experience of time, see Schilder (750, Chapter 13), Fenichel (180, pp. 282 ff.), Eissler (161 a). For developmental and comparative studies, see Werner (870) and Piaget (614), Rapaport (654, pp. 229–231), Rapaport (658, pp. 336–337, 360–361); also Stevens (808, Chapter 32), for a survey of experimental studies.

mic touching movements. The rhythmic sensations mediated by walking (tension alternating with release) should be particularly important; the various rhythmically ordered experiences would in time order themselves to the common tempo which is time-experience proper. Meumann's (551, 552, 553) and others' experimental investigations show that a rhythm is imposed upon auditory sense-impressions just as on movements. During the sequence of two tones we have a direct experience of time, which corresponds only approximately to objective time; it is now underestimated, now overestimated.

Though Wundt's considerations point out important partial factors of time-apprehension, they overlook the basic fact that it is "I" who lives in time, who strives from the past into the future. Therein lies a further unanalyzable basic fact of psychological life. Temporal-experiencing is closely interwoven with central attitudes; pathology as well as everyday observation shows that it is radically altered by the extent to which I am completely involved in a task or am in contradiction with myself.

Cases of depersonalization, whose total experience is splintered, all have an altered perception of time. In extreme cases, time seems to them to be at a standstill, or the present seems to be like the distant past. Revault d'Allonnes (27) has shown that these patients nevertheless show no objectively demonstrable disturbances of the time-sense. Are there any? In the Korsakow-syndrome, with its severe temporal disorientation, there are none.[22] Klien (425) has described epileptic states in which everything, one's own speech as well as the movements of others, seems to be speeded up. In the delirium of hashish, time seems to last an eternity.[23] In none of these cases was the estimating of short time-spans studied, however. Klien thinks that the sensory impressions fade too swiftly or too slowly, and thereby alter the experience of time. This issue is by no means settled yet (cf. Pick, 627). Besides this sensory factor of time-perception, Klien recognizes another related to the central attitudes of the personality: he speaks of psycho-energetic temporal signs.

To my mind, naturally, this central factor is important. Pathology knows no instance in which the patient loses his direct

[22] For a review of the pathology of the experience of time, see Rapaport (654, pp. 229–231).
[23] Cf. Werner (870).

experience of the present; so we may assert that it is unjustified to try to compound time-experiencing out of feeling-processes and sensations, even if they can alter it. Indeed, it is a question whether there is a stringent relationship between rhythmization and the experience of time at all, and whether the psychophysical tendency to rhythm, which experimental psychology has succeeded in demonstrating, does not simply depend upon time-experience. This assumption would be supported by a lack of anything rhythmic in the perception of time and by its uniform flow. In our view, experiencing time is most closely related to personality, is not compounded of rhythmic sensations, and is indeed the prerequisite for the perception of rhythm.

The life of every person is ordered into a temporal series, and naive observation assumes that this temporal series corresponds to the objective sequence of experiences. However, in his so-called complication-experiments, Wundt has shown that simultaneous impressions of disparate sensory areas are apprehended at varying times, depending on specific conditions of attention. Given two simultaneous stimuli, one acoustic and one visual, first one and then the other will appear to precede. Clearly, sensory material is not directly introduced into the temporal series, but is first elaborated. Let us keep in mind that not isolated elements, but wholes, are apprehended. A melody appears as a whole, though objectively it is extended in time; and we experience its first tone differently than we would experience the same tone in isolation, even when a "physiological" influence of the last tone on it is out of question. A uniform series of metronome-beats is rhythmicized and divided into a series of groups: this would not be possible unless the three or four tones of such a group were apprehended as a whole, in spite of their objective temporal distances. This implies, however, a principle important for psychology at large, which we have already encountered in discussing the formation and comprehension of sentences, and which also shows us that physical time and the present are not identical with each other.

While time-experience is a basic phenomenon of psychology in the narrower sense, rhythm appears to be a basic biological fact, though we encounter it continuously in psychological phenomena also. A few random points follow; it would lead us too far afield to study the nature of the various rhythmic processes and their relation to each other. All life-processes are rhythmical. The cycle of growth and propagation is just as rhythmic as heart-beat and breathing; uniform sequences of noises are grouped rhythmically, and walking shows rhythmic phases too; and there is rhythm in drive-gratification and renewed striving, as well as in their reflection in feelings. Rhythmic activity is more easily performed than arhythmic, and Buechner has shown how rhythm intervenes in and facilitates work. The pleasure in rhythmic movement always breaks through, in running, in the dance, etc.; and it is worth remembering that primitives ascribe a magic significance to dancing. Rhythm, arising from biological depths, pervades psychic life.

A principle which is related to rhythm may be termed motive-repetition.[24] Rhythmic activity always repeats something identical: rhythm is return. We find this pleasure in repetitive return in ornamentation, in the motif-repetitions of music, and in the course of thought too we encounter the same motif again and again. One might be led to surmise that the human psyche is always striving to represent anew what it has once experienced; naturally, the new presentation may be changed in its details.

4. PERSONALITY[25]

Goals of the personality and adopting of goals from people of the environment. Identification and mastery of reality. Ego-ideal and body. Formation of ego-ideal. Representation of ego-ideal in psychoses. Censorship. Adler's "directives." Will-to-power. Energy-source of repression. Splitting of the ego. Cases of double consciousness. Multilayeredness and inconstancy of ego-ideal. Psychology of suicide. Ego-ideal and neurosis. Partial restructuring and conservation of the ego-ideal in neurosis. Ego-ideal and psychosis.

We will now turn to the consideration of the personality, by which we mean all of the ego's experiences and its attitudes in so far as they have come to expression in experiences. We subsume under personality the experiences of loving, hating, choosing, preferring, valuing, in which the ego of the person manifests itself;

24 Cf. Schilder (752).

25 In this section Schilder again tackles various problems of ego-psychology. In the background of his considerations hovers the question, how to conceive of the role of an ego in a psychology of drives? The treatment is piecemeal and no solution is reached. Cf. Schilder's (749) later statement of the issue, also the attempts of present-day psychoanalytic ego-psychology to solve this problem (321, 318, 320, 321 a, 656, 657).

but we also include all the externals, such as influence, power, clothing, position.[26] We speak of personality where the ego has manifested itself in specific experiences.[27] All these experiences have a common factor; a common principle underlies them. Here we come in touch with everyday usage: we speak of a man's true and false personality, and by that mean whether or not the ego has manifested itself fully in the experiences in question.

We speak of a consciousness of the self, referring to the ego's observing its objective experiences—that is, its acts; and we speak of a consciousness of the personality, when the ego scrutinizes its subjective experiences. As the prototype of changed consciousness of personality, we might cite those experiments of Richet with hypnotized people in which, for instance, he gave a servant-maid a suggestion which made her into a general. One might assume that the personality is built of sexual partial-drives and of ego-drives, the latter being directed at object-values, such as maintenance of one's own person and subservience to the goals of society. Psychological observation, however, indicates that these matters are far more complicated. It is in the nature of education that we cannot set ourselves goals as we please; rather, they are transmitted to us by the people who raise us. The recent psychology of language-development has irrefutably shown that the child does not create language according to his own needs, but takes it over from adults, though his own organization also helps in this process; similarly, he adopts his goals from his environment also, for example the goal of cleanliness.[28]

The primitive youthful organism seeks to gratify its drives by the shortest path. As already shown, drive-objects have no structure articulated according to the laws of things, but shade into one with the body. The full structure of reality is not amenable to the child; he is not yet adequate to it. The child is biologically dependent on the people who take care of him. His relation to these people must therefore have definite laws. They appear to the child first of all as objects of his erotic tendencies, but also as mediators of other drive-gratifications, e.g., food-needs, and as

26 Schilder's later intense interest in the social process and its role in psychological development and dynamics is not yet reflected in this volume. See, however, Schilder (745, 746, 748, 749, 752 a).

27 Cf. Schilder (690).

28 Cf. Piaget (612, 617), but also Werner (870).

obstacles to certain of them. For instance, undoubtedly he has inclinations to derive pleasure from playing with stools and urine; he gives these up only reluctantly under the compelling force of education. In this process the adults appear as the compelling elements of reality, and adaptation to their demands is adaptation to reality; an idiot, for instance, is incapable of this.[29]

The child's attitude toward his environment is in many ways quite tyrannical; his tendency is to make use of his environment and to become master of it. Here the aggressive drive and the tendency to master reality are coupled, and the pleasure in mastering reality implies sexual pleasure also.[30] The pride in and love of one's own body and power (narcissism) are there to begin with; but later they spread to thinking and, in general, to one's whole mode of experiencing, one's whole personality. The tendency to master reality has the character of a drive, it is in its nature dissatisfied and insatiable: as soon as it attains a goal it creates a new one, and in this respect it is quite like the sex-drive.

The child soon recognizes that mastery of the external world is simply not always possible, and that, in comparison to adults, he is at a disadvantage. To catch up with them becomes his new directive, his new tendency. Here we have the levers for the identification that comes about between the child and his educators; the father is the most important of these, since he is the most successful in mastering reality.[31] By identification the child himself becomes the father; but he expresses this identification not only in single symptoms, but also in setting himself quite definite goals. There is not only an affectionate attachment, but also a more or less complete imitation in action: it is a followership. In identifications we must distinguish two aspects, one the identification proper, the other the ego-projection. Initially the ego-projection is very incomplete: the "ego" can be displaced only into the child's own body. But now suddenly the body with its drives loses its hegemony; it faces a new, a less tangible ego, which has arisen from the identification with the father.

[29] Concerning the relation of drives, ego-apparatuses and adaptation, see Hartmann (321).

[30] But compare Buehler (122) on "function pleasure," Hendrick (334, 335) on the "drive for mastery," and Erikson (166, particularly Chapter VII).

[31] For the concept of identification, see Freud (239) and Fenichel (180). But note that the general role of identification in mastering reality to which Schilder points has been little appreciated.

Here there is an advance in the ego, a new stage which relates to the rest of the ego as the father to his child (Freud, 239). This psychological ego, which we love even more than the bodily one, we can call the ego-ideal or superego, and we see in it the resultant of a series of identifications. That is, later on the child identifies not only with the father, but with other people who teach him and raise him; particularly in puberty these identifications with teachers and leaders play an extraordinarily great role. Man's goals and purposes, his striving after ideals, all have come about on the detour through identification.[32] His strivings are not only toward positive goals, but toward the suppressing of drive-impulses which are not compatible with such goals. Here then is the censor, the repressing institution; and here too is the germinal form of conscience, because the ego-ideal reproaches us even for the past.

It should not be assumed that the identification underlying the ego-ideal must remain hidden. Actually, for many individuals it becomes the leading motif: they want to become like a certain other person. Many students try to walk in the footsteps of the master, many sons in the footsteps of the father. Nor must it be assumed that the ego-ideal is built on identifications alone; other drive-strivings too find their fulfillment in it. In other words, the formation of the ego-ideal depends in part on erotic bonds, in part on other drive-strivings: that is, it is built of drive-constellations just as complicated as those of the neurotic symptom. On the one hand various partial drives, on the other the demands of adapting to reality, come to expression in it.

In certain psychoses, this ego-ideal becomes personified, and scrutinizes all of the individual's experience to find objectionable drive-impulses. In alcoholic hallucinosis, the composite figure of conscience dissolves into a manifold of single persons, becomes again the voices of society (Freud, 217, 225): the patient hears criticizing or cursing voices. In one of my schizophrenic patients the ego-ideal was represented by his surroundings, which reproached him continuously for being a homosexual among other things. The mass of exclusively male criticizers also represented

---

[32] While "identification" is one of the important factors in the development of the ego and socialization, it is certainly not the only one. Schilder himself saw that man is born with the equipment of the potentially social animal (749, 750). See, e.g., Ginzberg et al. (281) for the insufficiency of identification to explain vocational choice and for the role of "equipment" in such choice.

the object of the proscribed drive-impulse. The ego-ideal is formed only after a conflict between drives. Uninhibited ego-drive would as little need to form an ideal as would uninhibited sex-drive. The ego-ideal serves basically to gratify both: it is a compromise-formation, just like the neurotic symptom.

It makes an essential difference what relation the ego-ideal has to the other components of personality, whether it is mild or strict toward them. Everyone has times when he sets high demands for himself, and others when he is more lenient. In depression, where the patient continuously accuses himself of worthlessness, we are faced with excessive demands by the superego. In mania, the individual sets himself in place of his ego-ideal (Freud, 233). It is Adler's (11, 12) merit to have pointed out the enormous significance, for the entire psychic life, of those "directives" which each individual sets for himself. It must be admitted that the theme of power plays a significant role in these. Adler speaks of man's attempts to maintain his manly role (the masculine protest) and points up the techniques and tricks used, particularly by neurotics, to maintain mastery and power in spite of a dim awareness (feeling of inferiority) that they are inadequate to meet the situation, to maintain power and rule. No doubt, this conception implies recognizing the significance which attaches to the intendings of reality-structures, both of social life and inanimate nature. After all, one may consider sexuality too as a part of reality which demands objective mastery; sexual problems are, indeed, always problems of the total personality. Naturally, one must not forget that the goals of sexuality are more egotistic and lead back to the body, rather than outward into the world. Freud reduced the mastery of reality to the pressure of necessity, and I believe he was not quite justified in doing so: to my mind there is also a drive implied, namely, what Nietzsche called the will-to-power.[33]

Freud (225) himself considered narcissism the link between ego-drives and sexual drives. He meant by the ego both the ego-drives, in the narrower sense, and narcissism; ascribing to it the functions of reality-testing, conscience, and self-observation. He

[33] It is still an open question whether we must introduce a plurality of drives, or whether the double set of libidinous and aggressive drives within the framework of a structural (ego-id-superego) framework is a conceptual tool sufficient to apprehend psychological phenomena. Indeed, it is still possible to resort to a monistic drive-theory.

also maintained (239) that the ego has a particular relationship to the system Cs (consciousness). The nature of repression is understandable only by means of the understanding we now have of the total personality. Since the ego binds to itself both ego-drive and libidinous energies, the sources of energy for repression are now clear: ego-drive and narcissistic energies feed the repressive mechanism, and these energies are connected with the images and thoughts which come about under the influence of the ego-ideal. Thus, every impulse seems to arise against the ego, as it were, and dividedness of the personality seems to be more the rule, harmony more the exception; or more correctly, the two parts of the personality strive for unity, but as soon as unity is reached, division begins again.[34] Clearly, the unifying tendency of thinking reflects, in essence, the same state of affairs.[35]

The question arises whether one can nevertheless speak of a unity of the ego.[36] The divisions just mentioned are all within the realm of the ego, and pervaded by the same unitary basic tone. Indeed, it seems to be the essence of the ego that it is multifarious in its unity. This statement itself takes a stand on the phenomena of the so-called cases of double consciousness, the most famous of which is Azam's.[37] His patient Felida had two quite distinct psychological states. In one she appeared quiet and reticent, in the other gay, cheerful, and inclined to frivolous carelessness. In the first, her normal, state, she was altogether ignorant of the other; but in this other she had clear cognition of the first. Other cases of this sort show that many variations and transitions exist between clear cognition and unawareness of the "other" state. Azam's case and the related cases of Mitchel (560), Prince (638, 639), MacNish (526), Wilson (888), Bourru and Burot (97), as well as Janet's (377) artificial[38] Felida, differ only in regard to the amnesia from those more easily understood cases where various aspects of the personality arise in salutatory fashion.

That this amnesia is due to repression needs no further

[34] For the relation of the instinctual drives, see A. Freud (200).

[35] Cf. Nunberg (582) on the synthetic function of the ego, also Appendix, p. 345, infra.

[36] See Freud's (248) last discussion of this issue.

[37] Schilder refers to Azam (39); for a review of the literature on multiple personalities, see Rapaport (654, VII, 4. c.).

[38] I.e., hypnotically induced.

demonstration, in view of our discussion of memory. The difference is merely that these patients deny a part of their personality, and it is this denial[39] which manifests itself in amnesia. A part of the experiences of the personality is not tolerated by the ideals of the personality. These ideals, i.e., directives, fluctuate, presumably according to whether gratification has or has not been reached. Every fulfillment leads to the setting of new goals, and our ego-ideal fluctuates with our drives. The ego-ideal need not be a simple structure; rather, several such ideals may stand side by side. The constancy of personality depends on these factors, based on drives, which in turn are rooted in organic ground. This point is demonstrated by the fluctuations of ego-ideal encountered in circular psychoses. But there are fluctuations of a purely physiological character also. Note in Dostoevsky's *Brothers Karamazov* the following passage:

". . . forgivable, if we consider that he was a man fifty years old, that is, he had already reached the age at which a clever, well-situated man of the world becomes ever more respectful of his own person, even if without noticing it."

The value which man attaches to his ideals, to his ego-ideal, is enormous: he experiences it as a piece of himself. Self-love, which originally pertained only to the body, is extended to the psychological personality and its goals. We experience continuously our value and valuelessness; and even when we despise ourselves our emphasis is on the despiser in us, as Hebbel understood very well. It is questionable whether anything living can renounce a self-value; self-condemnation may be the strongest expression of the tendency to regard one's own person as perfect. Even the suicidal person passes judgment on himself, and by his action redeems his value.[40] We arrive at the general proposition that one of the basic characteristics of everything psychological is to hold fast to its essence, to its belief in its own value.

The example of suicide may give us some understanding of the finer structure of these matters. Statistics show that suicides are somehow related to economic conditions; that they are more frequent in urban than in rural populations; and that there are certain ethnic groups and segments of the population in which

[39] This is again not the defense-mechanism of "denial" in the technical sense.
[40] Cf. Schilder and Bender (744).

the inclination to suicide is particularly pronounced (cf. Weich-brodt's[41] recent study). All this teaches us little about the psychology of suicide. Psychological study points to a number of superficial motivations which again may be divided into two groups, corresponding to our general schema: social and erotic. The social motivations show a great variety of shadings, such as poverty, disappointed ambition, loss of social position. If we go deeper, however, we find in the suicide sadistic impulses directed against his own person.

An example will illustrate this state of affairs. A thirty-year-old man is admitted to the hospital with superficial cuts, inflicted with his pen-knife, on face and chest in the neighborhood of his heart, at which a shallow stab has been made. A fight with his beloved preceded this. She had feared he would do something to her, and to prove her fear groundless, he reported, he made this suicidal attempt. It is transparent that her fear was not unjustified: he had such intentions but rejected them, and the sadistic impulse turned against himself. Presumably this also implies a self-punishment for the hostile intention. The consequence of repression here is that the drive turns against one's own person (cf. Freud, 226); but the act also implies an identification with the beloved. So we see again that identification may result in the emergence of a partial personality, and is often incomplete: the patient is both judge and defendant, though he is not aware of this. Here too we see a splitting of personality. Often we find, as a motivation in the outer layers of the psyche of suicidal persons, the intention to sadden someone, or to make him understand an injustice; it is only a cover for deeper-lying strivings. Freud (233), to whom we owe our knowledge of this process, assumes that the suicidal inclination of depressives rests also upon a turning of sadistic impulses against one's own ego. Great as the psychological probability of this view may be, I have not yet found it empirically corroborated. In any case, suicide appears to be a way of doing justice to the demands of the ego, the personality, and maintaining self-value; and the manner in which this task is mastered simultaneously gratifies deeper-lying drives.[42]

From this vantage-point we begin to understand the genesis

41 See Weichbrodt (862); cf. also Durkheim (152).

42 The aggressive meaning of depression and suicide is here—as too often—by-passed: the depressed person by his state, and the suicidal person by his act, is directly aggressing against those attached to and surrounding him.

of actions in normals, and the origin of neuroses and psychoses. The neurotic is continuously faced with tasks he does not succeed in mastering, with structures he cannot, but according to his ego-ideal should, master. If he does not want to give up his old goals, or turn to new ones by altering his demands toward life, he must so transform reality that he can master it. Here is the very source of neurotic regression: gratification on a higher level is interdicted, whereupon gratification on a lower level occurs. But the ego-ideal remains unaffected, and thus the demands of society are recognized. Naturally, parts of the ego-ideal must be restructured. Neuroses may be characterized as permitting drive-gratification, on a lower level, while maintaining the ego-ideal.

Psychoses take a different path: the ego-ideal itself is decomposed to permit gratification. While in neuroses the process is closely linked to an external conflict, in psychoses the decomposition of the ego-ideal occurs in relative independence of the task to be mastered: the task of reality-adaptation is no longer achieved.[43] In psychoses, satisfaction with one's own person—maintenance of one's experience of self-value—is possible only by an alteration of the ego-ideal; in neuroses, the personality maintains its self-value at the price of distorting reality.

Every neurosis and psychosis thus begins with the experience of self-value becoming shaky; and they represent simply the restoration of self-value[44] by either a change in ego-goals or a restructuring of reality. Mayer-Gross (545) has observed that, after an acute psychotic episode, schizophrenics build up their ego, and by means of this new-built ego repress the memory of the episode. In the acute catatonic episode, according to Nunberg (580, 581), and in general paresis, according to Ferenczi and Hollos (184), there is a decomposition of the ego-ideal. The ego-ideal is the carrier of the relations to reality, to the external world[45]; consequently, when it is decomposed, an unarticulated world demanding drive-gratification takes the place of the structured world. The

[43] This formulation oversimplifies the actual state of affairs; cf. Freud (241, 242).

[44] Here we see Schilder developing Adler's ideas which, under the heading "self-esteem," became the slogan of the neo-Freudian schools. For the treatment of self-esteem in the framework of psychoanalytic theory proper, see Fenichel (180); cf. also Hartmann (320).

[45] It is unclear how this could be the case. If it were, the ego-ideal would perform a lion's share of ego functions.

more primitive the drives, the less articulated the world. With the development of higher drive-levels, ever more essential parts of reality are apprehended: there seems to be a close parallel between the drive-level and the possibility of apprehending reality-structures.[46]

The theory of ego-ideal and superego goes back to Adler's (11, 12) theory of directives. However, it was Freud's discovery of the significance of identification for the ego-ideal that opened the way to essential progress: cf. his *Group Psychology* (237) and *The Ego and the Id* (239). Clearly, the term ego-ideal embraces a group of very complicated processes which are all interrelated, and still in need of detailed exploration. The danger of being seduced by this comfortable concept into neglecting individual analysis must be avoided. For discussions of the experience of self-value, see Storch (809) and Stern (802).

5. ATTITUDES TO ONE'S OWN ILLNESS[47]

"Stand" to pain. Stomach-disorders. Movement-disorders. Exercise-treatment of tabes.

After these discussions, necessary for the understanding of the nature of one's psychological attitude and of the forces which act in it, we may state that such stands permeate and dominate the tasks of everyday life. Only the person's concrete goals and intentions can make all of his drives fully comprehensible to us.

The attitudes people take to their somatic illnesses are of particular importance to us. We have become too accustomed to regard the symptoms of somatic illnesses as direct expressions of local processes which are tangible on the dissecting table. Nothing could be less correct. There is no doubt that discomfort and pain travel a long psychological route before they appear clearly in consciousness. My attitude toward my pain determines what effect it will exert on me. In this respect it is noteworthy that, on vestibular stimulation, paretics occasionally do not feel or acknowledge nausea, though they show all its somatic indications. The manic does not feel pain at the height of his excitement. But pain in a joint will determine whether or not the person will move it. If one succeeds in disregarding the pain, then the limitation of function usual to the organic disorder will not come about, but this

---

[46] This appears to be a cardinal and little appreciated corollary of ego-development: not only establishment of delay and detour, but also the differentiation and "taming" of motivations, affects, and experiences are crucial aspects of ego development. Cf. Rapaport (656, 660).

[47] Cf. Schilder (740, 749, Chapters 9, 10, 11, and 731); for a recent survey, see Barker et al. (44 a).

will not be as a result of an added function. Such considerations may be applied to every somatic illness; and no doubt the stand taken by the patient to it makes his organic suffering appear in a different light. Organic complaints attain different dimensions when bad mood and depression are present.

Remembering what we learned of the somatic influence of affects, it must be noted that the attitude taken, that is, the attention directed toward the organ, cannot be irrelevant even physiologically. I believe that these matters are particularly important in mild organic disorders of the gastro-intestinal tract: whether an organic disorder of the stomach will cause vomiting is in great measure dependent upon the stand the individual takes toward it. Not all organic complaints are due to gross anatomic changes; there are toxically determined irritations also, the effects of which must depend on the patient's attitude. I remind the reader here that sleeplessness after morphine withdrawal—which is due to somatically tangible toxicity—may be influenced by hypnosis, and that hypnosis may in general be used to save anesthetics. Clearly, there is good reason for internal medicine to be interested in the stand of the patient toward his illness, even if the illness is unquestionably traced to somatic causes. It must be stressed that a patient whose attitude is not directed at overcoming his complaints is not therefore necessarily a hysteric.

The problems of the disorders of movement-organs cannot be solved at all without taking the patient's stand into consideration. Older bedridden patients tend to forget movements, though in such cases the presence of minor organic senile brain-changes may be assumed. Nevertheless, it is by disuse that these patients have unlearned how to cope with their organic disturbances. The case is similar with tabes. It is always baffling to see how tabitic patients with high grades of ataxia become able to use their sensations of movement purposefully through treatment by proper exercise. It is probable that these are cases who, under the first impact of the disorder, had despaired and arrived at an attitude of "not trying any more," which they could not then alter without aid. From varied approaches, we always come back again to the borders of the organic. The exercise-therapy of tabes rests in part on involving visual aids. Taking a stand involves also whether or not possible aids can be enlisted. It would be of the greatest psychological interest to study a group of severely ataxic tabetics from this point of view.

The concept of attitude demands further analysis. We must assume that there are attitudes based on relatively primitive premises, e.g., on the grounds of the body-image, and others on higher levels. A theory of such attitudes will make it possible for us to act purposefully not only in relation to neurotics, but also to the organically ill.[48] It must be kept in mind that, in each attitude taken, the human being appears as a whole personality; and we have seen that it is not solely the store of preserved memories which guarantees the unity of personality, but also its structure. This is of great complexity and multiplicity: it masters partial tasks by means of identifications—splitting the personality—which in final analysis are integrated in a unitary ego.

6. GENERAL CONSIDERATIONS. COGNIZING OTHER PERSONALITIES

Ego and values. Psychological causality. Various levels of psychic experiencing. The organism in service of strivings. Perception of the alien ego. Analogue-inference theory. Empathy-theory. Imitation-drive as pre-stage of identification. Imitation does not lead to cognizing alien experience. Direct perception of alien experience. The genetic problem: how is the inanimate perceived at all? More against empathy-theory. The avenue to apprehending other personalities. Intuitive apprehension. Character types: schizothyme and cyclothyme. Jung's typology. Psychography. Psychoanalytic considerations concerning the theory of character.

We have seen that psychology becomes possible only on the assumption of an articulated world, one which consists of an object-world and a value-world.[49] Of these, only what corresponds to the height of our own organizational level becomes apprehensible to us: a more richly articulated world corresponds to a higher level of organization. Consequently biological organization and value are closely related. Psychology shows that a full personality-experiencing can unfold only in a richly articulated external world, and even there only when experience centers on this ex-

48 Experience with the Kenny treatment of infantile paresis, and with the rehabilitation of amputees, has brought home this point forcefully; cf. Dembo et al. (472, 473, 882), also (554). In relation to psychiatric disorders, the "secondary gain of illness" (Freud 213, p. 336) is one of the problems in point. Others, such as the patient's attitude on entering a hospital, have been until recently little studied.

49 Schilder implies that the articulation of our world of necessity includes hierarchies of value, because object-relations alone do not vouchsafe articulation of and orientation in the world.

ternal world and not on one's own person or self-value. In other words: personality unfolds only when it is directed at tasks and goals, not when it sets its own unfolding as its goal. This inference is drawn from our study of depersonalization, and it may well be considered the criterion for the psychology of ethics and ethical attitudes.[50] Although it is by concrete psychological processes that we gain insight into structures, cognize and realize values, we must not forget, even when involved in psychology, that the worlds of values and objects are beyond those psychological processes and have an objective existence.

Now we must turn to the question of whether ego, person, and personality suffer changes in pathological processes, and if so, what are these changes?[51] From our previous considerations it is clear that ego and person are beyond all pathological processes. The ego cannot be destroyed; only its effects can be inhibited or suppressed. Psychoses change only in the external achievements of the personality, the psychological processes involved abide by causality (cf. Introduction) even if the structure of the mind, of the ego, can by no means be considered a causal sequence. Psychic causality appears accordingly as an unbreakable chain: every psychological experience is followed by a stand taken to it by the individual, which occurs on a different "level." This point becomes clearest if we consider dreams, which show a different kind of stand from that of the waking-state. The attitude taken in dreams is on a lower level, the characteristics of which are a greater wealth of images and of un-unified meanings, and a more explicit retention of the past. This "lower level" approximates what was called "pure memory" by Bergson (63), who has tellingly compared the various psychological levels with a cone, the vertex of which penetrates into the present, while its base represents pure memory. Yet it must not be forgotten that the vertex contains the whole cone in a structuralized form.[52*] Object-relevant actions unify the

50 Cf. Schilder (690).

51 Much as this formulation smacks of philosophical idealism and teleology, it is a bold attempt to reflect: a) the observations pertaining to the unremitting integrative work of the ego, on whatever level these observations occur; b) the experience of the therapist, who in his work even with completely foundered human beings gets some glimpse of what they could have become. Whether or not Schilder's formulation is felicitous, its referents are observations which have not yet been theoretically encompassed.

52* I cannot discuss Bergson's theories in detail here, yet I must under-

entire past, which then chimes along in a muted way, while in lower-level forms of experience the past reverberates more explicity.

In other words, we may speak of displacements of accent within the sphere; but we must distinguish two main forms: one changes the relation of past to present, while the other— the form of dementia—eliminates directly the possibility of apprehending structures. Even in the most severe degrees of dementia, however, the individual past has its effects, and psychological causality is sustained. This second form of disorder is often connected with gross disturbances of the organism; and we come closer to their psychological understanding if we bring the organism into direct relation with the apprehension of the structure of the external world and regard it as an instrument in the service of such apprehension. To do so is justified by the developmental history of organisms. Since, following Uexkuell (841), we can infer the environment of an animal only from its organization, we must consider a progressive evolution as prerequisite for the apprehension of a more richly articulated reality.

So far we have spoken of personality, regardless of whether it was our own or an alien one. We have also evaded the question: how do we arrive at assuming the existence of alien personalities? The earlier naive answer was, "On the basis of inference by analogy." Against this view—recently defended by Kronfeld (464, 465)—Lipps (513) justly objected that the inference by analogy would be that, since the movement of my hand is connected with an ego-experience, my ego partakes in similar hand-movements of others. Lipps consequently developed the concept of empathy,[53*] by which he means: I displace my experience into others, I project myself into others, I feel myself into others; moreover, I displace not only my ego, but also my feelings and passions, into them. The threatening gesture of another arouses in me the instinct of imitation, and by imitation I experience myself as threatening, which I then displace into the other. Now no doubt there are imitative tendencies of a very primitive kind; they are seen

---

score a mistake he made: he totally misrecognized the dignity of action, and therefore did not see that if a return to lower psychological levels has no relation to action, it can be only an apparent enrichment.

[53*] Geiger's (264) review of the literature gives a complete survey of the problem. [See also Geiger (263, 265, 266).]

in children, but also in adults. The barking of the dog prompts
the child to make similar sounds; the horse's running makes the
child run. Watching an acrobat, we go through his contortions
with him, to a mild degree; the crying of others makes our faces
drawn; and we accompany the movement of the bowling-ball with
our own movements. Here it seems justified to speak with Lipps
of an instinct of imitation. Pathology shows us the same phenomena in sharp relief.[54]

There are hallucinating patients who speak aloud what they
hear in hallucination, and others who act out what they see in
visual hallucination—indeed, they become the image which they
see. Quite generally, we may put it thus: every image, every im-
ageable psychological experience, carries within it a tendency to
an action. There are two possibilities: either we act as though we
were the image, or we take a stand to it which lets it be the object.
The behaviors of co-experiencing and imitation are of great importance: they are pre-stages of identification. This statement permits us a deeper understanding of the nature of imitation.

Doubt now arises as to whether by this avenue we can arrive
at cognizing others' personalities: when I instinctively imitate, it
is still my own person which experiences, and we are again faced
with explaining how our own experiences can become those of
others. When I see someone angry, it has nothing to do with my
anger: I do not experience my anger. If I share the anger of a
friend over an injustice inflicted on him, my sharing the anger
stands side-by-side with my perception of his anger, and is essentially independent of it.

Thus, empathy does not lead out of one's own ego, and we
are back at the need to assume an independent apprehension of
alien egos and alien personalities. Just as we cannot reduce perception to sensations, so we cannot compound the perception of
alien egos and personalities out of our own experiences. There is
a direct perception of others' psychological experiences, of alien
egos, which belongs to the basic facts of psychological life and
cannot be further dissected.[55] Naturally, the motives originating

54 Cf., however, Piaget (617).

55 Schilder centers attention here on a grossly neglected problem of psychology (and psychotherapy). His avowal that the phenomenon is not further
analyzable is called into question by Piaget's (617) observations; but it should
be an antidote both to Miller and Dollard's (559) view according to which this

in our own psychological life do play into this apprehension of other people; but I no more perceive an alien ego by projecting my feelings, affects, and strivings, than I perceive by projecting my sensations. Objective observations on children indicate that all events of the external world are regarded by them as psychological happenings, as acts of will, which clearly implies a primitive ego.[56] In other words, in certain developmental stages of childhood, every object is animate; and genetically it would therefore be more correct to ask how we arrive at the assumption of inanimate objects, rather than at that of psychological existence in others. The crowning point of the magic world-view of primitives is that all events are reducible to will-causation.[57] Connected with this is the view that every part of the object contains the will equally. Only later do the child and the primitive renounce the assumption that all effects are effects of someone's will.

The perception of the inanimate seems to have its main source in the perception of the immobile. Thus, if a genetic derivation be undertaken at all, the inanimate would have to be reduced to the animate, not vice versa. Lipps does not limit the theory of empathy to the perception of other personalities, but assumes that we can empathize with inanimate nature also. A landscape appears to us sad or gay; the thunder is angry; the column strives upwards, or braces itself against the crossbeam. But these too are qualities of objects: the gay landscape is not gay because it makes me gay; in spite of its gaiety I can be despondent. The column does not strive upwards because I stretch upwards, but because this is its quality as an object; feelings adhere to objects, and only this makes it possible for our apprehension of things to be continuously enriched. If all of it came from within us, it would be incomprehensible how we could ever apprehend other individualities: the world would be a hopeless mirror of our own individuality, and there would be no experience.[58]

It must be admitted, however, that the affective mechanisms discussed (particularly ego-projection, and projection in gen-

---

too, like everything else in their universe, is learned, and to the frequently encountered "psychoanalytic" view that it is a product of "projection."

56 Cf. Piaget (611), also Werner (870).

57 Cf. Levy-Bruehl (488), Werner (870).

58 See the reference to projection in footnote 55, supra. For a similar view, compare also Koehler (435).

eral) do continuously intervene, modifying the basic process of simple perception; and moreover, that even correct cognitions may come about in this way. When my affectivity is correctly attuned, I will project into others only those portions of my own experience which by their nature objectively justify being projected. Nonetheless, we must assume that a framework of objective perceptions of what is alien to us exists independent of any sort of projection, and is actually the prerequisite for projection. The whole theory of projection and identification would be untenable if, on the one hand, we were to assume the existence of personalities of others, and on the other, deny them by relegation into the category of projections. The final boundary-line between "I" and "you" is in any case drawn by affectivity.

We can apprehend another's total personality intuitively; and this is what we do every day, and with great accuracy. Bearing and intonation, facial play and gestures tell us infinitely more than can be expressed verbally. Expressive movements, the articulation, intonation, and word-choice of speech, are all intimately connected with affectivity and drive-life. F. Krueger (466) has shown that there are musical differences between the same sentence uttered as assertion, as doubt, as question, and as joyous announcement. In these expressive movements we see not only the other's affects, but also his nature. Physique too doubtless gives essential information about the personality. These things have been made scientifically tangible by the observations of Kretschmer (457). I spoke earlier of a direct communication between the unconscious (system Ucs) of two persons. If we conceive of a person as the totality of all his attitudes, then we can see a bridge leading from the understanding of single actions to the understanding of the total personality. The single attitudes of an individual do not stand unrelated, side by side; in each of them the total personality is implied. Even in everyday life, a mean action at a decisive point suffices for us to say the one who committed it is a mean character.

There are many attempts at classifying characters. The most significant seems to me Kretschmer's (455, 457), which pursues the two great types of psychoses, circular and schizophrenic, into types within the normal range. As mentioned, he divides people into cyclothymes and schizothymes. For him, the psychological tempo and the moods are decisive. To the first type belong, on the one hand, the soft natures inclined to sadness, sympathetic and empathic; on the other, the gay, active, clear-headed, deliberate men of success. To the second type belong the cold, unapproachable, rude natures, who are now fiery and fierce, now cool and calm; despots, bossy people, unpredictable moody characters whose feeling-life is hard to understand. The first type, more oriented and tied to reality, is encountered among empirically-oriented scientists, humorists, epic poets; the second type is more frequent in speculative philosophers and dramatists. Though this theory of types does not account for the full range of reality, it is at present the most promising beginning for the scientific mastery of these problems.

It is far superior to Jung's (396) typology which distinguishes an extroverted and an introverted type: the extroverted is oriented toward goals in the external world, the introverted sees things in the mirror of his own self. Even less satisfactory are the results achieved so far by psychography, which attempts to characterize the individual by means of psychological tests.[59] In such undertakings one must consider the order of experiences both in cross-section and in longitudinal (that is, temporal) sequence. The psychographic investigation must consider ability to learn, power of memory, knowledge, observational ability, vividness of imagery; also the tempo of development, speed, etc.; moreover, motor skill, cleverness, relation to and independence of other people's opinion, adaptiveness, general work-ability (whether constant or spasmodic, persevering or not), moral attributes (just, truthful), recreations (games, reading, art), general mood, attitude toward self (self-awareness), attitude toward others (sympathetic, critical), reaction to attitudes of others toward him or others (social), attitude to reality (practical), sexuality, factors of stability (religion and ideals—according to Wells, 869, and Froebes, 258). Extensive details on this topic will be found in Baade (40), Lipmann (504) and Stern (800).

We are indebted to psychoanalysis for important information concerning personality-types.[60] First of all, it has demonstrated

[59] Schilder wrote this before the many advances made by psychodiagnostic testing (see, e.g., Schafer, 686) in the last three decades. Although these have met many of the requirements Schilder sets forth, his subsequent familiarity with them seemed never to overcome his initial distrust.

[60] Cf. Freud (228), Abraham (6), also Fenichel (180).

with certitude that the painstakingness, steadiness, and orderliness of compulsion-neurotics is related to certain drive-attitudes. Furthermore, it has demonstrated that penuriousness, thrift, is beyond question connected with anal drives,[61] and that self-appraisal has to do with narcissistic drives.[62] Naturally, here again it proves extremely difficult to decide which aspects of a character-picture are constitutional and which due to experience.[63] We can establish, particularly in those neuroses that we cure, essential differences between the neurotic and the non-neurotic personality; and this is important because broad segments of neuroses do reach into the realm of so-called normality. The affects of hatred and mistrust may spread from single experiences to the entire psychic life, and finally make the personality appear in an entirely different light. All these matters completely escape the psychographic approach, because, though in theory it demands consideration of the longitudinal section, in reality it remains a consideration of the cross-section.[64]

7. Geniuses and Their Creativity[65]

Interest and organ. Mastery of object-structure. Organ-inferiority. Supernormal memory. Pathology in the genius. Two phases of artistic creativity. Execution of the ingenious conception. Genius and psychosis. Nature of inspiration and its relation to the ego. Psychology of conversion. Ecstasy of mystics.

We come to the question: how are truly great gifts to be understood? Perhaps two factors, ability and interest, should be distinguished. Ability might be thought of as closely tied to the

61 Cf. Freud (210, 230), also Abraham (6).

62 Cf. Freud (225).

63 For a comparison of the older and the more recent approaches to this problem, see Freud (223) and Loewenstein (517).

64 Schilder here again spoke out clearly on an issue which under the headings "normality" and "mental health" has only recently been treated in the psychoanalytic literature, and even now not decisively. (Cf. Glover, 283; Waelder, 858; Jones, 387; Hartmann, 317; Knight, 430; Hacker, 312.) Yet he seems to have been mistaken about the relation of psychodiagnostics (psychography) to this problem. It has not eluded psychodiagnostics; they have contributed considerably to its clarification.

65 Though many psychoanalysts tackled fringes of this problem (for a review of the literature see Levey, 487), only Kris (460, 461) faced its core as Schilder does. With Schilder the approach remained mainly a program; Kris has put forth concrete evidence and progressed to specific theoretical implementation.

organ, and interest as coupled with affectivity in general, sexuality in particular. This sketch requires further explanation. The organs of individuals are no doubt not all of equal value. We know little about the details of it, but specific gifts seem to go with specific brain-organization.[66]

For instance, the development of the central gyri on the brain of Menzel is striking; and according to Pfeiffer (604), the development of Heschl's transverse gyrus is a measure of musical endowment. Moebius (562), following Gall, relates mathematical endowment to certain parts of the left frontal lobe. One might assume that particular development of the corresponding parts of the brain would follow interests, and that one could attempt to explain these interests by purely psychological connections. This assumption has, however, little probability if taken exclusively: true, quite a few endowments, such as those for music and mathematics, manifest themselves early; but many interests just as intense as those of geniuses are never followed by mastery of the object of interest. It must be assumed that particular endowments consist in the successful direction of interests into a particular area: that is, the brain-apparatus in question must be moldable by the interest.[67]

Thus, no doubt, there is a psychogenesis of endowments, but success depends on factors which have nothing to do directly with the binding of interests and affectivity. Yet it appears that the possibility of mastering a certain area, which an endowment offers, maintains interest in that very area. Endowment in the visual field makes for seeing more of visual structures; and this binds the interest, once it has turned there by chance, continuously in that direction. The mathematical genius discovers characteristics of numbers which others do not see at all. Let us remember that Gauss, as a child, had already made his school-assignment easy by discovering the characteristics of arithmetic series—namely, that the sum of their first and last members must equal the sum of the second and the penultimate, and that therefore the sum of the

[66] While the assumption of a relation of specific talents to specific brain-organizations is certainly untenable, our present-day theoretical understanding of ego-apparatuses (321, 658) and of vocational choice (281) does support the assumption of some connection between talent and ego-apparatuses.

[67] Cf. Hebb (328). The hypotheses Schilder puts forth here appear promising and not eclipsed either by alternative ones or by empirical findings.

series must be equal to half the sum of the first and last members, multiplied by the total number of members.

Let us note that not only scientific, but artistic endowment too discovers new structures of objects. This requires particular apparatuses. The genius is a discoverer of object-structures in the scientific, artistic, or ethical realm: he encompasses parts of reality which are not easily amenable to others.[68] Adler (11) attempted to demonstrate that organ-inferiority initiates a development of psychic superstructure upon the organ. He considered the example of Demosthenes to be typical, and referred to Beethoven's deafness. We can admit that organ-inferiority facilitates the turning of special interest to the organ; yet inferiority cannot be considered a necessary condition, and the empirical facts speak against the generalization of this mechanism, however important it is in individual cases. This view would not be vitiated by the demonstration of the close relation occasionally observed between higher cerebral development and peripheral inferiority.

It is not the interest alone that is decisive, but the increased ability to apprehend object-structures, an ability which surely is closely related to cerebral structures. So far, hypernormal memory is the most closely studied phenomenon of this sort, and it has been demonstrated that interest plays a great role in it. G. E. Mueller's (569) subject Rueckle used a wealth of aids in memorizing his long rows of numbers in an amazingly short time; he grouped the numbers and ordered them—and he could group and order them only because, due to his interest in numbers since his earliest youth, he knew their characteristics intimately (see above, p. 158). Here too the crucial role of interest becomes clear.[69]

Thorough knowledge of the so-called pathological is prerequisite for the understanding of the so-called healthy and normal. According to the view developed in these pages, the phenomena of neurosis are but changes of the level of effects of personality; and these changes may be considered as due to inhibitions and obstructions. But who is not subject to such inhibitions and obstructions? Let us note also that the dream is altogether similar to the phenomena of psychosis, and that every thought must pass through

---

[68] A unique definition binding all areas of creativity into unity. Cf. Rapaport (652).

[69] Cf. Bartlett (46); also (658, Part VII).

a dream-like, psychosis-like, phase before it reaches final maturity. Actually the lives of great men show greater or lesser deviations from the so-called normal. Indeed, more or less clear psychotic phenomena are found in many: Hoelderlin became schizophrenic, Lenau and Nietzsche perished in paresis, K. F. Meyer had a psychosis belonging to the manic-depressive form-circle, Strindberg was schizophrenic and Dostoevsky perhaps epileptic, Van Gogh had a psychosis of schizophrenic character, Rousseau was paraphrenic [cf. Birnbaum's (77) survey]. This list could be extended indefinitely, and even in the lives of apparently healthy people we find puzzling features bordering on psychosis: Moebius (562) described such features in Goethe. Lombroso (520) deserves credit for having opened up this field of problems, even though he was mistaken as to particulars and failed to recognize the real relationships.

The urgent question is: how are mental illness and valuable achievements compatible? First we must remember that the psychiatric-clinical concept of mental illness is not a negative valuation. The biological concepts of health and sickness do not imply ethical valuations. A person mentally ill in the psychiatric sense may well be a valuable personality. Nobody has seen this more clearly than Dostoevsky; *The Idiot* depicts an epileptic who, though intellectually disturbed, must be considered an ethical genius. The value of a piece of art is independent of whether or not it was created during psychosis.[70] Recently Prinzhorn (640), in an excellently illustrated volume, has made accessible many valuable paintings and sculptures of schizophrenics. Jaspers's (381) studies of Strindberg and Van Gogh show irrefutably that these artists created when they were already psychotic. Past periods have persistently compared inspiration and ecstasy with psychosis, and the question arises whether psychosis is not even a prerequisite for valuable creation.

Earlier we saw that those transactions which make possible a rich apprehension of reality take place in the sphere. In psychosis,

---

[70] Kris (460, 461) has put forth considerable evidence and developed a theory which seriously calls this proposition into question. Kris does not simply negate this formulation, but shows that it answers the wrong question. The creative invention—as Schilder also discusses below—is followed by an elaboration which changes it from magic into communication. The work of the ego in elaboration often fails, or in psychoses may even be in abeyance.

however, the spheric experiences become pronounced and fill the foreground; renewed connection with banal everyday thought is reached only later, when the illness becomes chronic. In place of closed, stereotyped, rigid thoughts, there comes a more live process; thus it seems plausible that psychosis can be a prerequisite of artistic creation, by liberating thinking from its rigidity and reviving its freshness and originality. I cannot help feeling that the poems Hoelderlin wrote at the beginning of his illness are among his most beautiful.[71] Naturally, as illness progresses, the possibility of apprehending relationships and approaching things becomes ever more limited: then not only are the stereotypes shattered, but the outlines of things beyond the sphere are no longer seen. The enticement of works of art consists essentially in that, though they point to new object-structures, they do not forsake the sphere. Unclosedness and manifold meaning are the main characteristics of artistic fantasy, in contrast to scientific thinking.

We must distinguish two phases of the artistic creative process.[72] In the first, the individual tears himself loose from preconceptions which he must overcome, he dissolves the customary differentiated forms and adaptations; thinking remains on some primitive level within the sphere. If it remained there, it would be an unformed dream, without an avenue back to the world of objects. But in the second phase, creative activity begins with a new adaptive process, a new formation, which evaluates in terms of reality the relationships acquired by having descended into the sphere. Thus, the degree of regression alone will not decide whether the results of the dissolution will be valuable; the tendency to return to objects, from this submersion in the sphere, will also play a role. The degree of regression that is the optimal condition for creativity is an open question. Psychosis can achieve only the necessary breaking-up of burdening prejudices, can only shake off the bourgeois man, and thereby prepare the unfolding of the pure personality.

Ingenuity is, in final analysis, only the ability to see things in a new light. This ability has two components: first, that creative

71 A systematic study of critical responses to Hoelderlin's poetry might provide an objective test of Schilder's vs. Kris's theory.

72 Here Schilder anticipates Kris's theory and gives one of the most sensitive impressionistic accounts of creativity we have, though he does go to excess in extolling the "liberating" effects of psychoses.

force which we encounter in the thinking of every child; second, a particular talent which goes further. If one observes schizophrenic episodes with an unprejudiced eye, one often sees that a ray of ingeniousness breaks through, so that the patient appears to rise above his usual existence. The admiration we pay to children's actions and sayings also hints at the heavy sacrifices exacted of us by adjustment to the everyday world.

The work of art in its multi-colored images still shows the tendency towards reality; thus it gratifies the demands both of object-structures and of the sphere. Purely descriptively, we may say that all experiences of inspiration, whether artistic, religious, scientific, or practical, imply the tendency either to return to reality or to die away in the twilight of dreaming. If Schopenhauer's *The World as Will and Idea* emerged in him in the form of a single idea (and there is no reason to doubt his statement) then the very conception implied the possibility of, and tendency to, its final formation. The formative process may be disrupted by later vicissitudes; and when so often the admirable ingeniousness of schizophrenic conceptions does not lead to final creation, it may be the fault not of the conception as such, but rather of obstructions concomitant with increasing withdrawal from reality. It might be put thus: the potentiality of schizophrenic experiences is often extraordinary, but cannot unfold.[73]

This brings us to a new aspect of the matter. Great energy is needed to execute the possibilities of mastering reality offered by inspiration and ecstasy. Much that was ingeniously conceived trickles away for want of self-confidence and force. When in manic phases self-confidence and force mount, and inhibitions are brushed aside, execution may also be facilitated; thus mild manic phases may be regarded as prerequisites for happier activity, but only if the excess energy is brought to bear on a real conception. If it leads to decreased self-criticism and overestimation of the conception, the result will be a forceful execution of unimportant things—a caricature of this being those people in state hospitals, who are active continuously, move constantly, fill stacks of papers with their doodlings, and whose restlessness leads to no fulfillment.

[73] In this paragraph Schilder appears to come near to contradicting his previous point and reaching the formulation Kris put forth later. Cf. particularly footnote 70, supra.

This basic schema may help us to understand the relation of genius and psychosis. Moebius (562) is probably right that parts of *Zarathustra* were written in the beginning of Nietzsche's paresis: general paresis has manic phases. In the *Ecce Homo* the manic excitement is obvious; but *Zarathustra* is a majestic work, and even the *Ecce Homo* contains values that are more significant than those in many non-psychotic writings.

What is the relation of inspiration to personality? Inspiration seems to break in on its recipient, and creative people always stress that it came over them without their doing, "unconsciously"; they speak also of *"grace"* and often refer it to an active principle external to their personality.[74] There can be no doubt these are ego-experiences; indeed, the experience of inspiration is representative of the total personality; it unifies all its tendencies and is the expression of all drive-strivings, which imply the past, present, even the future of the person. This is unification itself, the absolute antithesis of depersonalization; and in it the personality finds its purest expression. It is the clearest indicator that full experiencing is possible only when we pay attention not to experiencing as such, but only to the object: we are most purely ourselves when turned toward objects. The full unfolding of personality is vouchsafed by the rich variability of the world, and every real inspiration has for its object not simply the world, but an articulated structured world. This much we learn from phenomenology. Considering the genesis of inspiration, we note that it is preceded by a continuous occupation with the object, a continuous wish to penetrate and obtain mastery over it. Inspiration always lies in the direction of attitudes, whether these are drives in the narrower sense or of the decisions of the will. Attitudes prepare the ground for inspiration; and if in the moment of inspiration the preparatory work of drives is not conscious, then this is a case of the disregard or repression of our own psychic experiences that we have so often encountered above.

It is instructive to consider in this context Starbuck's (788) studies of the psychology of sudden conversion.[75] According to Starbuck, it makes no difference whether or not the will is set

---

[74] Cf. Kris (461, Chapter 13) "On Inspiration."
[75] Cf. James (374), also Moen (562 a), Burney (127), and Bergman (59).

in motion in these experiences; and regardless of the direction in which it is set in motion, the crucial step of psychological renascence is that the personal will is given up—though it seems necessary that, before this happens, the individual should have striven toward the new life. Before the experience of conversion there is a feeling of imperfection and doubt; there are feelings of "incompleteness": "I feel a longing, a restlessness, a painful emptiness which the world did not fill," or "I feel mentally and morally twisted," or "I had a desperate feeling of helplessness." During the conversion itself: "I fell beside my bench on my face, and attempted to pray, I made a last effort to call to God for mercy, because I was about to choke and die; and the last thing of that time I remember was that with the same invisible hand on my throat, I fell backwards on the ground. As I came to, a throng was around me praising the Lord; all the heavens seemed open, rays of light and glory streaming down." According to Starbuck, attention is narrowed and concentrated. The following illustrates the moment of transition: "I felt the Lord's condemning judgment come over me, as over all who refused to accept Christ as their saviour. After much effort to avoid God's mercy, I finally gave in. That night the Lord did not give me as clear a proof of his accepting me as he did next morning when I walked in the forest alone. I will never forget the sweet peace of soul I had then." Or: "I felt sorrow over my sins, but an unspeakable feeling of joy came over me."

After conversion "the ego rises to a new significance": "I felt I belonged to a new category of creatures, nobler and more worthy to exist. The Bible was a new book for me. I read it with joy and felt that its commands were all warnings and promises to me." "Nature seemed to feel with me." "Suddenly light and peace came into my soul as tenderly as the sun rising on a June morning. Earth and heaven seemed to unite. All was love . . ." Converts mostly feel as though they were living in a new world. "As I rose from my knees, I cried: 'The old is gone, and everything is new now.' " "It was like an entrance into a new world—a new state of existence . . . My spiritual vision became so clear that I saw beauty in every material object. The forests resounded with heavenly music." "Day and night, floods of light and glory seemed to stream through my soul; and oh, how changed I was! Everything was new. My horses and pigs and everybody were changed." "I felt the unfolding of truth and the unveiling of the ways of God. I experienced a moral and intellectual revival." Conversion is accompanied by the feeling of great bliss. "I felt joy so great that I nearly cried." "The bliss was intense, I could have sung, but the whole house was quiet." "Now followed a marvelous feeling with love toward God."

One of the immediate results of conversion is that the person is internally driven to active sympathy with the external world. Here it becomes clear that the course of conversion follows a quite general scheme: doubt, and the overcoming of doubt. We will understand these primitive attitudes better if we consider the situations of life in which they occur, rather than if we try to understand complex formations from analyzing primitive experiences. The feelings of imperfection, and the doubts preceding conversion, correspond to a clash of drive-attitudes, and to the apathy of attitudes from other levels. Doubt is the reflection of experiencing contradictions fully; even when the doubter does tend to a certain view, it is not with the whole of his personality; some ego-tendencies oppose it. True, doubt is a continuous internal struggle for belief and certitude, but it is inherent to doubt that the character of intending is changed so that these are not attainable. But the doubt itself indicates whether it can be overcome or must remain un-unified: there exist both victorious doubt and doubt which implies a lasting inability to come to rest. Both forms are rooted in drive-attitudes, and the conquest of doubt is equivalent with the unification of motivations. I stress again that every object-experience shows a layering that reaches down to the earliest experiences of childhood, and that drive-attitudes attach to these layers also. The unification of contradictory tendencies, the surmounting of doubts, represents anew the picture of action, of decision . . .

Starbuck's studies appear significant from yet another angle. They pertain mainly to American Protestants, particularly Methodists. Conversion in the Methodist sense is a sudden transition from an imperfect to a perfect life, which usually occurs within a certain age-period. In women the first maximum is at 13, the second and more important at 16, and the last at 18 years of age. In men it is the 12th, 16th, and 19th years of life. This suggests that the somatic factors of puberty must play a role here too; and I want to point out again that the effect-value of psychic experiences depends on purely somatic factors also.[76]

Let us note that the psychology of conversion and doubt throws light not only on many everyday experiences, but on neuroses too. Here I refer to what was said about depersonalization and the significant role of doubt in compulsion-neuroses. Furthermore, there are psychoses which follow the course of doubt and conquest of doubt; this is particularly observable in acute schizophrenic episodes, where the conquest of doubt is possible only at the price of neglecting reality and the emergence of archaic formations. It is worth noting also that conversions are frequently accompanied by hallucinations, or at least by awarenesses which are not objectively justifiable.

Studying the dynamics of such a process, we find them determined by previous drive-attitudes. No doubt conversions and mystic experiences are in general fed by sexual energy and libido: genetically considered, the ecstasy of the mystics is not conceivable without converted sexuality. Leuba (486) speaks of a tendency to sensual pleasure in Christian mystics: their language and similies are erotic, they speak of marriages, intoxicating excitement, bodily joys, and the Virgin Mary appears in their prayers as the Lady of their longing and rapture. Indeed, occasionally we hear of ejaculations and, in women, orgastic feelings. But nothing would be less correct than therefore to see mystic ecstasy only as sexuality, and fail to recognize the unique specificity of the experience. We come again to the recognition that the dynamics of an event clarify neither its value nor its phenomenological character. It belongs to the basic facts of the existence of the psyche that it unfolds always afresh, and spreads out into multifarious, ever new forms; and though the sequences can be explained from the dynamisms, the inexhaustible wealth of psychic formations cannot.

[76] No systematic studies since Starbuck's in 1909 seem to have been made. It is a promising field of exploration. Starbuck's age-data gain further significance in the light of Erikson's (166) studies.

APPENDIX

PAUL SCHILDER'S CONTRIBUTION TO THE THEORY OF THOUGHT-PROCESSES[1]

DAVID RAPAPORT, PH.D.

Ladies and Gentlemen,

I feel awed and privileged to be here to give your Schilder Memorial Address—awed by the task of sketching Schilder's contribution to the theory of thinking, and privileged by the opportunity offered. Let me hasten to say that it is due to Dr. Lauretta Bender, and the chance by which she discovered that I am familiar with and have studied most of Schilder's writings, have become involved in them and, through them, in the man Paul Schilder. I became acquainted with Schilder's writings in the course of my studies on the psychology of thought, over the last fifteen years. I am delighted to have the opportunity to talk about Paul Schilder.

Let me tell you why by way of a story: there was once a king who was entertaining another one. And since he was the king who had originated the idea that a king should have a cabinet, he introduced his cabinet to his guest. The guest asked who was the most important member of the cabinet. The king pointed to one so far not introduced. "And what is his portfolio?" asked the guest. "Oh, he is the Minister without Portfolio"—and seeing the bewilderment of his guest, he added—"He knows what the rest of them are doing, and tells me about it." That is how I feel about Paul Schilder. Indeed there is hardly any area of psychiatric and psychological problems which Schilder did not recognize, tackle, and illuminate; scarcely a syndrome which he did not study, whether schizophrenia, mania, depression, aphasia, amentia, paresis, or Korsakow; hardly a function which he did not explore, whether memory, perception, consciousness, motility, language;

1 Schilder Memorial Address given to the Schilder Society, New York, 18 January, 1951. First published in *The International Journal of Psycho-Analysis*, Volume XXXII, Part IV, 1951.

few indeed are the problems with which he did not deal, whether they pertain to the form varieties of conscious experience, psycho-somatic relationships, neuro-psychological interrelations, episte-mological foundations of our relation to reality, or the nature of man's socialization; and exceptional the psychiatric phenomenon or symptom which he did not describe, whether depersonalization, *déjà vu*, or body-image. His was an encyclopaedic mind—he was a psychiatric polyhistor in our time.

I would like to discuss three topics. First, I would like to demonstrate that it is worth while for psychiatrists to be concerned with the theory of thinking, indeed that the theory of thinking is in a way a measuring rod of the status of the theory of psychiatry. Second, I would like to discuss some of the salient contributions of Schilder to the theory of thinking, demonstrating that in many ways he pointed ahead to theoretical developments which we have only recently reached, and to much that is yet to be reached. Finally, I would like to discuss the present state of psychiatric theory—characterized as it is by competing factions—to establish Schilder's position in this picture, in the hope of contributing something to the understanding of the role of the individual sci-entist and of the meaning of factions in the development of a science.

I

Let us then turn to the theory of thought-processes. What is the basic paradox with which any broad theory of thinking has to cope? Excepting a few "die-hards" all agree that human be-havior, and thus human thought also, is motivated by funda-mental needs, drives, or instincts, if you please. Yet human thought so motivated is adapted to the reality of objects and society. How to reconcile the motivatedness with the social, as well as objective, reality-adaptedness of thought, is the basic paradox faced by the psychology of thinking. Indeed this is the question faced by every psychiatrist treating every patient. But in therapy the patient's own synthetic forces, as well as the psychiatrist's intuition, steadily cope with this problem and prevent it from emerging in stark nakedness. In theoretically treating this problem no such merciful disguises obtain; the stark nakedness of the problem becomes threatening and the paradox has been faced only but by a few giants. Freud saw it clearly. He described those thought-processes which prevail when primary, unconscious motivation exerts its effect directly, as for instance in dreams. He discerned and described their mechanisms, such as condensation, displacement, substitution, symbolization, and labelled them the primary process. He saw clearly that in everyday life, superimposed over the thinking organized in terms of the primary process, a different kind of thinking obtains which abides by the laws of logic and is adapted to social and objective reality—this he labelled the secondary process. He devoted incomparably more interest to the exploration of the primary process than to that of the secondary process, and it may seem that he solved the paradox by erecting a dichotomy.[2] Actually in the seventh chapter of "The Interpretation of Dreams" (204), in "Wit and Its Relation to the Unconscious" (207), and in the papers "Formulations Regarding the Two Principles in Mental Functioning" (216), "Repression" (227), "The Unconscious" (229), and "Negation" (243), he laid down the cornerstones for the exploration of the secondary process, and indicated that he did not regard the dichotomy as hard and fast. Not only was this little noted, but two decades after the first publication of "The Interpretation of Dreams" we find Freud complaining in a footnote to a new edition that, even as regards the primary process, people were concerned mainly with rules of thumb for finding the latent dream-thought in the manifest dream-content, and utterly disregarded the dream-work by which the latent thought is translated into the manifest content,—that is, the primary process. He reiterated that the dream was primarily a thought-process. He was aware of the fact that his followers became interested, to the exclusion of almost everything else, in the content of thought.[3]

Here then is the first demonstration of how the theory of thinking becomes a measuring rod of the status of psychiatric theory: lack of interest in theoretical foundations is early expressed by disregard of thought-processes in favor of thought-content. The central role of the theory of thinking in psychiatric theory becomes more generally clear if we call to mind that, for instance, the obsessional person is one with a certain personality organization and drive dynamics, but that the obsessive compulsive activity, characterological or symptomatic, is prepared for by thought-processes which are interposed between the personality organization and drive dynamics on the one hand, and the obsessive compulsive behavior or symptoms on the other. And this also holds for other kinds of personality structures and their expression in behavior. Personality organization and drive dynamics

[2] Cf. Rapaport (655).
[3] See Freud (204, pp. 466–467).

translate themselves into behavior and symptoms through thought-processes, and indeed the psychiatrist in his everyday work deals with these mediating processes rather than directly with the symptom or directly with the personality. Direct dealing with the symptom we usually regard with healthy skepticism, and as for dealing directly with the personality, we do not even know how to go about it. While content often serves as a reliable guide to the relation of symptom and dynamics, fundamentally only the dynamics, economics, and topography of the thought-processes give full information as to what is going on. Our intuition may in everyday practice make concern with the formal characteristics of thought-processes unnecessary, but disregard of them will certainly leave us out on a limb when confronted with theoretical claims such as those of Sullivan or Fromm—in one word, the culturalists who, having become involved with the role of culture in personality organization and pathology, claim for it the crucial and exclusive position in personality development. What they disregard is again that without the understanding of the mediating processes, which are thought-processes—in the broad sense in which I use this term here (658)—there is no understanding of socio-cultural impact, and that without understanding of motivation and mediation there is no understanding of socialization. Psychoanalysts often retreat from facing the paradox of motivation vs. socialization and reality-adaptation of thinking, to an exclusive concern with basic motivation and thought-content as its indicator. The culturalists also retreat from facing this basic paradox of the theory of thinking, to an exclusive concern with socialization and adaptation, and the derivative motivations corresponding to these. We can make clear the error of the culturalists only if we do not make the opposite error of considering thought and behavior only in its motivated and not in its adaptive and socialized aspect as well.

II

Let me turn now to Schilder's contribution to the theory of thinking to show that he did not make either kind of retreat. Schilder faced squarely the question of how thought can be both motivated and adaptive-socialized, which is tantamount to the question of what is the relationship between the primary and secondary process. He saw clearly that primary-process phenomena, such as are encountered in dreams, free association, schizophrenic and other pathology of thought, are also present in the course of normal thinking. We know that Freud was aware of this

when he wrote: "The tendency of the thinking process must always be to free itself more and more from exclusive regulation by
the pleasure-principle . . . but we are aware that this . . . is
seldom completely successful . . . and that our thinking always
remains liable to falsification by the intervention of the pleasure-
principle" (204, p. 536). Schilder, however, went further and
demonstrated in various studies summarized in his paper, "On the
Development of Thoughts" (695), that thought-formations seen
in thought-disorders appear in normal thinking as preliminary
phases of problem-solving, remembering, etc. Thus he arrived at
the bold generalization that every thought of the human individual undergoes a development before it becomes conscious in its
final form. He asserted that this development proceeds from indefinite to definite forms, passing through associatively related ideas,
and that in the early phases of this development, imagery is more
prevalent, and personal affective influences—that is, primary-process mechanisms—play a greater role than in the later phases of the
development, which are increasingly object- and reality-oriented.
Accordingly, he considered the pathological forms of thought to
result when these processes of thought-development come to a premature close, bringing to consciousness forms which are normally
only preliminary phases of thought-development instead of completed thoughts. He also inferred from his observations that even
when such thought-developments reach completion, image-like
and affect-distorted preliminary developmental forms may come
into consciousness alongside the completed thought. It is clear—
and Schilder said so—that this conception was based on the idea
that ontogenesis recapitulates phylogenesis, a pattern so prevalent
in the thinking of the beginning of this century. We need not discuss here the validity of this bold assumption. Some aspects of it
have been borne out by recent empirical investigations; compare,
for example, R. Schafer (685a). Schilder, however—unlike Stekel
who offered a similar conception in his "The Polyphony of
Thought" (795a)—was not satisfied with this solution. Indeed this
conception of thought-development would imply that whenever
any thought comes to consciousness it is preceded by a battle of
the Titans, enacted by all our fundamental impulses, reaching
down to and shaking the foundations of our psychological existence, only to give birth to a meek mouse of an idea. Schilder
had to get away from this conception, and he did. He studied with
great care an array of thought-disorders; aphasia, agnosia, Meynert's amentia, paretic and other dementias, schizophrenia, and
neuroses. He came to the surprising finding that in all of these

disorders the same fundamental forms of thought-disorder were present (752). He described these in great detail, and in summary stated that they all boil down to this fact: the whole cannot be differentiated into parts, and the parts cannot be integrated into a whole. What then is the distinctive character of each of these disorders? he asked. The answer which he gave was this: the psychic apparatus is so built that its central core of impulse-dynamics is surrounded by means-layers which serve it in expressing and executing the impulses. The layer of perception and verbalization is the one farthest removed from the central core. It has an autonomous synthetic function of its own, which is the one affected in aphasic and agnosic disorders. The perceptual material synthetically integrated by this means-layer of the psyche serves as raw material for the apperceptive means-layer, which integrates it on another level establishing the object-relationships of the percepts. This integrative, synthetic function is the one affected in Meynert's amentia. The material thus integrated in turn serves as the raw material of another means-layer of the psyche which integrates and evaluates it conceptually. This is the synthetic function affected in dementia. The process of final, personal integration in terms of drives—operating by methods we would call the mechanisms of the primary process—is laid bare in dream-work, in neurotic symptoms and schizophrenic thought-disorders. Everywhere the pattern of the thought-disorder is the same, but its substratum in each disorder is a different one of these means-layers.[4] This conception, however vulnerable, and in parts outdated by more recent explorations, contains factual discoveries and theoretical assumptions which have only recently been approximated by psychoanalytic ego-psychology, through the studies of Nunberg (582), Hartmann, Kris, and Loewenstein (321, 318). It implies the assumption of ego apparatuses which have a relative autonomy and serve drive dynamics as an integral apparatus.[5] It implies the recognition of synthetic functions layered over each other in a hierarchic series. It implies also the recognition that the secondary process is not as a whole juxtaposed to the primary process, but that there is a whole series of levels on each of which derivative motivations, progressively further removed from the basic drive, bring about primary-process-like phenomena, counteracted or replaced by more and more successfully socialized and reality-adapted secondary-process phenomena.[6] To show more concretely

4 See Schilder (752, pp. 566–568, 577–580).
5 See Rapaport (656).
6 See Kris (460). Compare Rapaport (658, Part VII).

Schilder's insight, let me present to you his discussion of the relation of common slips of the tongue to the parapraxes of aphasics.
We all remember Freud's discussion of the nature of parapraxes:
that if, when robbed of my pocketbook in a dark street, I complain
to the police that darkness robbed me of my money, I am mistaken,
because darkness provided only the occasion for the robbery.
Similarly—he continued—we are mistaken when we attribute slips
of the tongue to fatigue, which gives only the occasion for impulses
to break through in the form of slips of the tongue.[7] In discussing
aphasic parapraxes Schilder shows that they are not specifically
related to repressed impulses as are our common slips of the
tongue. The synthetic function inherent in the process of verbalization is itself affected in aphasia by an organic damage, and therefore the parapraxes are diffuse and not impulse-specific. Yet we
know that when an aphasic becomes excited his parapraxes also
become more pronounced and specific, even though the disorder is
otherwise diffuse. In turn, with normal people the more fatigue
and other general factors interfere with the effectiveness of the
synthetic function of verbalization, the more occasion is given for
the impulse to do its slip-producing work. Indeed the relationship
between diffuse thought-disorder and specific impulse interference
with autonomous psychic apparatuses is nowhere in our literature
presented with the lucidity of Schilder's discussion.[8] Not even in
the Silberer-Jones controversy,[9] which had the same core, did it
attain such clarity. Silberer (782) claimed that the hypnagogic
state by its very nature, owing to its low energy level, is conducive
to symbolization, while Jones[10] insisted that only repressed impulses are symbol-producing. Whatever the final fate of Schilder's
theoretical construction may be, he did point out with unforget-
table clarity the fact that thought-disorders do become diffuse and
generalized, and it is rather the exception for them to be specific
and traceable to single impulse dynamics, as are common slips of
the tongue, and that there is a fluid transition between the dynamics of a diffuse and an impulse-specific thought-disorder.

Schilder, having recognized the fluid transition between the
primary and secondary process, the multiple layering of synthetic
and controlling energy distributions—which Hartmann, Kris and
Loewenstein (319) recently described as the progressive neutraliza-
tion or binding of drive-cathexes—proceeded to create a conception

7 See Freud (205, esp. p. 50).
8 See also Schilder (752, pp. 565–566).
9 See Nachmansohn (575, esp. pp. 283–284).
10 See "The Theory of Symbolism" in (388).

of the thought-process in keeping with the conception of autonomous means-layers, or as recent psychoanalytic ego-psychology would put it: in keeping with the conception of autonomous ego-apparatuses.[11] I shall choose four salient points to sketch Schilder's conception.

III

To outline Schilder's view of the thought-process, I shall attempt to sketch his conception of the motivation of thought-processes, of the nature of concepts, of anticipations, and of judgment.

Motivations. Our task would be easy if Schilder had anywhere directly expressed himself concerning the nature of the motivating forces of the thought-process, but it would have been quite unlike him to do so. We must not forget that, though a man of insatiable thirst for facts and unceasing urge to make sense of these facts by hunch and theory, Schilder was not a systematizer. There can be no question that instincts, drives, and libido were to his mind the ultimate motivators of psychic events. There can be no question but that he was aware of their role at every point of the way. But when it came to the motivations of thought-processes we hear him talk about tasks, goals, determining tendencies, readiness, attitudes (*Einstellungen*), intentions, interests, strivings, affects, drive-orientations instead of drives. In other words, as soon as he began to talk about motivations of thought-processes other than the pure primary thought-process, his terminology was other than that of libido, drive, or instinct. This much is obvious to anyone who studies his writings. From here on it takes work—at times arduous work—to discover what he means. One has to wander from his *Brain and Personality* (729) to the "Studies Concerning the Psychology and Symptomatology of General Paresis" (752), and from there to his *Mind: Perception and Thought* (750), and painstakingly piece together Schilder's concept that the motivations of thought form a hierarchy, all deriving from the fundamental drives, all having an autonomy, that is, are capable of exerting their motivating role, once they are stimulated either by more fundamental motivations or by perceptions from the external world. Thus, not only do the means-layers of the psyche have a hierarchy, but so do the motivations of thought. This conception may remind one of the more recent—or let us say Neo-Freudian—conceptions, in which defensive structures and the energies related

[11] See pp. 56, 72, 104–105, supra.

to them are considered to be basic motivations of human behavior, as in Horney and Fromm. The difference is only that Schilder never forgets, or lets us forget, that higher-level motivations derive from the more fundamental ones, even though he remains keenly aware of the relative autonomy of the former.[12]

Schilder conceived of the role of motivations in thinking as follows. An impulse—which to begin with implies an object-directedness—is checked (or as Freud would have put it: delayed in discharge), either by another impulse or by structural characteristics of the psyche. Such checking, braking-effect, or delay, gives rise to thought which in itself is both an indicator of the lack of fulfillment of the impulse and a carrier of the undischarged tension. Thoughts so arising develop from an indistinct, imageless, and wordless form into more distinct image-like and verbal forms, by being again and again modified by other similarly developing thoughts and structural obstacles. Thus thoughts, being resultants of both impulses and of delaying influences, express not only the original impulse and its object, but also these intrapsychic and the objective delaying influences; they become progressively more reality-adapted, point the way to the object in reality, and so fulfill the original aim of the impulse.[13] What is not fulfilled by the diffuse, imageless thought is fulfilled by the discrete image, what is not fulfilled by the discrete image comes closer to fulfillment by the process of verbalization, and what is not fulfilled even by the verbalized thought is experienced by us as meaning; and this final residue points directly to the object of the impulse and cannot be fulfilled except by the action on the object toward which the impulse was originally directed.[14] Thus Schilder carried a long way further what Freud sensed and expressed when he wrote: thought is experimental action with small quantities of energy (216, p. 16).

Concepts.[15] This still was not specific enough for Schilder; he was not satisfied with the realization that the process of thought can be initiated by motivations from any level of the motivational hierarchy, either by intra-psychic or external perceptions, nor with the implied recognition of the relative autonomy of the levels of motivation. He seems to have reasoned: if thought leading to action can be initiated on any of the autonomous levels of motivation, then thought itself must also have relatively autonomous building-stones (707). These he found first of all in concepts. He

12 See pp. 197 ff., supra.
13 See pp. 190 ff., supra.
14 See (752, pp. 528–530).
15 See (752, pp. 528–529); also (695, pp. 515–518).

was aware that ethnopsychology argues that primitive concepts are action-concepts, that is, for a dog trained to jump on a chair the verbal signal "chair" means something to jump up and crouch down on, and anything that can be so acted on is subsumed under the primitive concept "chair." In one word, he was aware that primitive concepts refer to things-of-action.[16] He maintained that in order to act one has to have stable objects. In a world of constant change, lacking stability, in a world of piecemeal perception without synthetic integration, no action (that is, intentional action) is possible. He was aware that this is one of the fundamental implications of obsessive and schizophrenic doubt, indecision, and inactivity. This then is where concepts come in: they extract out of the world of objects the most constant and reliable features, and provide thereby reliable orientations and objects for action. Indeed he insisted that concepts which guarantee us the stability of objects are in essence but action-readinesses directed toward specific objects (752, p. 529). Furthermore, he maintained that to be successful, action requires insight into object-relationships, and realized that effective concepts do indeed comprise such insight (752, pp. 522–524). He knew that concepts do not have to be given birth to again and again, every time they come up in our thinking, but once they come about they are at our disposal as ready-made parts, apparatuses of our thinking. They are an expression of, and serve as a guarantee for, the autonomy of the secondary process. He was also aware, however, that in the course of our thinking these concepts undergo progressive growth and remoulding; though they appear ready-made, relatively stable, even quite rigid in some people (for example, feeble-minded) (752, pp. 562 ff.), in others—and at certain times in most people—they can become fluid again. He saw that in creative thinking they are resolved at times even into complete fluidity, only to be reborn from a battle of Titans in an entirely new form, in that of new artistic or scientific invention. He knew that concepts have a constancy, an autonomy, but he knew also that this autonomy is only relative, and creative processes can dissolve it and rebuild it again more richly.[17] He conceived of every concept as surrounded by a halo of connected associations which he termed "the sphere," and believed that it is in these spheres that motivations of any level find concepts to orient them toward finding their object in reality, and lead them to action and discharge on these objects; and also

16 See Werner (870).
17 See pp. 122 ff., supra.

that it is within these spheres that concepts are remoulded in the course of intellectual growth as well as in the heat of creative invention.[18]

Anticipations. But Schilder was not satisfied with inserting concepts and their spheres as autonomous apparatuses to explain the relation and transition between the primary and secondary process. He observed that motivations imply as expectancies the objects toward which they are directed. This expectancy begins even with the drive in the sense that drive discharge becomes possible only in the presence of its satisfying object.[19] Freud showed this and Schilder never forgot it. He also learned from the experiments of Selz that in the course of thought-processes directed toward problem-solving, schematic expectations of the solution precede the solution itself (752, pp. 537–539). It is no surprise that Schilder knew Selz, who delivered one of the first decisive blows at conventional academic association-psychology, for he knew this conventional psychology as well as Gestalt-psychology and Lewin. Indeed with the exception of only a few psychoanalysts who are our contemporaries, he may be described as the psychiatrist most broadly versed in the psychological literature. For these expectations accompanying any and all motivation, he adapted from Selz the concept of anticipation-patterns. Thought does not develop merely from the clash, or delay, of motivations by the structural hierarchy of the psychic apparatus, nor by these motivations using crystallized concepts to guide them to action; but motivations carry with them, to greater or lesser degree, structuralized anticipation-patterns which guide them in selecting the proper concepts.[20] These anticipations, like concepts, are again, as it were, relatively autonomous apparatuses in the service of the thought-process. If we talk about selectiveness in memory, in perception, in thought, we are referring to the effect of these anticipations. It is clear from Schilder's writing that he was guided in his formulation of the role of anticipations by Bleuler's description of hysterical mechanisms as "occasional apparatuses," but it is also clear that he went far beyond Bleuler in perceiving the significance of such apparatuses.[21] Again it is clear that though such anticipations may and do come about anew in creative as well as in everyday productive

18 See Schilder (695, pp. 515–518); see also pp. 330 ff., supra.

19 See pp. 168 ff., supra.

20 See (695, pp. 507–509); also (750, pp. 324–325, p. 271); also (752, pp. 532–537).

21 See Schilder (729, pp. 68–70) and p. 144, supra. See also Hartmann (321, pp. 392–396).

thinking, many of them, once crystallized, stay with us and guarantee the reality-adaptedness of the thought-process and the socially shared character of communication.[22] For instance, if I now say the word "although," I have elicited in all of you the anticipation that I will follow this word "although" with two coordinate and antithetic sentences. Indeed all the conjunctions of the language are verbal expressions of such highly structuralized (automatized) and socially shared anticipations, which, as we know, do not exist in such primordial forms of thought as for instance the dream (750, p. 261).

The conception of structuralization, automatization, of apparatuses implicit in Schilder's view of concepts and anticipations was explicitly and systematically put forth in 1937 by Hartmann (321). This conception proved in Hartmann's treatment to be an inevitable corner-stone in the systematic theory of psychoanalytic ego-psychology.

Judgment. Finally let me discuss Schilder's concept of judgment. It is clear that both in his "Formulations Regarding the Two Principles in Mental Functioning" and "Negation" Freud had set the concept of judgment in the center of the function of reality-testing; yet he left the formal characteristics of this function unexplored. Schilder studied the function in various thought-disorders and demonstrated that judgment, when functioning in relation to action, consists of a matching of the percept of the object to be acted on and the result of the action, with the anticipation and the concept of the object to which the motivation was directed. He also demonstrated that judgment, when functioning in relation to thought, consists in a matching of the anticipation-pattern accompanying the motivation, with the memory-associations of the sphere through which the thought-development had passed. In other words, passing through the various associations of the sphere, judgment matches the various associations met with by the anticipation-pattern implicit to the motivation.[23]

These conceptions alone would seem to be important contributions. Yet Schilder went further. Merlan (549 a) and Bernfeld (64a) recently reported evidence that Freud had studied with Brentano and was familiar with act-psychology and with the philosophy of phenomenology. Indeed those who did text-critical work on Freud's writings have been anticipating something like this, since traces suggestive of Brentano's influence are again and again

22 See Schilder (692, pp. 45 ff.).
23 See (752, pp. 532–537).

encountered in Freud's writings.[24] But here is the difference between Freud and Schilder. Freud digested whatever in Brentano
and phenomenology fitted his purpose and his thinking. Schilder
studied these and set out deliberately to apply their thinking to
psychiatric research.[25] Their thinking fitted in well with his great
interest in describing pathological phenomena. Applying act-psychology to the issues of reality-testing led him to see that human
thinking and consciousness is such that we are capable of having
ideas in our consciousness as specific memories, as facts of general
knowledge, as daydreams, as future expectations, as facts, as assumed, doubted, certain, etc. He showed that it is useful to subsume all these as form-varieties of the function of judgment, and
that without these forms of conscious experience implied in judgment, the refinement of reality-testing, that is, the function of the
reality-principle, would be altogether crude and far short of the
stage it has reached.[26] Schilder's awareness of these forms of conscious experience is so far-reaching that at times he gives the
impression of assuming that these varieties of conscious experience
generalize into autonomous states of consciousness, of which there
again exists a broad, but hierarchically ordered, variety. To my
mind, the understanding of the phenomena of transition between
the waking and the dream state, and of many pathological conditions (for example, fugues, amnesias, schizophrenic blockings, etc.),
is not possible without making some such assumption.[27] But let me
resist the temptation, so great at this point,[28] which would lead me
away from what are certainly Schilder's ideas, to where my own
would inevitably, if imperceptibly, creep in.

IV

Now that I have attempted to sketch the nature of Schilder's
contribution to the theory of thinking, I feel I have delayed long
enough in presenting Schilder's two fundamental points of departure, which he held with an intensity amounting to articles
of faith, and the validity of which he endeavored to demonstrate
in multifarious ways. These two fundamental premises are:

First: human thinking is directed toward an existing world
of objects, and without assuming the existence of such a world

24 See particularly Freud (232).
25 See Schilder (690, 707).
26 See pp. 124 ff., supra.
27 See pp. 105, 269–270, supra; and (729, pp. 11–13).
28 See Rapaport (659).

of objects, no theory of thinking can be built.[29] Clearly this is an epistemological stand, and you may wonder why psychiatrists should be bored with the tedious nonsense of philosophizing, and you may ask who anyhow would doubt such a simple fact. Yet the thinkers of Western civilization, from Heraclitus to Schopenhauer, have struggled for 2,500 years with this issue and offered many contradictory solutions to it. In psychoanalytic writing also there has been a good deal of confusion about it.[30] When thinking is considered only in its motivated aspects, and not in its reality-adaptive and socialized aspects as well, what we perceive may indeed appear as mere projection of the objects of our motivation. Schilder insisted early, just as did Freud in his last writings (244, 246), that human psychic life is not a product of conflicts only. It is Hartmann's (321) merit to have formulated this issue systematically: we are born with apparatuses—those of memory, perception, musculature, etc.—which exist before the ego and id have become differentiated, and which are integrated after this differentiation into the ego, and then subserve its functions. Hartmann realized that these inherited apparatuses potentially guarantee reality-adaptation—providing that maturation and integration take place relatively unhampered. Schilder (707) stated his epistemological stand as early as 1923, and though never advanced to the level of the formulations of Hartmann, the spirit of this epistemological stand permeated all his writings. Projection is indeed a fundamental corollary of the basic motivated nature of thought, and without projection and introjection the formation of the ego, the differentiation of the "me" and the "not-me" is hardly conceivable to those who grew up on Freud's "Metapsychological Supplement to the Theory of Dreams" (232), and *Beyond the Pleasure Principle* (236). Yet neither projection nor introjection are conceivable without the perceptual and motor apparatuses, these preformed and inherited guarantees of human adaptation. Reality-adaptation is not a late acquisition in man's ontogenesis: it is also his fundamental inherited potentiality, though its unfolding occurs in the course of ontogenesis, and is contingent upon the conditions and conflicts of ontogenesis.[31] Schilder was right, and present-day psychoanalytic ego-psychology came to the same conclusion: without this postulate, psychological life is not understandable. If an illusion to the contrary could be sustained in any other area of psychology, a consistent attempt at building a

[29] See pp. 56 ff., supra; and (752, pp. 519–527).
[30] See Hermann (342 a, 342 b).
[31] See Hartmann (319 a).

theory of thinking would certainly break such an illusion to bits.

' The *second* basic premise of Schilder was that socialization, just like reality-directedness, is not an acquisition of thinking or human psychological life, but a basic implication of it.[32] He endeavored to demonstrate this on drive actions and expressive movements, showing that these forms of behavior are already directed to an audience, are communications. He linked language to expressive movements, tracing thus its fundamentally socialized character (752, pp. 524 ff.). He stressed that the very motivations of thought and the corresponding anticipations and concepts imply, to begin with, the socialized character of man, and though experience, learning, and the corresponding development of the higher levels of motivation, anticipation, and conceptual abstraction lead to more and more adequate reality and socially shared (socialized) forms of thought, socialization is not just acquired but lies in the very nature of human psychic organization. Here again Schilder did not break the continuity between drive and primary process on the one hand, and experience, learning, cultural influence, socialization and secondary process on the other, but rather insisted that there is a continuous development from the one to the other, and that socialization and secondary process cannot be understood without realizing the basically, even if only potentially, socialized implications of the fundamental motivations, and of the thought-forms of the primary process that pertain to them. Though deeply interested in all the matters so dear to the heart of the present-day, so-called culturalist, schools of psychoanalysis, he could not afford to forget the fundamental motivations in favor of the higher-level, defensive and adaptive motivations to which these schools resorted as ultimate explanatory principles of behavior.

It is curious to see how the environmentalist and culturalist thinking pushes *learning* into the foreground of psychological interest, and how it is inclined to accept conditioned-reflex and conditioned-response theories of learning. Schilder, however, though he was fully cognizant of and deeply interested in conditioning, saw and stated clearly the fallacy of such a procedure.[33] He argued: though we see complex motor mechanisms built up on simple re-

---

[32] See, e.g., Schilder (750, p. 244): "The body image as well as the object are built by continuous interchange with other human beings; they are therefore socialized. Socialization is thus a fundamental form of human experience." See also (750, p. 261). Compare also Piaget, "Principal Factors Determining Intellectual Evolution from Childhood to Adult Life" in Rapaport (658).

[33] See pp. 152 ff. supra.

flex mechanisms, it would be a mistake here, as elsewhere, to start with the analysis of the simplest forms. Obviously he had Coghill and Minkowsky in mind. The simple reflex mechanisms are crystallizations of previous global and undifferentiated processes. So do habits automatize into relatively stable occasional apparatuses from undifferentiated flexible and goal-seeking processes.[34] The understanding of habits becomes possible, therefore, only on the basis of an understanding of those automatization processes, which are the fate of many complex psychological dynamisms. This is a crucial point which has in academic psychology been most clearly perceived by Kurt Lewin[35], and in psychoanalytic ego-psychology by Heinz Hartmann (321).

The two points of departure of Schilder's psychiatric thinking in general, and of his theory of thinking in particular, are the belief in the basic directedness of all psychological processes toward objects of an existing reality, and the belief in the basically socialized character of the human psychic apparatus—which matures in the course of experience and learning, but is not created by them.

V

Schilder is the "Minister without Portfolio," and the Minister without Portfolio is supposed to tell us about what all the rest are doing. Let us then ask: What does he tell us about all the rest?

As you can see from the scattered comments I have made about Freud's theory of thinking, Freud centered on the issue of the fundamental motivation of thought, and though he opened up the problems of the theory of thinking in many directions beyond this fundamental interest, he had to pay for his systematic singleness of purpose by doing little exploration of the adaptive and socialized nature of thought. On the other hand, we see how the interest in adaptation, culture, societal influences, results in centering much of contemporary psychoanalytic interest upon defenses, values, socialization, and learning, and we know how the psychoanalysts so interested—for instance, Horney, Fromm and Sullivan—pay for this interest. They lose contact with, and in fact have to turn forcibly against, what we have learned of the basically motivated nature of man's behavior and thought.

I am sure you are by now asking yourself, "Was Schilder the only man who did not pay anything, since he could see all of it?"

[34] See Schilder (729, pp. 65–71).
[35] See Lewin (495), esp. pp. 129–130, 141–143.

This is certainly not the impression I would want to give you. This encyclopaedic mind, this psychiatric polyhistor of our time, paid dearly for his discarding the claim to any portfolio. He never developed systematically any of the infinitely rich observations and countless hunches he developed in well-nigh all fields of psychiatric interest. Unresting and fruitful, he spread his effort all around, sowing rich seed without being interested in a definitive harvest. And so it happens that the full scope of his contribution has been hardly assessed, and that his writing is often so difficult to read.

So it is in the development of science. For every achievement we pay dearly by turning away and indeed cutting ourselves away from other possibilities and facts. No individual and no school can encompass the riches of phenomena in any science, and even less so in the science of man, with which we are concerned. I believe the "Minister without Portfolio" tells us that none of us can behold all aspects of man at once, and the one who attempts to do that will give a rich and intuitive but scattered picture. He makes it easier for us to understand why, in exploring cultural influence in personality development, one is prone to forget basic motivation by showing us that a high price has to be paid, by every one of us, for what we would discover.

This price is determined by what our interest centers on, and our interest in turn flows from our character and personal proclivities. It is a different person with partly different values who is possessed with the discovery of basic motivation, from the one who finds defensive and socializing motives to be the ultimate ones. So with Schilder too: personal proclivities, values, and urges, determined ultimately the choice of the price he paid. Let us, however, not ask what the personal proclivities of Schilder were that shaped the character of his scientific creativity; let us rather honor the man, so rare in our time, who sowed seeds richly and was little concerned with the harvest.

BIBLIOGRAPHY

1. AALL, A. "Ein neues Gedaechtnisgesetz?" *Z. Psychol.*, 66:1–50; 1913.
2. ABRAHAM, K. "The Experiencing of Sexual Traumas as a Form of Sexual Activity," pp. 47–63. In: *Selected Papers of Karl Abraham*, London, Hogarth, 1948.
3. ABRAHAM, K. "Hysterical Dream-States," pp. 90–124. In: *Selected Papers of Karl Abraham*, London, Hogarth, 1948.
4. ABRAHAM, K. "The First Pregenital Stage of the Libido," pp. 248–279. In: *Selected Papers of Karl Abraham*, London, Hogarth, 1948.
5. ABRAHAM, K. "Manifestations of the Female Castration Complex," pp. 338–369. In: *Selected Papers of Karl Abraham*, London, Hogarth, 1948.
6. ABRAHAM, K. *Selected Papers*, London, Hogarth, 1948.
7. ACH, N. *Ueber die Willenstaetigkeit und das Denken. Eine experimentelle Untersuchung mit einem Anhang: Ueber das Hippsche Chronoskop,* Goettingen, Vandenhoeck and Ruprecht, 1905.
8. ACH, N. *Ueber den Willensakt und das Temperament. Eine experimentelle Untersuchung,* Leipzig, Quelle and Meyer, 1910.
9. ACH, N. "Determining Tendencies; Awareness," pp. 15–38. In: Rapaport, D., *Organization and Pathology of Thought,* New York, Columbia University Press, 1951.
10. ADCOCK, C. J. "A Factorial Examination of Sheldon's Types," *J. Personal.*, 16:312–319; 1948.
11. ADLER, A. *Studien ueber Minderwertigkeit von Organen,* Berlin, Urban und Schwarzenberg, 1907.
12. ADLER, A. *The Neurotic Constitution; Outlines of a Comparative Individualistic Psychology and Psychotherapy,* New York, Moffat, Yard, 1917.
13. ALBRECHT, O. "Drei Faelle mit Antons Syndrom," *Arch. Psychiat. Nervenk.*, 59:883; 1918.

14. ALEXANDER, F. "Der biologische Sinn psychischer Vorgaenge," *Imago*, 9:35–57; 1923.

15. ALEXANDER, F. "Fundamental Concepts of Psychosomatic Research," *Psychosom. Med.*, 5:205–210; 1943.

16. ALLERS, R. "Nervensystem und Stoffwechsel. Ein Versuch einer Darstellung der nervoesen Einfluesse auf die Organe und Funktionen des Koerperhaushaltes. (Referate)," *Z. Neurol. Psychiat.*, 19:209–262; 1919.

17. ALLERS, R. and BORAK, J. "Zur Frage des 'Muskelsinnes'," *Wien. med. Wochenschr.*, 70:1165–1168; 1920.

18. ALLERS, R. "Bild und Gedanke," *Z. Neurol. Psychiat.*, 76:1–17; 1922.

19. ALLERS, R. "Sexualpsychologie." In: *Handbuch der vergleichenden Psychologie. Band 3: Die Funktionen des abnormen Seelenlebens,* ed. Von Kafka, Muenchen, Reinhardt, 1922.

20. ALLERS, R. and TELLER, I. "Ueber die Verwertung unbemerkter Eindruecke bei Associationen," *Z. Neurol. Psychiat.*, 89:492–513; 1924.

21. ALLPORT, G. "Eidetic Imagery," *Brit. J. Psychol.*, 15:99–120; 1924.

22. ALLPORT, G. "The Eidetic Image and the After-Image," *Amer. J. Psychol.*, 40:418–425; 1928.

23. ALLPORT, G. and VERNON, P. *Studies in Expressive Movement,* New York, Macmillan, 1933.

24. ALLPORT, G. "Attitudes," pp. 798–844. In: *A Handbook of Social Psychology,* ed. Carl Murchison, Worcester, Mass., Clark University Press, 1935; also in (26).

25. ALLPORT, G. *Personality: a Psychological Interpretation,* New York, Holt, 1937.

26. ALLPORT, G. *The Nature of Personality: Selected Papers,* Cambridge, Addison-Wesley Press, 1950.

27. D'ALONNES, G. REVAULT. "Rôle des sensations internes dans les émotions et dans la perception de la durée," *Rev. philos.*, 60:592–623; 1905.

28. ALPERS, B. J. "Personality and Emotional Disorders With Hypothalamic Lesions—A Review," *Psychosom. Med.*, 2:286–303; 1940.

29. ALRUTZ, S. "Problems of Hypnotism: an Experimental Investigation," *Proceedings of the Society for Psychical Research,* 32:151–178; 1921.

30. ALT, F. *Ueber die Melodientaubheit und musikalisches Falsch-hoeren,* Leipzig und Wien, Deuticke, 1906.

31. ALVERDES, F. *Neue Bahnen der Lehre vom Verhalten der nie-deren Organismen,* Berlin, Springer, 1923.

31a. ANGYAL, A. *Foundations for a Science of Personality,* New York, Commonwealth Fund, 1941.

32. ANTON, G. "Beitraege zur klinischen Beurtheilung und der Lokalisation der Muskelsinnstoerungen im Grosshirne," *Z. Heilkunde,* 14:313–348; 1893.

33. ANTON, G. "Ueber die Selbstwahrnehmung der Herderkrank-ungen des Gehirns durch den Kranken bei Rindenblind-heit und Rindentaubheit," *Arch. Psychiat. Nervenk.,* 32: 86–127; 1899.

34. ASCHAFFENBURG, G. *Das Verbrechen und seine Bekaempfung. Kriminalpsychologie fuer Mediziner, Juristen und Sozio-logen; ein Beitrag zur Reform der Strafgesetzgebung,* Heidelberg, Winter, 1903.

35. ASCHAFFENBURG, G. "Experimentelle Studien ueber Assozia-tionen," *Psychol. Arbeiten,* ed. E. Kraepelin, 1:209–299; 1896, 2:1–83; 1899, 4:235–273; 1904.

36. AUBERT, H. "Ueber den Raumsinn der Netzhaut," *Jahres-Bericht der Schlesischen Gesellschaft fuer vaterlaendische Kultur,* 34:33–34; 1856.

37. AUSTIN-LUND, K. *Peter Moen's Diary,* London, Faber and Faber, 1951.

38. AXELRAD, S. and MAURY, L. "Identification as a Mechanism of Adaptation," pp. 168–184. In: *Psychoanalysis and Cul-ture,* eds. G. Wilbur and W. Muensterberger, New York, International Universities Press, 1951.

39. AZAM, C. M. E. *Hypnotisme, double conscience et altérations de la personnalité,* Paris, Bailliere, 1887.

40. BAADE, W. "Gibt es isolierte Empfindungen?" pp. 30–31. In: *VI Kongress f. exper. Psychol.,* Leipzig, Barth, 1914.

41. BAERWALD, R. *Zur Psychologie der Vorstellungstypen, mit be-sonderer Beruecksichtigung der motorischen und musi-kalischen Anlage,* Leipzig, Barth, 1916.

42. BAK, R. "Discussion of Dr. Wexler's Paper," pp. 202–215. In: *Psychotherapy With Schizophrenics,* eds. E. Brody and F. Redlich, New York, International Universities Press, 1952.

43. BALASSA, L. "Zur Psychologie der Seelentaubheit," *Dtsch. Nervenk.,* 77:143–156; 1923.

44. BALINT, R. "Seelenlaehmung des 'Schauens,' optische Ataxie, raeumliche Stoerung der Aufmerksamkeit," *Monat. Psychiat. Neurol.*, 25:51–81; 1909.

44a. BARKER, R., WRIGHT, B. and GONICK, M. *Adjustment to Physical Handicap and Illness*, New York, Social Sci. Res. Council, 1946.

45. BARTEMEIER, L. "Micropsia," *Psychoanal. Quart.*, 10:573–582; 1941.

46. BARTLETT, F. C. *Remembering: a Study in Experimental and Social Psychology*, Cambridge, England, Cambridge University Press, 1932.

47. BARTLEY, S. and CHUTE, E. *Fatigue and Impairment in Man*, New York, McGraw-Hill, 1947.

48. BASTIAN, H. *Ueber Aphasie*, Leipzig, Engelmann, 1902.

49. BEACH, F. *Hormones and Behavior*, New York, Hoeber, 1948.

50. BENDER, LAURETTA. *A Visual Motor Gestalt Test and Its Clinical Use*, Res. Monogr. Amer. Orthopsychiat. Assn., No. 3, 1938.

50a. BENDER, LAURETTA. *Child Psychiatric Techniques*, Springfield, Illinois, Thomas, 1952.

51. BENDER, MORRIS and FURLOW, L. "Phenomenon of Visual Extinction in Homonymous Fields and Psychologic Principles Involved," *Arch. Neurol. Psychiat.*, 53:29–33; 1945.

52. BENDER, MORRIS and TEUBER, H. "Phenomena of Fluctuation, Extinction and Completion in Visual Perception," *Arch. Neurol. Psychiat.*, 55:627–658; 1945.

53. BENDER, MORRIS and TEUBER, H. "Disturbances in Visual Perception Following Cerebral Lesions." Paper read at the Twelfth International Congress of Psychology, Edinburgh, Scotland, July 24, 1948.

54. BENEDIKT, M. *Anatomical Studies Upon Brains of Criminals*, Baltimore, William Wood, 1885.

55. BENUSSI, VITTORIO. "Die Atmungssymptome der Luege," *Arch. Psychol.*, 31:244–273; 1914.

56. BENUSSI, VITTORIO. "Kinematographische Auffassungsformung," Barth, *Ber. VI Kongress fuer experimentelle Psychologie*, 1914.

57. BERGER, H. *Ueber die koerperlichen Auesserungen psychischer Zustaende. Experimentelle Beitraege zur Lehre von der Blutzirkulation in der Schaedelhoehle des Menschen*, II, Jena, Fischer, 1907.

58. BERGER, H. *Untersuchungen ueber die Temperatur des Gehirns*, Jena, Fischer, 1910.

59. BERGMAN, P. "A Religious Conversion in the Course of Psychotherapy." (Unpublished manuscript.)

60. BERGSON, H. "Le Souvenir du présent et la fausse reconnaissance," *Rev. philos.*, 66:561–593; 1908.

61. BERGSON, H. *Time and Free Will: an Essay on the Immediate Data of Consciousness,* New York, Macmillan, 1910.

62. BERGSON, H. *Creative Evolution,* New York, Holt, 1911.

63. BERGSON, H. *Matter and Memory,* New York, Macmillan, 1912.

64. BERNFELD, S. "Bemerkungen ueber Sublimierung," *Imago,* 8:333–344; 1922.

64a. BERNFELD, S. "Turning Points in Freud's Life," Lecture at Yale University, Department of Neuropsychiatry, April, 1951.

65. BERNHEIM, H. *Hypnotisme, suggestion, psychothérapie, études nouvelles,* Paris, Doin, 1891.

66. BERTALANFFY, L. VON. *Das biologische Weltbild,* Vol. I, Bern, Francke, 1949.

67. BERZE, J. *Die primaere Insuffiziens der psychischen Aktivitaet,* Leipzig und Wien, Deuticke, 1914.

68. BERZE, J. "Zur Frage der Lokalisation der Vorstellungen," *Z. Neurol. Pychiat.,* 44:213–285; 1919.

69. BETLHEIM, S. and HARTMANN, H. "On the Parapraxes in the Korsakow Psychosis," pp. 288–307. In: Rapaport, D., *Organization and Pathology of Thought,* New York, Columbia University Press, 1951.

70. BEZZOLA, N. "Zur Analyse psychotraumatischer Symptome," *J. Psychol. Neurol.,* 8:204–219; 1907.

71. BIBRING, E. "The Development and Problems of the Theory of the Instincts," *Int. J. Psychoanal.,* 22:102–131; 1941.

72. BIBRING, E. "The Conception of the Repetition Compulsion," *Psychoanal. Quart.,* 12:486–519; 1943.

73. BICKEL, H. *Die wechselseitigen Beziehungen zwischen psychischem Geschehen und Blutkreislauf, mit besonderer Beruecksichtigung der Psychosen,* Leipzig, Veit, 1916.

74. BINSWANGER, L. "Psychoanalyse und klinische Psychiatrie," *Int. Z. Psychoanal.,* 7:137–165; 1921.

75. BINSWANGER, L. *Einfuehrung in die Probleme der allgemeinen Psychologie,* Berlin, Springer, 1922.

76. BINSWANGER, L. *Ausgewaehlte Vortraege und Aufsaetze, Band I, Zur phaenomenologischen Anthropologie,* Bern, Francke, 1947.

77. BIRNBAUM, K. *Psychopathologische Dokumente,* Berlin, Springer, 1920.

78. BIRNBAUM, K. *Kriminal-Psychopathologie,* Berlin, Springer, 1921.

79. BIRNBAUM, K. *Der Aufbau der Psychose,* Berlin, Springer, 1923.

80. BLAKE, R. and RAMSEY, G., eds. *Perception, an Approach to Personality,* New York, Ronald Press, 1951.

81. BLEULER, E. "Die Schizophrenie." In: *Handbuch fuer Psychiatrie,* Vol. V, Aschaffenburg, Wien, Deuticke, 1911.

82. BLEULER, E. "Der Sexualwiderstand," *Jahrb. Psychoanal. Psychopath. Forsch.,* 5:442–452; 1913.

83. BLEULER, E. "Das Unbewusste," *J. Psychol. Neurol.,* Vol. XX, suppl. 2, pp. 1–11, 1913.

84. BLEULER, E. "Zur Theorie der Sekundaerempfindungen," *Z. Psychol. Physiol. Sinnesorg.,* 65:1–39; 1913.

85. BLEULER, E. *Naturgeschichte der Seele und ihres Bewusstwerdens,* Berlin, Springer, 1921.

86. BLEULER, E. *Textbook of Psychiatry,* New York, Macmillan, 1924.

87. BLEULER, E. "Autistic Thinking," pp. 399–437. In: Rapaport, D., *Organization and Pathology of Thought,* New York, Columbia University Press, 1951.

88. BLEULER, E. "Autistic-Undisciplined Thinking," pp. 438–450. In: Rapaport, D., *Organization and Pathology of Thought,* New York, Columbia University Press, 1951.

89. BLEULER, E. "The Basic Symptoms of Schizophrenia," pp. 581–649. In: Rapaport, D., *Organization and Pathology of Thought,* New York, Columbia University Press, 1951.

90. BLOOMFIELD, L. *Language,* New York, Henry Holt, 1933.

91. BLUEHER, H. *Die Rolle der Erotik in der maennlichen Gesellschaft,* Jena, Diederichs, 1919–1920.

92. BOHN, G. *Die Entstehung des Denkvermoegens. Eine Einfuehrung in die Tierpsychologie,* Leipzig, Thomas, 1910.

93. BOHN, G. *Die neue Tierpsychologie,* Leipzig, Veit, 1912.

94. BONHOEFFER, K. "Doppelseitige symmetrische Schlaefen- und Parietallappenherde als Ursache vollstaendiger dauernder Worttaubheit bei erhaltener Tonskala, verbunden mit taktiler und optischer Agnosia," *Monat. Psychiat. Neurol.,* 37:17–38; 1915.

95. BORING, E. *Sensation and Perception in the History of Experimental Psychology,* New York, Appleton-Century, 1942.

95a. BORING, E. "Cutaneous Sensation After Nerve-Division, *Quart. J. Exper. Physiol.,* 10:1–95; 1916.

96. BORING, E. *A History of Experimental Psychology*, New York, Appleton-Century, 1950.

97. BOURRU, H. and BUROT, P. *Variations de la personnalité*, Paris, Alcan, 1888.

98. BRAUN, F. "Vom Seelenleben gefangener Voegel," *Naturwissenschaften*, 10:833–838; 1922.

99. BRAUN, L. *Herz und Psyche in ihren Wirkungen aufeinander*, Leipzig, Deuticke, 1920.

100. BRAZIER, M. "A Neuronal Basis for Ideas," *Dialectica*, 4:73–78; 1950.

101. BRENMAN, M., GILL, M. and HACKER, F. "Alterations in the State of the Ego in Hypnosis," *Bull. Menninger Clin.*, 2:60–66; 1947.

102. BRENMAN, M. and GILL, M. *Hypnotherapy, a Review of the Literature*, Menninger Foundation Monograph, No. 5, New York, International Universities Press, 1947.

103. BRENMAN, M. "Phenomena of Hypnosis," pp. 123–163. In: *Problems of Consciousness*, Transactions of the First Conference, March 1950, New York, Josiah Macy, Jr. Foundation, 1951.

103a. BRENMAN, M. "Dreams and Hypnosis," *Psychoanal. Quart.*, 18:455–465; 1949.

104. BRENMAN, M. "On Teasing and Being Teased: and the Problem of 'Moral Masochism,' " pp. 264–285. In: *The Psychoanalytic Study of the Child*, Vol. VII, New York, International Universities Press, 1952.

105. BRENMAN, M., GILL, M. and KNIGHT, R. P. "Spontaneous Fluctuations in Depth of Hypnosis and Their Implications for Ego-Function," *Int. J. Psychoanal.*, 33:22–33; 1952.

106. BRENMAN, M. "Psychology of the Hypnotic Relationship." (Unpublished Manuscript.)

107. BRENTANO, F. *Psychologie vom empirischen Standpunkt*, Leipzig, Dunker and Humbolt, 1874.

108. BREUER, J. and FREUD, S. *Studies in Hysteria*, Nervous and Mental Disease Monograph, No. 61, New York, Nervous and Mental Disease Monograph, 1937.

109. BRODMANN, K. "Experimenteller und klinischer Beitrag zur Psychopathologie der polyneuritischen Psychose," *J. Psychol. Neurol.*, 3:1–48; 1904.

110. BRODMANN, K. *Vergleichende Lokalisationslehre der Grosshirnrinde in ihren Prinzipien dargestellt auf Grund des Zellenbaues*, Leipzig, Barth, 1909.

111. BRODMANN, K. "Feinere Anatomie des Grosshirns," *Handbuch Neurol.*, 1:206–298; 1910.

112. BROWN, T. "Die Reflexfunktionen des Zentralnervensystems, besonders vom Standpunkt der rhythmischen Taetigkeiten beim Saeugetier betrachtet," *Ergebn. Physiol.*, 13: 279–453; 1913.

113. BRUECKNER, A. "Zur Frage der Lokalisation des Kontrastes und verwandter Erscheinungen in der Sehsinnsubstanz," *Z. Augenheilk.*, 38:1–14; 1917.

114. BRUNER, J. and POSTMAN, L. "Tension and Tension Release as Organizing Factors in Perception," *J. Personal.*, 15: 300–308; 1947.

115. BRUNER, J. and POSTMAN, L. "Perception Under Stress," *Psychol. Rev.*, 55:314–323; 1948.

116. BRUNER, J., POSTMAN, L. and McGINNIES, E. "Personal Values as Selective Factors in Perception," *J. Abnorm. Soc. Psychol.*, 43:142–154; 1948.

117. BRUNER, J. and POSTMAN, L. "On the Perception of Incongruity: a Paradigm," *J. Personal.*, 18:206–223; 1949.

118. BRUNER, J. and KRECH, D., eds. *Perception and Personality*, Durham, Duke University Press, 1950.

119. BRUNSWIK, E. *Systematic and Representative Design of Psychological Experiments*, Berkeley and Los Angeles, University of California Press, 1947.

120. BUBER, M. *Ekstatische Konfessionen*, Jena, Diederichs, 1909.

121. BUEHLER, K. "Tatsachen und Probleme zu einer Psychologie der Denkvorgaenge. I. Ueber Gedanken," *Arch. ges. Psychol.*, 9:297–365; 1907. "*Ibid.*, II. Ueber Gedankenzusammenhaenge," *Arch. ges. Psychol.*, 12:1–123; 1908. Also: "On Thought Connections," pp. 39–57. In: Rapaport, D., *Organization and Pathology of Thought*, New York, Columbia University Press, 1951.

122. BUEHLER, K. *The Mental Development of the Child. A Summary of Modern Psychological Theory*, New York, Harcourt, 1930. Also: *Die geistige Entwicklung des Kindes*, Jena, Fischer, 1922.

123. BUERGER-PRINZ, H. and KAILA, M. "On the Structure of the Amnesic Syndrome," pp. 650–686. In: Rapaport, D., *Organization and Pathology of Thought*, New York, Columbia University Press, 1951.

124. BULL, N. *Attitude Theory of Emotion*, New York, Nervous and Mental Disease Monographs, #81, 1951.

125. BUMKE, O. *Das Unterbewusstsein. Eine Kritik*, Berlin, Brockhaus, 1922.

126. BURKAMP, W. *Die Kausalitaet des psychischen Prozesses und die unbewussten Aktionsregulationen*, Berlin, Springer, 1922.

127. BURNEY, C. *Solitary Confinement*, London, Clerke and Cockeran, 1952.

128. BURROW, T. and GALT, W. "Electroencephalographic Recordings of Varying Aspects of Attention in Relation to Behavior," *J. Gen. Psychol.*, 32:269–288; 1945.

129. BURROW, T. and SYZ, H. "Studies With the Lifwynn Eye-Movement Camera," *J. Biological Photographic Association*, 17:155–170; 1949.

130. BYCHOWSKI, G. "Psychopathologische Untersuchung ueber die Folgezustaende nach der Encephalitis epidemica, insbesondere den Parkinsonismus," *Z. Neurol. Psychiat.*, 83:201–246; 1923.

131. CAMERON, E. *Objective and Experimental Psychiatry*, New York, Macmillan, 1941.

132. CAMERON, N. *The Psychology of Behavior Disorders*, New York, Houghton Mifflin, 1947.

133. CHARCOT, J. M. "Cas de suppression brusque et isolée de la mémoire des signes," *Progrès médical*, Paris, 1883.

134. CHOWRIN, A. N. *Experimentelle Untersuchungen auf dem Gebiete des raeumlichen Hellsehens*, Muenchen, Reinhardt, 1919.

135. CLAPARÈDE, E. "Recognition and 'Me-Ness,'" pp. 58–75. In: Rapaport, D., *Organization and Pathology of Thought*, New York, Columbia University Press, 1951.

136. CRAFTS, L., SCHNEIRLA, T., ROBINSON, E. and GILBERT, R. *Recent Experiments in Psychology*, New York, McGraw-Hill, 1950.

137. CSAPODY, ISTVÁN. "A szemizombénuldst követö gerde fejtavtas egy nem méltatott okáról." *Szemészet*, 2:8; 1922.

138. CUSHING, H. "A Note Upon the Faradic Stimulation of the Postcentral Gyrus in Conscious Patients," *Brain*, 32:44–53; 1909.

139. DARROW, C., HENRY, C., BRENMAN, M. and GILL, M. "Inter-Area Electroencephalographic Relationships Affected by Hypnosis. A Preliminary Report," *Electroencephalography and Clin. Neurophysiology*, 2:231; 1950.

140. DARWIN, C. *Expression of the Emotions,* London, Murray, 1904.

141. DAVID, H., ed. "Symposium on Fatigue," *Psychosom. Med.,* 5:152–165; 1943.

142. DELACROIX, H. *Etudes d'histoire et de psychologie du mysticisme,* Paris, Alcan, 1908.

143. DELBRUECK, M. "A Physicist Looks at Biology," *Trans. Conn. Acad. Arts Sci.,* 38:173–190; 1949.

144. DEUTSCH, F. "Psychoanalyse und Organkrankheiten," *Int. Z. Psychoanal.,* 8:290–306; 1922.

145. DEUTSCH, F. "Gehaeuftes Auftreten von Morbus Basedowii," *Med. Klin.,* 19:678–680; 1923.

146. DEUTSCH, H. "Ueber die pathologische Luege," *Int. Z. Psychoanal.,* 8:153–167; 1922.

147. DIETHELM, O. and JONES, M. "Influence of Anxiety on Attention, Learning, Retention and Thinking," *Arch. Neurol. Psychiat.,* 58:325–326; 1947.

148. DILTHEY, W. "Ideen ueber beschreibende und zergliedernde Psychologie," *Sitzungsber. d. Preuss. Akad. d. Wiss.,* Phil-hist. Kl., 1894.

149. DOLLARD, J. and MILLER, N. *Personality and Psychotherapy: an Analysis in Terms of Learning, Thinking and Culture,* New York, McGraw-Hill, 1950.

150. DRIESCH, H. *The Science and Philosophy of the Organism,* New York, Macmillan, 1907–1908.

151. DUNBAR, F. *Emotions and Bodily Changes,* 2nd ed., New York, Columbia University Press, 1938.

152. DURKHEIM, E. *Le Suicide,* Paris, Librairie Alcan, 1912.

153. EBBINGHAUS, H. *Grundzuege der Psychologie,* 3 Aufl., Bd. 1 u. 2, 1911 u. 1913.

154. EBBINGHAUS, H. *Memory: a Contribution to Experimental Psychology,* New York, Teachers College, 1913.

155. EBBINGHAUS, H. and BUEHLER, K. *Grundzuege der Psychologie,* 4 Aufl., Leipzig, von Veit & Co., 1919.

156. ECONOMO, CONSTANTIN VON. *Encephalitis Lethargica,* London, Oxford University Press, 1931.

157. EHRENFELS, C. VON. "Ueber Gestaltqualitaeten," *V. wissen. Philosophie,* 14:249–292; 1890.

158. EHRENREICH, G. "Historical Survey of Hypnotizability," 1948. (Unpublished ms.)

159. EHRENREICH, G. "Report on Group Hypnotizability Data," 1948. (Unpublished ms.)

160. EHRENREICH, G. "The Relationship of Certain Descriptive

Factors to Hypnotizability," *Trans. Kansas Acad. Sci.*, 52:24–27; 1949.

161. EISSLER, K. "Remarks on the Psychoanalysis of Schizophrenia," pp. 130–167. In: *Psychotherapy With Schizophrenics*, E. Brody, and F. Redlich, eds., New York, International Universities Press, 1952.

161a. EISSLER, K. "Time Experience and the Mechanism of Isolation," *Psychoanal. Rev.*, 39:1–22; 1952.

162. ELIASBERG, W. and FEUCHTWANGER, E. "Zur psychologischen und psychopathologischen Untersuchung und Theorie des erworbenen Schwachsinns dargestellt an einem Fall von forschreitender Demenz nach Hirnverletzung," *Z. Neurol. Psychiat.*, 75:516–596; 1922.

163. ELLIS, W. *Sourcebook of Gestalt Psychology*, New York, Harcourt, Brace, 1938.

164. ERDMANN, B. "Die psychologische Grundlage der Beziehungen zwischen Sprechen und Denken," *Archiv. f. systematische Philosophie*, 2:210–218; 1896.

165. ERDMANN, B. and DODGE, R. *Psychologische Untersuchungen ueber das Lesen auf experimenteller Grundlage*, Halle, M. Niemeyer, 1898.

166. ERIKSON, E. *Childhood and Society*, New York, Norton, 1950.

167. ERIKSON, E. "The 'Dream Specimen' of Psychoanalysis." (In press.)

168. ESCALONA, S. "The Effect of Success and Failure on the Level of Aspiration in Manic-Depressive Psychoses," *Univ. Iowa Studies Child Welfare*, 16:199–302; 1940.

169. EXNER, S. "Optische Bewegungsempfindungen," *Biologisches Zentral.*, 8:437–448; 1888–1889.

170. EXNER, S. "Ueber Sensomobilitaet," *Pflüger's Archiv. Physiol.*, 48:592–613; 1891.

171. FARBER, M. *Philosophical Essays in Memory of Edmund Husserl*, Cambridge, Harvard University Press, 1940.

172. FECHNER, G. T. *Elemente der Psychophysik*, Leipzig, Breitkropf and Härtel (2 aufl. 1884), 1860.

173. FECHNER, G. *Das Buechlein vom Leben nach dem Tode*, Hamburg, Voss, 1900.

174. FEDERN, P. "Die Ichbesetzung bei den Fehlleistungen," *Imago*, 19:312–338, 433–453; 1933.

175. FEDERN, P. "Zur Unterscheidung des gesunden und krankhaften Narzissmus," *Imago*, 22:5–39; 1936.

176. FEDERN, P. "Psychoanalysis of Psychoses," *Psychiat. Quart.*,

I. "Errors and How to Avoid Them," 17:3; 1943. II. "Transference," 17:246; 1943.

177. FEDERN, P. "Principles of Psychotherapy in Latent Schizophrenia," *Amer. J. Psychotherapy,* 1:129; 1947.

177a. FEDERN, P. *Ego Psychology and the Psychoses,* New York, Basic Books, 1952.

178. FENICHEL, O. "Zur Kritik des Todestriebes," *Imago,* 21:458–466; 1935.

179. FENICHEL, O., ed., WINDHOLZ, E., OLDEN, C., DERI, F., MAENCHEN, A., BERLINER, B. and SIMMEL, E. "Symposium on Neurotic Disturbances of Sleep," *Int. J. Psychoanal.,* 23:49–68; 1942.

180. FENICHEL, O. *The Psychoanalytic Theory of Neurosis,* New York, Norton, 1945.

181. FENICHEL, O. "On Identification." In: Fenichel, O., *Collected Papers,* New York, Norton, 1953. (In press.)

182. FENICHEL, O. "Screen Memories." In: Fenichel, O., *Collected Papers,* New York, Norton, 1953. (In press.)

183. FERENCZI, S., ABRAHAM, K., SIMMEL, E. and JONES, E. *Psycho-Analysis and the War Neuroses,* London, International Psycho-Analytic Press, 1921.

184. FERENCZI, S. and HOLLOS, S. *Psycho-Analysis and the Psychic Disorder of General Paresis,* New York, Nervous and Mental Disease Publishing Co., 1925.

185. FERENCZI, S. "Introjection and Transference," pp. 35–93. In: *Sex in Psychoanalysis,* New York, Brunner, 1950.

186. FERENCZI, S. "Stages in the Development of a Sense of Reality," pp. 213–239. In: *Sex in Psychoanalysis,* New York, Brunner, 1950.

187. FISCHER, O. "Ueber Makropsie und deren Beziehungen zur Mikrographie, sowie ueber eine eigentuemliche Stoerung der Lichtempfindung," *Monat. Psychiat. Neurol.,* 19:290–305; 1906.

188. FISCHER, O. "Ein weiterer Beitrag zur Klinik und Pathogenese der hysterischen Dysmegalopsie," *Monat. Psychiat. Neurol.,* 21:1–19; 1906.

189. FLECHSIG, P. *Die Leitungsbahnen im Gehirn und Rueckenmark des Menschen auf Grund entwicklungsgeschichtlicher Untersuchungen,* Leipzig, Engelmann, 1876.

190. FLECHSIG, P. *Gehirn und Seele,* Leipzig, Veit & Co., 1896.

191. FLECHSIG, P. "Bemerkungen ueber die Hoersphaere des menschlichen Gehirns," *Neur. Centbl.,* 27:2–7, 50–58; 1908.

192. FOERSTER, O. "Das phylogenetische Moment in der spasti-

schen Laehmung," *Berlin. klin. Wochenschr.*, 50:1217–
1220; 1913, 50:1255–1261; 1913.

193. FOERSTER, O. "Zur Analyse und Pathophysiologie der striaeren Bewegungsstoerungen," *Z. Neurol. Psychiat.*, 73:1–
169; 1921.

194. FORD, A. "Attention Automatization," *Amer. J. Psychol.*,
41:1–32; 1929.

195. FORD, C. and BEACH, F. *Patterns of Sexual Behavior*, New
York, Harper and Hoeber, 1951.

196. FOREL, A. *Hypnotism: or, Suggestion and Psychotherapy: a
Study of the Psychological, Psycho-physiological and
Therapeutic Aspects of Hypnotism*, New York, Regman
Company, 1907.

197. FRAENKEL, F. "Der psychopathologische Formenreichtum der
Eunuchoiden," *Z. Neurol. Psychiat.*, 80:560–574; 1923.

198. FRANK, L. *Affektstoerungen. Studien ueber ihre Aetiologie
und Therapie*, Berlin, Springer, 1913.

199. FRAZER, J. G. *The Golden Bough*, London, Macmillan, 1911–
1913.

200. FREUD, A., (1937). *The Ego and the Mechanisms of Defence*,
New York, International Universities Press, 1946.

201. FREUD, S., (1891). *Zur Auffassung der Aphasien*, Vienna, Deuticke, 1891. *On Aphasia*, transl. E. Stengel. New York,
Int. Univ. Press, 1953.

202. FREUD, S., (1895). "The Justification for Detaching from Neu-
rasthenia a Particular Syndrome: the Anxiety Neurosis,"
pp. 76–106. In: *Collected Papers*, Vol. I, London, Hogarth, 1948.

203. FREUD, S., (1896). "Further Remarks on the Defence Neuro-
Psychoses," pp. 155–182. In: *Collected Papers*, Vol. I,
London, Hogarth, 1946.

204. FREUD, S., (1900). "The Interpretation of Dreams," pp. 183–
549. In: *The Basic Writings of Sigmund Freud*, New
York, Modern Library, 1938.

205. FREUD, S., (1904). *The Psychopathology of Everyday Life*,
New York, Macmillan, 1914.

206. FREUD, S., (1905). *Three Essays on the Theory of Sexuality*,
London, Imago, 1949.

207. FREUD, S., (1905). "Wit and its Relation to the Unconscious,"
pp. 633–803. In: *The Basic Writings of Sigmund Freud*,
New York, Modern Library, 1938.

208. FREUD, S., (1906). "Psycho-Analysis and the Ascertaining of
Truth in Courts of Law," pp. 13–24. In: *Collected Papers*, Vol. II, London, Hogarth, 1948.

209. FREUD, S., (1907). "Obsessive Acts and Religious Practices," pp. 25–35. In: *Collected Papers*, Vol. II, London, Hogarth, 1948.

210. FREUD, S., (1908). "Character and Anal Erotism," pp. 45–50. In: *Collected Papers*, Vol. II, London, Hogarth, 1948.

211. FREUD, S., (1908). "On the Sexual Theories of Children," pp. 59–75. In: *Collected Papers*, Vol. II, London, Hogarth, 1948.

212. FREUD, S., (1908). "The Relation of the Poet to Day-Dreaming," pp. 173–183. In: *Collected Papers*, Vol. IV, London, Hogarth, 1948.

213. FREUD, S., (1909). "Notes on a Case of Obsessional Neurosis," pp. 293–383. In: *Collected Papers*, Vol. III, London, Hogarth.

214. FREUD, S., (1910). "Contributions to the Psychology of Love. A Special Type of Choice of Object Made by Men," pp. 192–202. In: *Collected Papers*, Vol. IV, London, Hogarth, 1948.

215. FREUD, S., (1910). *Leonardo da Vinci. A Study in Psychosexuality*, New York, Random House, 1947.

216. FREUD, S., (1911). "Formulations Regarding the Two Principles in Mental Functioning," pp. 13–21. In: *Collected Papers*, Vol. IV, London, Hogarth, 1948. Also: Rapaport, D., *Organization and Pathology of Thought*, New York, Columbia University Press, 1951, pp. 315–328.

217. FREUD, S., (1911). "Psycho-Analytic Notes Upon an Autobiographical Account of a Case of Paranoia," pp. 387–466. In: *Collected Papers*, Vol. III, London, Hogarth, 1948.

218. FREUD, S., (1912). "Contributions to the Psychology of Love. The Most Prevalent Form of Degradation in Erotic Life," pp. 203–216. In: *Collected Papers*, Vol. IV, London, Hogarth, 1948.

219. FREUD, S., (1912). "A Note on the Unconscious in Psycho-Analysis," pp. 22–29. In: *Collected Papers*, Vol. IV, London, Hogarth, 1948.

220. FREUD, S., (1912). "Totem and Taboo," pp. 807–930. In: *The Basic Writings of Sigmund Freud*, New York, Modern Library, 1938.

221. FREUD, S., (1912). "Types of Neurotic Nosogenesis," pp. 113–121. In: *Collected Papers*, Vol. II, London, Hogarth, 1948.

222. FREUD, S., (1913). "Further Recommendations in the Technique of Psycho-Analysis. Observations on Transference-Love," pp. 377–391. In: *Collected Papers,* Vol. II, London, Hogarth, 1948.

223. FREUD, S., (1913). "The Predisposition to Obsessional Neurosis," pp. 122–132. In: *Collected Papers,* Vol. II, London, Hogarth, 1948.

224. FREUD, S., (1914). "Fausse Reconnaissance (Déjà Raconté) in Psycho-Analytic Treatment," pp. 334–341. In: *Collected Papers,* Vol. II, London, Hogarth, 1948.

225. FREUD, S., (1914). "On Narcissism: an Introduction," pp. 30–59. In: *Collected Papers,* Vol. IV, London, Hogarth, 1948.

226. FREUD, S., (1915). "Instincts and Their Vicissitudes," pp. 60–83. In: *Collected Papers,* Vol. IV, London, Hogarth, 1948.

227. FREUD, S., (1915). "Repression," pp. 84–97. In: *Collected Papers,* Vol. IV, London, Hogarth, 1948.

228. FREUD, S., (1915). "Some Character-Types Met With in Psycho-Analytic Work," pp. 318–344. In: *Collected Papers,* Vol. IV, London, Hogarth, 1948.

229. FREUD, S., (1915). "The Unconscious," pp. 98–136. In: *Collected Papers,* Vol. IV, London, Hogarth, 1948.

230. FREUD, S., (1916). "On the Transformation of Instincts With Special Reference to Anal Erotism," pp. 164–171. In: *Collected Papers,* Vol. II, London, Hogarth, 1948.

231. FREUD, S., (1917). *Introductory Lectures on Psycho-Analysis,* London, Allen and Unwin, 1922.

232. FREUD, S., (1917). "Metapsychological Supplement to the Theory of Dreams," pp. 137–151. In: *Collected Papers,* Vol. IV, London, Hogarth, 1948.

233. FREUD, S., (1917). "Mourning and Melancholia," pp. 152–170. In: *Collected Papers,* Vol. IV, London, Hogarth, 1948.

234. FREUD, S., (1918). "Contributions to the Psychology of Love. The Taboo of Virginity," pp. 217–235. In: *Collected Papers,* Vol. IV, London, Hogarth, 1948.

235. FREUD, S., (1918). "From the History of an Infantile Neurosis," pp. 473–605. In: *Collected Papers,* Vol. III, London, Hogarth, 1948.

236. FREUD, S., (1920). *Beyond the Pleasure-Principle,* London, Hogarth, 1948.

237. FREUD, S., (1921). *Group Psychology and the Analysis of the Ego,* New York, Boni and Liveright, 1922.

238. FREUD, S., (1922). *Kleine Schriften zur Neurosenlehre,* Bd. 1–5, Vienna, Int. Psa., Verlag.

239. FREUD, S., (1923). *The Ego and the Id,* London, Hogarth, 1947.

240. FREUD, S., (1924). "The Economic Problem of Masochism," pp. 255–268. In: *Collected Papers,* Vol. II, London, Hogarth, 1946.

241. FREUD, S., (1924). "The Loss of Reality in Neurosis and Psychosis," pp. 277–282. In: *Collected Papers,* Vol. II, London, Hogarth, 1946.

242. FREUD, S., (1924). "Neurosis and Psychosis," pp. 250–254. In: *Collected Papers,* Vol. II, London, Hogarth, 1946.

243. FREUD, S., (1925). "Negation," pp. 181–185. In: *Collected Papers,* Vol. V, London, Hogarth, 1950. Also: Rapaport, D., *Organization and Pathology of Thought,* New York, Columbia University Press, 1951, pp. 338–348.

244. FREUD, S., (1926). *The Problem of Anxiety,* New York, Psychoanalytic Quarterly Press, 1936.

245. FREUD, S., (1932). *New Introductory Lectures on Psychoanalysis,* New York, Norton, 1933.

246. FREUD, S., (1937). "Analysis Terminable and Interminable," *Int. J. Psychoanal.,* 18:373–405; 1938.

247. FREUD, S., (1938). *Outline of Psychoanalysis,* New York, Norton, 1949.

248. FREUD, S., (1938). "Splitting of the Ego in the Defensive Process," pp. 372–375. In: *Collected Papers,* Vol. V, London, Hogarth, 1950.

249. FREY, M. "Beitraege zur Physiologie des Schmerzsinns," *Ber. saechs. Ges. Wiss.,* 46:185–196, 283–296; 1894. "Beitraege zur Sinnesphysiologie der Haut," *ibid.,* 47:166–184; 1895. "Untersuchungen ueber die Sinnesfunctionen der menschlichen Haut; Druckempfindung und Schmerz," *Abhandl. Saechs. Ges. Wiss.,* 23:175–266; 1896.

250. FRIEDLAENDER, H. *Ueber Hypnose und Hypnonarkose,* Stuttgart, Enke, 1920.

251. FRIEDLAENDER, H. "Die Wahrnehmung der Schwere," *Z. Psychol.,* 83:129–210; 1920.

252. FRIES, M. E., BROKAW, K. and MURRAY, V. F. "The Formation of Character as Observed in the Well-Baby Clinic," *Amer. J. Diseases of Children,* 48:28–42; 1935.

253. FRIES, M. E. "Importance of Continuous Collaboration of All

Agencies in Dynamic Handling of the Child," *The Nervous Child*, 3:258–267; 1944.

254. FRIES, M. E. "The Child's Ego Development and the Training of Adults in His Environment," pp. 85–112. In: *The Psychoanalytic Study of the Child*, New York, International Universities Press, 1946.

255. FRIES, M. E. "Diagnosing the Child's Adjustment Through Age-Level Tests," *Psychoanal. Rev.*, 34:1–31; 1947.

256. FRIES, M. E. "Psychological By-Products of a Physical Examination," *Psychiat. Quart.*, 21:671–682; 1947.

257. FRITSCH, G. and HITZIG, E. "Ueber die elektrische Erregbarkeit des Grosshirns," *Arch. Anat. Physiol. Wiss. Med.*, 37:300–320; 1870.

258. FROEBES, J. *Lehrbuch der experimentellen Psychologie*, Freiburg, Herder, 1923.

258a. FROMM, E. *The Forgotten Language*, New York, Rinehart, 1951.

259. FUCHS, W. "Untersuchungen ueber das Sehen der Hemianopiker und Hemiamblyopiker: I. Verlagerungserscheinungen," *Z. f. Psychol.*, 84:67–169; 1920. II. "Die totalisierende Gestaltauffassung," *ibid.*, 86:1–143; 1921.

260. FULTON, J. *Physiology of the Nervous System*, London, Oxford Press, 1938.

261. GARDNER, R. "Cognitive Styles in Categorizing Behavior," 1952. (Ph.D. Thesis, University of Kansas.)

262. DI GASPERO, H. *Hysterische Laehmungen. Studien ueber ihre Pathophysiologie und Klinik*, Berlin, Springer, 1912.

263. GEIGER, M. *Das Bewusstsein von den Gefuehlen*, Muenchner philosoph. Abh., 1911.

264. GEIGER, M. "Ueber das Wesen und die Bedeutung der Einfuehlung," *Ber. IV. Kongress f. exper. Psychol.*, 29–73; 1911.

265. GEIGER, M. "Zum Problem der Stimmungseinfuehlung," *Z. f. Aesthetik*, 6:1–42; 1911.

266. GEIGER, M. *Beitraege zur Phaenomenologie des aesthetischen Genusses*, Halle, Niemeyer, 1913.

267. GELB, A. "Ueber den Wegfall der Wahrnehmung von 'Oberflaechenfarben,'" *Z. Psychol.*, 84:66–257; 1920.

268. GELB, A. "Die Farbenkonstanz der Sehdinge," pp. 594–678. In: *Handbuch der normalen und pathologischen Physiologie*, Vol. XII, ed. A. Bethe, G. v. Bergmann, G. Embden and A. Ellinger, Berlin, Springer, 1925–1932.

269. GELEY, G. "La physiologie dite supra-normale et les phéno-

mènes d'idéoplastie," *Bull. Institut Général Psychologique*, 18:5–26; 1918.

270. GERSTMANN, J. and SCHILDER, P. "Studien ueber Bewegungsstoerungen. I. Eigenartige Formen extrapyramidaler Motilitaetsstoerung," *Z. Neurol. Psychiat.*, 58:266–275; 1920. "II. Ein eigenartiger Typus motorischer Reizerscheinungen," *ibid.*, 276–279; 1920. "III. Ueber die motorischen Symptome der chronischen Chorea und ueber Stoerungen des Bewegungsbeginnes," *ibid.*, 61:203–218; 1920. "IV. Zur Frage der Katalepsie," *Med. Klinik.*, 17:193–194; 1921. "V. Ueber die Typen extrapyramidaler Pseudobulbaerparalyse (akinetisch-hypertonisches Bulbaersyndrom)," *Z. Neurol. Psychiat.*, 70:35–54; 1921. "VI. Unterbrechung von Bewegungsfolgen (Bewegungsluecken), nebst Bemerkungen ueber Mangel an Antrieb," *ibid.*, 85:32–43; 1923. "VII. Das Fallen der Spaetencephalitiker," *ibid.*, 85:44–51; 1923. "VIII. Ueber Wesen und Art des durch striopallidaere Laesion bedingten Bewegungsuebermasses," *ibid.*, 87:570–582; 1923.

271. GIBBS, F. and GIBBS, F. *Atlas of Electroencephalography*, Cambridge, Massachusetts, Lew A. Cummings Company, 1941.

272. GIBSON, J. "A Critical Review of the Concept of Set in Contemporary Experimental Psychology," *Psychol. Bull.*, 38:781–817; 1941.

273. GIBSON, J. *The Perception of the Visual World*, Cambridge, Riverside Press, 1950.

274. GIERLICH, N. "Ueber die Beziehungen des Praedilektionstyps der hemiplegischen Laehmung zur phylogenetischen Entwicklung der Pyramidenbahnen," *Z. Neurol. Psychiat.*, 60:59–76; 1920.

275. GIERLICH, N. "Ueber die Beziehungen der angeborenen und frueh erworbenen hemiplegischen Laehmung zur Phylogenese," *Berlin. Klin. Wochenschr.*, 58:476–478; 1921.

276. GIESE, H. "Ueber 'Depersonalisation,'" *Z. Neurol. Psychiat.*, 81:62–126; 1923.

277. GILL, M. "Spontaneous Regression on Induction of Hypnosis," *Bull. Menninger Clin.*, 12:41–48; 1948.

278. GILL, M. and BRENMAN, M. "Hypnosis and Ego Boundaries." (Unpublished manuscript.)

279. GILL, M. "Hypnosis and Sleep." (Unpublished manuscript.)

280. GINSBURG, S. "Values and the Psychiatrist," *Amer. J. Orthopsychiat.*, 20:466–478; 1950.

281. GINZBERG, E., GINSBURG, S., AXELRAD, S. and HERMA, Y. *Occupational Choice,* New York, Columbia University Press, 1951.

282. GIRGENSOHN, K. *Der seelische Aufbau des religioesen Erlebens,* Leipzig, Hirzel, 1923.

283. GLOVER, E. "Medico-Psychological Aspects of Normality," *Brit. J. Psychol.,* 23:152–166; 1932.

284. GOLDSCHEIDER, A. "Ueber die Physiologie des Palpierens," *Klin. Wochenschr.,* 2:961–962; 1923.

285. GOLDSCHMIDT, B. *Die quantitative Grundlage von Vererbung und Auslese,* Berlin, Springer, 1920.

286. GOLDSTEIN, K. "Zur Theorie der Hallucinationen," *Arch. Psychiat. Nervenk.,* 44:584–655, 1036–1106; 1908.

287. GOLDSTEIN, K. and GELB, A. "Zur Psychologie des optischen Wahrnehmungs- und Erkennungsvorganges," *Z. Neurol. Psychiat.,* 41:1–142; 1918.

288. GOLDSTEIN, K. and GELB, A. *Psychologische Analysen hirnpathologischer Faelle,* Leipzig, Barth, 1920.

289. GOLDSTEIN, K. "Die Topik der Grosshirnrinde in ihrer klinischen Bedeutung," *Dtsch. Z. Nervenk.,* 77:7–124; 1923.

290. GOLDSTEIN, K. and GELB, A. "Ueber Farbennamenamnesie, nebst Bemerkungen ueber das Wesen der amnestischen Aphasie ueberhaupt und die Beziehung zwischen Sprache und dem Verhalten zur Umwelt," *Psychol. Forsch.,* 6:127–186; 1924.

291. GOLDSTEIN, K. *The Organism,* New York, American Book, 1939.

292. GOLDSTEIN, K. and SCHEERER, M. "Abstract and Concrete Behavior: an Experimental Study With Special Tests," *Psychol. Monogr.* 53, No. 2, Washington, D.C., Amer. Psychological Assn., 1941.

293. GOLDSTEIN, K. *Language and Language Disturbances,* New York, Grune and Stratton, 1948.

294. GOMPERZ, H. *Weltanschauungslehre. I. Methodenlehre,* Jena and Leipzig, Diederichs, 1905.

295. GRANICH, L. *Aphasia,* New York, Grune and Stratton, 1947.

296. GRASSET, J. "La sensation du déjà vu," *J. de psychol. norm. et pathol.,* 1:17–27; 1904.

297. GREGOR, A. "Beitraege zur Kenntnis der Gedaechtnisstoerung bei der Korsakowschen Psychose," *Monat. Psychiat. Neurol.,* 21:19–45, 148–166; 1907.

298. GREGOR, A. "Beitraege zur Psychopathologie des Gedaechtnisses," *Monat. Psychiat. Neurol.,* 25:218–255, 339–386; 1909.

299. GREGOR, A. *Leitfaden der experimentellen Psychopathologie,* Berlin, Karger, 1910.

300. GREGOR, A. "Beitraege zur Kenntnis des psychogalvanischen Phaenomens," *Z. Neurol. Psychiat.,* 8:393–412; 1911.

301. GREGOR, A. "Die hautelektrischen Erscheinungen in ihren Beziehungen zu Bewusstseinsprozessen," *Arch. Psychol.,* 27:241–284; 1913.

302. GRODDECK, G. *The Book of the It,* trans. V. M. E. Collins, New York, Funk and Wagnalls, 1950.

303. GRODDECK, G. "Ueber die Psychoanalyse des Organischen im Menschen," *Int. Z. Psychoanal.,* 7:252–263; 1921.

304. GROOS, K. *The Play of Animals,* New York, Appleton, 1915.

305. GROOS, K. *The Play of Man,* New York, Appleton, 1901.

306. GROSS, A. *Freud's Creative Period.* (Unpublished manuscript.)

307. GROSS, O. *Die zerebrale Sekundaerfunktion,* Leipzig, Vogel, 1902.

308. GRUHLE, H. "Psychologie abnormer Seelenzustaende," pp. 3–151. In: *Die Funktionen des abnormen Seelenlebens. Vol. 3. Handbuch der vergleichenden Psychologie,* ed. G. Kafka, Muenchen, Reinhardt, 1922.

309. GRUNDLAND, S. "Reaktionsversuche am Feder-Ergographen," *Arch. ges. Psychol.,* 35:252–408; 1916.

310. HAAS, W. *Ueber Echtheit und Unechtheit von Gefuehlen,* Nürnberg, B. Hilz, 1910.

311. HAAS, W. *Die psychische Dingwelt,* Bonn, F. Cohen, 1921.

312. HACKER, F. "The Concept of Normality and Its Practical Significance," *Amer. J. Orthopsychiat.,* 15:47–64; 1945.

313. HACKER, I. "Systematische Traumbeobachtungen mit besonderer Beruecksichtigung der Gedanken," *Arch. Psychol.,* 21:1–131; 1911.

314. HALSTEAD, W. "Chronic Intermittent Anoxia and the Dynamic Visual Field," *J. Psychol.,* 20:49–56; 945.

315. HARTMANN, F. *Die Orientierung,* Leipzig, Vogel, 1902.

316. HARTMANN, H. "Halluzinierte Flaechenfarben und Bewegungen," *Monat. Psychiat. Neurol.,* 56:1–14; 1924.

317. HARTMANN, H. "Psychoanalysis and the Concept of Health," *Int. J. Psychoanal.,* 20:308–321; 1939.

318. HARTMANN, H., KRIS, E. and LOEWENSTEIN, R. "Comments on the Formation of Psychic Structure," pp. 11–38. In: *The Psychoanalytic Study of the Child,* Vol. II, New York, International Universities Press, 1946.

319. HARTMANN, H., KRIS, E. and LOEWENSTEIN, R. "Notes on the

Theory of Aggression," pp. 9–36. In: *The Psychoanalytic Study of the Child*, Vol. III/IV, New York, International Universities Press, 1947.

319a. HARTMANN, H. "Comments on the Psychoanalytic Theory of Instinctual Drives," *Psychoanal. Quart.*, 17:368–388; 1948.

320. HARTMANN, H. "Comments on the Psychoanalytic Theory of the Ego," pp. 74–96. In: *The Psychoanalytic Study of the Child*, Vol. V, New York International Universities Press, 1950.

321. HARTMANN, H., (1937). "Ego Psychology and the Problem of Adaptation," pp. 362–396. In: Rapaport, D., *Organization and Pathology of Thought*, New York, Columbia University Press, 1951.

321a. HARTMANN, H. "The Mutual Influences in the Development of Ego and Id," pp. 9–30. In: *The Psychoanalytic Study of the Child*, Vol. VII, New York, International Universities Press, 1952.

322. HARTRIDGE, H. "Recent Advances in Color Vision," *Science*, 108:395–404; 1948.

323. HEAD, H. and HOLMES, G. "Sensory Disturbances From Cerebral Lesions," *Brain, V*, 34:102–254; 1895.

324. HEAD, H. "Sensation and the Cerebral Cortex," *Brain*, 41:57–253; 1948.

325. HEAD, H. "Some Principles of Neurology," *Brain*, 41:334–354; 1918.

326. HEAD, H. "Aphasia and Kindred Disorders of Speech," *Brain*, 43:87–165; 1920.

327. HEAD, H. *Studies in Neurology*, Vols. I and II, London, Frowde, 1920.

328. HEBB, D. O. *The Organization of Behavior*, New York, Wiley and Sons, 1949.

329. HEGGE, T. "Die phaenomenalen Gedaechtnisse," *Klin. Wochenschr.*, 742–744; 1922.

330. HEILBRONNER, K. "Die aphasischen, apraktischen und agnostichen Stoerungen," *Handbuch d. Neurol.*, 1:982–1093; 1910.

331. HEILER, F. *Prayer: a Study in the History and Psychology of Religion*, London, Oxford University Press, 1932.

332. HELMHOLTZ, H. *Die Lehre von den Tonempfindungen als physiologische Grundlage fuer die Theorie der Musik*, 1862.

333. HELMHOLTZ, H. *Treatise on Physiological Optics,* trans. 3rd German ed., ed. James P. C. Southall, Ithaca, Optical Society of America, 1924.

334. HENDRICK, I. "The Discussion of the 'Instinct to Master,'" *Psychoanal. Quart.,* 12:561–565; 1943.

335. HENDRICK, I. "Work and the Pleasure Principle," *Psychoanal. Quart.,* 12:311–329; 1943.

336. HENNIG, R. "Entstehung und Bedeutung der Synopsien," *Z. Psychol.,* 10:183–222; 1896.

337. HENNING, H. "Kuenstliche Geruchsfaehrte und Reactionstruktur der Ameise," *Z. Psychol.,* 74:161–202; 1916.

338. HENNING, H. "Pruefung eines Wuenschelrutengaengers durch eine wissenschaftliche Kommission," *Z. Psychol.,* 82:314–333; 1919.

339. HENRI, V. *Ueber die Raumwahrnehmungen des Tastsinnes,* Berlin, 1898.

340. HENSCHEN, S. "Ueber die Hoersphaere," *J. Psychol. Neurol.,* 22, (Ergaenzungsheft 3), 1918.

341. HERING, E. *Grundzuege der Lehre vom Lichtsinn,* Leipzig, 1920.

342. HERSCHMANN, H. and POETZL, O. "Bemerkungen ueber die Aphasie der Polyglotten," *Neurol. Zentral.,* 39:114–120; 1920.

342a. HERMANN, I. *Das Ich und das Denken,* Wien, Internationaler Psychoanalytischer Verlag, 1924.

342b. HERMANN, I. *Psychoanalyse und Logik,* Wien, Internationaler Psychoanalytischer Verlag, 1929.

343. HERRMANN, G. and POETZL, O. *Ueber die Agraphie, etc.,* Berlin, Karger, 1926.

344. HEYMANNS, G. "Eine Enquete ueber Depersonalisation und 'Fausse Reconnaissance,'" *Z. Psychol.,* 36:321–343; 1904.

345. HEYMANNS, G. "Weitere Daten ueber Depersonalisation und 'Fausse Reconnaissance,'" *Z. Psychol.,* 43:1–17; 1906.

346. HILLEBRAND, F. "Ruhe der Objekte bei Blickbewegungen," *J. Psychiat. Neurol.,* 40:213–265; 1920.

347. HILGARD, E. and MARQUIS, D. *Conditioning and Learning,* New York, Appleton, 1940.

348. HILGARD, E. *Theories of Learning,* New York, Appleton, 1948.

349. HIRSCHFELD, M. *Die Homosexualitaet des Mannes und des Weibes,* Berlin, Marcus, 1914.

350. HOEFFDING, H. *Der menschliche Gedanke, seine Formen und seine Aufgaben,* Leipzig, Reisland, 1911.

351. HOFFMANN, H. *Die individuelle Entwicklungskurve des Menschen,* Berlin, Springer, 1922.

352. HOFFMANN, H. *Vererbung im Seelenleben. Einfuehrung in die psychiatrische Konstitutions- und Vererbungslehre,* Berlin, Springer, 1922.

353. HOLT, R. and BELLAK, L. "Somatotypes in Relation to Dementia Praecox," *Amer. J. Psychiat.,* 104:713–724; 1948.

354. HOLT, R. "Review of Sheldon's *Varieties of Delinquent Youth,*" *J. Abnorm. Soc. Psychol.,* 45:790–795; 1950.

355. HOLZMANN, P. "Cognitive Attitudes of Leveling and Sharpening in Time-Error Assimilation Tendencies," 1952. (Unpublished Ph.D. Thesis, University of Kansas Library.)

356. HORNEY, K. "Zur Genese des weiblichen Kastrations-Komplexes," *Int. Z. Psychoanal.,* 9:12–26; 1923.

357. HORSLEY, J. *Narco-Analysis,* London, Oxford University Press, 1943.

358. HUMPHREY, G. *The Nature of Learning,* London, Kegan Paul, 1933.

359. HUMPHREY, G. *Directed Thinking,* New York, Dodd, Mead, 1948.

360. HUMPHREY, G. *Thinking: an Introduction to Its Experimental Psychology,* New York, Wiley, 1951.

361. HUNT, J. McV., ed. *Personality and the Behavior Disorders,* Vols. I and II, New York, Ronald Press, 1944.

362. HUSSERL, E. "Philosophie als strenge Wissenschaft," *Logos,* 1:289–341; 1921.

363. HUSSERL, E. *Ideen zu einer reinen Phaenomenologie und phaenomenologischen Philosophie. I. Buch: Allgemeine Einfuehrung in die reine Phaenomenologie,* Halle, Niemeyer, 1913.

364. HUSSERL, E. *Logische Untersuchungen,* 2 vols., Vol. I: *Prolegomena zur reinen Logik;* Vol. II: *Untersuchungen zur Phaenomenologie und Theorie der Erkenntnis,* Halle, Niemeyer, 1921.

365. ICHOK, G. "Die tuberkuloese Psychoneurose," *Z. Tuberkul.,* 31:334–350; 1920.

366. ISSERLIN, M. "Ueber Agrammatismus," *Z. Neurol. Psychiat.,* 75:332–410; 1922.

367. JACKSON, H. "Reprint of Some of Hughlings Jackson's Papers on Affections of Speech," *Brain,* 38:28–190; 1915.

368. JAENSCH, E. "Zur Analyse der Gesichtswahrnehmungen," *Z. Psychol.,* Suppl. Vol. IV, Leipzig, Barth, 1909.

369. JAENSCH, E. "Ueber die Wahrnehmung des Raumes," *Z. Psychol.*, Suppl. Vol. VI, Leipzig, Barth, 1911.

370. JAENSCH, E. "Ueber Grundfragen der Farbenpsychologie," *Z. Psychol.*, 83:257–265; 1920.

371. JAENSCH, E. "Zur Methodik experimenteller Untersuchungen an optischen Anschauungsbildern," *Z. Psychol.*, 85:37–82; 1920.

372. JAENSCH, E. *Eidetic Imagery*, London, Paul, Trench, 1930.

373. JAMES, W. *The Principles of Psychology*, 2 vols., New York, Holt, 1907.

374. JAMES, W. *The Varieties of Religious Experience*, 2 vols., New York, Holt, 1907.

375. JAMES, W. and LANGE, F. *The Emotions,* Baltimore, Williams and Wilkins, 1922.

376. JANET, P. *L'automatisme psychologique*, Paris, Alcan, 1889.

377. JANET, P. "Une ferida artificielle," *Rev. philos.*, 69:329–357, 483–529, 1910.

378. JASPERS, K. "Die Trugwahrnehmungen, Kritisches Referat," *Z. Neurol. Psychiat.*, Referate u. Ergebnisse, 4:289–354; 1912.

379. JASPERS, K. "Zur Analyse der Trugwahrnehmungen (Leibhaftigkeit und Realitaetsurteil)," *Z. Neurol. Psychiat.*, 6:460–535; 1911.

380. JASPERS, K. "Kausale und verstaendliche Zusammenhaenge zwischen Schicksal und Psychose bei der Dementia praecox (Schizophrenie)," *Z. Neurol. Psychiat.*, 14:158–263; 1913.

381. JASPERS, K. *Strindberg und Van Gogh,* Leipzig, Bircher, 1922.

382. JASPERS, K. *Allgemeine Psychopathologie,* Berlin, Springer, 1948.

383. JENNINGS, H. *Behavior of the Lower Organisms,* New York, Columbia University Press, 1906.

384. JOERGER, J. *Psychiatrische Familiengeschichten,* Berlin, Springer, 1919.

385. JOHANNESSON, A. "The Gestural Origin of Language," *Nature,* 166:60–63; 1950.

386. JOHANNESSON, A. *Gestural Origin of Language,* Oxford, Blackwell, 1952.

387. JONES, E. "The Concept of a Normal Mind," *Int. J. Psychoanal.*, 23:1–8; 1942.

388. JONES, E. *Papers on Psychoanalysis,* 5th ed., Baltimore, Williams and Wilkins, 1948.

389. deJong, H. "Die Hauptgesetze einiger wichtiger koerperlichen Erscheinungen beim psychischen Geschehen von Normalen und Geisteskranken," *Z. Neurol. Psychiat.,* 69:61–141; 1921.

390. Jung, C. *Die psychologische Diagnose des Tatbestandes,* Halle, Marhold, 1906.

391. Jung, C. *Die Bedeutung des Vaters fuer das Schicksal des Einzelnen,* Wien, Deuticke, 1909.

392. Jung, C. *Diagnostische Assoziationsstudien. Beitraege zur experimentellen Psychopathologie,* 2 Bd., Leipzig, Barth, 1910.

393. Jung, C. "Wandlungen und Symbole der Libido," *Jahrb. Psychoanal. Psychopath.,* 3:120–227; 1911.

394. Jung, C. "Versuch einer Darstellung der psychoanalytischen Theorie," *Jahrb. Psychoanal. Psychopath.,* 5:307–441; 1913.

395. Jung, C. *Psychology of the Unconscious,* New York, Moffat, 1921.

396. Jung, C. *Psychological Types,* London, Routledge and Kegan Paul, 1949.

397. Kafka, G. "Tierpsychologie," pp. 11–144. In: *Die Entwicklungsstuffen des Seelenlebens. Vol. III. Handbuch der vergleichenden Psychologie,* ed. G. Kafka, Muenchen, Reinhardt, 1922.

398. Kahn, E. "Psychopathen als revolutionaere Fuehrer," *Z. Neurol. Psychiat.,* 52:90–106; 1919.

399. Kammerer, P. *Allgemeine Biologie,* Stuttgart, Deutsche Verlagsanstalt, 1915.

400. Kandinski, V. K. *Kritische und klinische Betrachtungen im Gebiete der Sinnestaeuschungen,* Berlin, Friedlaender, 1885.

401. Kant, I. *Critique of Pure Reason,* New York, Dutton and Company, 1945.

402. Karpinska, L. v. "Experimentelle Beitraege zur Analyse der Tiefenwahrnehmung," *Z. Psychol. Physiol.,* 57:1–88; 1910.

403. Karplus, J. and Kreidl, A. "Gehirn und Sympathicus. I. Zwischenhirnbasis und Halssympathicus," *Arch. Physiol.,* 129:138–144; 1909. "II. Ein Sympathicuszentrum im Zwischenhirn," *ibid.,* 135:401–416; 1910.

404. Karsten, A. "Psychische Saettigung," *Psychol. Forsch.,* 10:142–254; 1928.

405. Katz, D. "Die Erscheinungsweisen der Farben und ihre Be-

einflussung durch die individuelle Erfahrung," *Z. Psychol.*, Suppl. vol. VII, Leipzig, Barth, 1911.

406. KATZ, D. "Psychologische Versuche mit Amputierten," *Z. Psychol.*, 85:83–117; 1920.

407. KATZ, D. and KELLER, H. H. "Das Zielen bei Tieren," *Z. Psychol.*, 95:27–35; 1923.

408. KATZ, D. *The World of Colour,* London, Kegan Paul, 1935.

409. KAUDERS, O. *Zur Klinik und Analyse der psychomotorischen Stoerung,* Berlin, Karger, 1931.

410. KEHRER, F. "Beitraege zur Aphasielehre mit besonderer Beruecksichtigung der amnestischen Aphasie," *Arch. Psychiat.*, 52:103–300; 1913.

410a. KILPATRICK, F. P., ed. *Human Behavior from the Transactional Point of View,* Princeton, Institute Associated Research, 1952.

411. KINSEY, A., et al. *Sexual Behavior in the Human Male,* New York, Saunders, 1948.

412. KLAGES, L. *Die Probleme der Graphologie. Entwurf einer Psychodiagnostik,* Leipzig, Barth, 1910.

413. KLEIN, G. and KRECH, D. "Cortical Conductivity in the Brain-Injured," *J. Personal.*, 21:118–148; 1952.

414. KLEIN, G. and SCHLESINGER, H. "Where is the Perceiver in Perceptual Theory?" *J. Personal.*, 18:32–47; 1949.

415. KLEIN, G. "The Personal World Through Perception," pp. 328–355. In: *Perception: an Approach to Personality,* eds. R. Blake and G. Ramsey, New York, Ronald, 1951.

416. KLEIN, G. and KRECH, D. "The Problem of Personality and Its Theory," *J. Personal.*, 20:2–23; 1951.

417. KLEIN, G. "Control Processes: an Oversight in Measuring Need," presented in the symposium on, "The Measurement of Human Motives," at the A.P.A. Convention, Washington, D.C., 1952.

418. KLEIN, G. "Studies in Cognitive Style and the Regulation of Need: I, Estimations of Size Under Conditions of Thirst," presented at the A.P.A. Convention, Washington, D.C., 1952.

419. KLEIST, K. "Corticale (innervatorische) Apraxie," *J. Psychiat. Neurol.*, 28:46–112; 1907.

420. KLEIST, K. *Die psychomotorischen Stoerungen Geisteskranker,* Leipzig, Klinkhardt, 1908.

421. KLEIST, K. "Der Gang und der gegenwaertige Stand der Apraxieforschung," *Ergebn. Neurol. Psychiat.*, 1:343–452; 1912.

422. KLEIST, K. "Die psychomotorischen Stoerungen und ihr Verhaeltnis zu den Motilitaetsstoerungen bei Erkrankungen
der Stammganglien," *Monat. Psychiat. Neurol.*, 52:253–
302; 1922.

423. KLEITMAN, N. *Sleep and Wakefulness*, Chicago, University
of Chicago Press, 1939.

424. KLEITMAN, N. "The Sleep-Wakefulness Cycle," pp. 15–61. In:
Problems of Consciousness, ed. H. Abramson, New York,
Macy Foundation, 1951.

425. KLIEN, H. "Beitrag zur Psychopathologie und Psychologie des
Zeitsinns," *Z. Pathopsychol.*, 3:307–362; 1919.

426. KLUEVER, H. "Visual Disturbances After Cerebral Lesions,"
Psychol. Bull., 24:316–358; 1927.

427. KLUEVER, H. "Eidetic Imagery," pp. 699–722. In: *A Handbook of Child Psychology*, 2nd. ed., ed. C. Murchison,
Clark University Press, 1933.

428. KLUEVER, H. "Functional Significance of the Geniculo-Striate
System," *Biological Symposia*, 7:253–299; 1942.

429. KNAUER, A. and BILLIGHEIMER, E. "Ueber organische und
funktionelle Stoerungen des vegetativen Nervensystems
unter besonderer Beruecksichtigung der Schreckneu-
rosen," *Z. Neurol. Psychiat.*, 50:199–283; 1919.

430. KNIGHT, R. P. "Determinism, 'Freedom' and Psychotherapy,"
Psychiatry, 9:251–262; 1946.

431. KNIGHT, R. P. "Borderline States," *Bull. Menninger Clin.*,
17:1–12; 1953. Also in: *Drives, Affect, Behavior*, ed. R.
Loewenstein, New York, International Universities
Press, 1953.

432. KOEHLER, W. "Ueber unbemerkte Empfindungen und Urteils-
taeuschungen," *Z. Psychol. Physiol.*, 66:51–80; 1913.

433. KOEHLER, W. "Akustische Untersuchungen, III," *Z. Psychol.
Physiol.*, 72:1–192; 1915.

434. KOEHLER, W. "Zur Theorie des Sukzessivvergleichs und der
Zeitfehler," *Psychol. Forsch.*, 4:115–175; 1923.

435. KOEHLER, W. *Gestalt Psychology*, New York, Liveright, 1929.

436. KOEHLER, W. and HELD, R. "The Cortical Correlate of Pattern Vision," *Science*, 110:414–419; 1949.

437. KOFFKA, K. "Beitraege zur Psychologie der Gestalt- und
Bewegungserlebnisse. III. Zur Grundlegung der Wahr-
nehmungspsychologie. Eine Auseinandersetzung mit V.
Benussi," *Z. Psychol.*, 73:11–90; 1915.

438. KOFFKA, K. *The Growth of the Mind*, 2nd ed., London,
Kegan Paul, 1928.

439. KOFFKA, K. *Principles of Gestalt Psychology,* New York, Harcourt, Brace, 1935.

440. KOGERER, H. "Der Fall Maria D. Ein Beitrag zur Frage des hypnotischen Verbrechens," *Wien. med. Wochenschr.,* 70:2104–2110; 1920.

441. KOGERER, H. "Die posthypnotische Geburtsanalgesie," *Wien. klin. Wochenschr.,* 35:513–517, 538–540, 558–561; 1922.

442. KOSTER, W. "Zur Kenntniss der Mikropsie und Makropsie," *Arch. Ophthalmol.,* 42:134–178; 1896.

443. KRAEPELIN, E. *Ueber die Beeinflussung einfacher psychischer Vorgaenge durch einige Arzneimittel; Experimentelle Untersuchungen,* Jena, Gustav Fischer, 1892.

444. KRAEPELIN, E. "Die Arbeitskurve," *Philosoph. Studien,* 19: 459–507; 1902.

445. KRAEPELIN, E. *Ueber Sprachstoerungen im Traume,* Leipzig, Engelmann, 1906.

446. KRAEPELIN, E. *Psychiatrie. Ein Lehrbuch fuer Studierende und Aerzte,* (8 Aufl.), Leipzig, Barth, 1909–1913.

447. KRAFFT-EBING, R. v. *Psychopathia Sexualis, mit besonderer Beruecksichtigung der kontraeren Sexualempfindung, etc.,* (14 Aufl.), Stuttgart, Encke, 1912.

448. KRECH, D. "Dynamic Systems, Psychological Fields and Hypothetical Constructs," *Psychol. Rev.,* 57:283–290; 1950.

449. KRECH, D. "Dynamic Systems as Open Neurological Systems," *Psychol. Rev.,* 57:345–362; 1950.

450. KRETSCHMER, E. "Die Gesetze der willkuerlichen Reflexverstaerkung in ihrer Bedeutung fuer das Hysterie- und Simulationsproblem," *Z. Neurol. Psychiat.,* 41:354–385; 1918.

451. KRETSCHMER, E. *Der sensitive Beziehungswahn,* Berlin, Springer, 1918.

452. KRETSCHMER, E. "Ueber psychogene Wahnbildung bei traumatischer Hirnschwaeche," *Z. Neurol. Psychiat.,* 45:272–300; 1919.

453. KRETSCHMER, E. "Zur Kritik des Unbewussten," *Z. Neurol. Psychiat.,* 46:368–387; 1919.

454. KRETSCHMER, E. "Seele und Bewusstsein. Kritisches zur Verstaendigung mit Bleuler," *Z. Neurol. Psychiat.,* 53:97–102; 1920.

455. KRETSCHMER, E. *Medizinische Psychologie,* Leipzig, Thieme, 1922.

456. KRETSCHMER, E. "Konstitution und Rasse," *Z. Neurol. Psychiat.,* 82:139–147; 1923.

457. KRETSCHMER, E. *Physique and Character,* New York, Harcourt, Brace, 1925.

458. KRETSCHMER, E. *Hysteria,* Nerv. ment. dis. Monogr., #44, 1926.

459. KRIES, J. v. "Die Gesichtsempfindungen." In: Nagel, W., ed., *Handbuch d. Physiol. d. Menschen,* Vol. III, Braunschweig, Viehweg, 1905.

460. KRIS, E. "On Preconscious Mental Processes," pp. 474–491. In: Rapaport, D., *Organization and Pathology of Thought,* New York, Columbia University Press, 1951. Also in (461).

461. KRIS, E. *Psychoanalytic Explorations in Art,* New York, International Universities Press, 1952.

462. KROH, O. *Subjektive Anschauungsbilder bei Jugendlichen. Eine psychologisch paedagogische Untersuchung,* Goettingen, Vandenhoech and Ruprecht, 1922.

463. KRONFELD, A. "Ueber neuere pathopsychische phaenomenologische Arbeiten," *Z. Neurol. Psychiat.,* 28:441–459; 1919.

464. KRONFELD, A. *Das Wesen der Psychiatrischen Erkenntnis,* Berlin, Springer, 1920.

465. KRONFELD, A. "Eine Bedenklichkeit der 'angewandten' Psychiatrie," *Z. Neurol. Psychiat.,* 65:364–367; 1921.

466. KRUEGER, F., "Rhythmus und Tonmodulation im Satze," pp. 390–436. In: Wundt, W., Chapter VII, *Voelkerpsychologie,* Bd. 2, Leipzig, Engelmann, 1912.

467. KRUEGER, F. "Beobachtungen ueber Zweiklaenge," *Philos. Studien,* 16:307–379, 568–664; 1900.

468. KRUEGER, F. "Die Tiefendimension und die Gegensaetzlichkeit des Gefuehlslebens," *Festschrift f. Volkelt,* 1918.

469. KUELPE, O. "Der gegenwaertige Stand der experimentellen Aesthetik," III, *Kongress fuer experimentelle Psychologie,* 1906–1907.

470. KUELPE, O. "Ueber die moderne Psychologie des Denkens," *Int. Monat. Wiss.,* 6:1069–1110; 1912.

471. KUEPPERS, E. "Ueber die Deutung der plethysmographischen Kurve," *Z. Psychol.,* 81:129–180; 1919.

472. LADIEU, G., HANFMANN, E. and DEMBO, T. "Studies in Adjustment to Visible Injuries: Evaluation of Help By the Injured," *J. Abnorm. Soc. Psychol.,* 42:169–192; 1947.

473. LADIEU, G., ADLER, D. and DEMBO, T. "Studies in Adjustment

to Visible Injuries; Social Acceptance of the Injured," *J. Soc. Issues,* 4:55–61; 1948.

474. LANDAUER, K. "Handlungen des Schlafenden," *Z. Neurol. Psychiat.,* 39:329–351; 1918.

475. LANG, A. *The Making of Religion,* London, Longmans, Green, 1898.

476. LANGE, L. "Die einfache Reaktion auf Sinneseindruecke," *Wundts Philosoph. Studien,* 4:479–510; 1888.

476a. LASHLEY, K. "The Thalamus and Emotion," *Psychol. Rev.,* 45:42–61; 1938.

477. LASHLEY, K., CHOW, K. and SEMMES, J. "An Examination of the Electrical Field Theory of Cerebral Integration," *Psychol. Rev.,* 58:123–136; 1951.

478. LAUENSTEIN, O. "Ansatz zu einer physiologischen Theorie des Vergleichs und der Zeitfehler," *Psychol. Forsch.,* 17: 130–177; 1933.

479. LEHMANN, A. and BLEULER, E. *Zwangsmaessige Lichtempfindung durch Schall,* Leipzig, 1881.

480. LEHMANN, A. *Die Hauptgesetze menschlichen Gefuehlslebens,* Leipzig, D. Reisland, 1892.

481. LEHMANN, A. *Die koerperlichen Aeusserungen psychischer Zustaende,* Leipzig, D. Reisland, 1899–1905.

482. LEHMANN, A. *Aberglaube und Zauberei von den aeltesten Zeiten an bis in die Gegenwart,* (2 Aufl.), Stuttgart, Enke, 1908.

483. LEIDLER, R. "Versuch einer psychologischen Analyse des Schwindels," *Monat. Ohren.,* 55:144–164; 1921.

484. LENZ, F. "Zur Pathologie der cerebralen Sehbahn unter besonderer Beruecksichtigung ihrer Ergebnisse fuer die Anatomie und Physiologie," *Arch. Ophth.,* 72:1–85, 197–273; 1909.

485. LENZ, F. "Zwei Sektionsfaelle doppelseitiger zentraler Farbenhemianopsie," *Z. Neurol. Psychiat.,* 71:135–186; 1921.

486. LEUBA, J. "Les tendances fondamentales des mystiques chrétiens," *Rev. philos.,* 54:1–36, 441–487; 1902.

487. LEVEY, H. "A Critique of the Theory of Sublimation," *Psychiatry,* 2:239–270; 1939.

488. LEVY-BRUEHL, L. *Primitive Mentality,* London, Allen and Unwin, 1923.

489. LEWIN, B. D. *The Psychoanalysis of Elation,* New York, Norton, 1950.

490. LEWIN, K. "Die psychische Taetigkeit bei der Hemmung von

Willensvorgaengen und das Grundgesetz der Assoziation," Z. Psychol., 77:212–247; 1916.

491. LEWIN, K. "Kriegslandschaft," Z. Psychol., 12:440–447; 1917.

492. LEWIN, K. "Das Problem der Willensmessung und das Grundgesetz der Assoziation," Psychol. Forsch., 1:192–302; 2:65–140; 1922.

493. LEWIN, K. A Dynamic Theory of Personality, New York, McGraw-Hill, 1935.

494. LEWIN, K. "Comments Concerning Psychological Forces and Energies, and the Structure of the Psyche," pp. 76–94. In: Rapaport, D., Organization and Pathology of Thought, New York, Columbia University Press, 1951.

495. LEWIN, K. "Intention, Will and Need," pp. 95–153. In: Rapaport, D., Organization and Pathology of Thought, New York, Columbia University Press, 1951.

496. LICHTHEIM, L. "On Aphasia," Brain, 7:433–484; 1885.

497. LIEBAULT, A. Du sommeil et des etats analogues consideres surtout au point du vue de l'action morale sur le physique, Nancy and Paris, 1866. Also: Vienna, Deuticke, 1892.

498. LICHTENSTEIN, R. and STEINACH, E. "Umstimmung der Homosexualitaet durch Austausch der Pubertaetsdruesen," Muench. med. Wochenschr., 65:145–148; 1918.

499. LIEPMANN, H. "Das Krankheitsbild der Apraxie ('motorische Asymbolie') auf Grund eines Falles von einseitiger Apraxie," Monat. Psychiat. Neurol., 8:15–44, 102–132, 182–197; 1900.

500. LIEPMANN, H. Ueber Ideenflucht, Halle, Marhold, 1904.

501. LIEPMANN, H. Drei Aufsaetze aus dem Apraxiegebiet, Berlin, Karger, 1908.

502. LIEPMANN, H. and PAPPENHEIM, M. "Ueber einen Fall von sogenannter Leitungsaphasie mit anatomischem Befund," Z. Neurol. Psychiat., 27:1–41; 1914.

503. LIEPMANN, H. "Apraxie," Ergebnisse der Medizin, ed. von Brugsch, 1:516; 1920.

504. LIPMANN, O. Abzaehlende Methoden und ihre Verwendungen in der psychologischen Statistik, Leipzig, Barth, 1921.

505. LINDWORSKY, J. Das schlussfolgende Denken, Freiburg, Harder, 1916.

506. LINDWORSKY, J. "Wahrnehmung und Vorstellung," Z. Psychol., 80:201–225; 1918.

507. LINDWORSKY, J. *Der Wille,* Leipzig, Barth, 1919.

508. LINKE, P. *Grundfragen der Wahrnehmungslehre,* Muenchen, Reinhardt, 1918.

509. LIPMANN, O. "Die Spuren interessenbetonter Erlebnisse und ihre Symptome (Theorie, Methoden und Ergebnisse der 'Tatbestandsdiagnostik')," *Beihefte, Z. angew. Psychol.,* Vol. I, Leipzig, Barth, 1911.

510. LIPPS, T. *Aesthetik,* Hamburg, L. Voss, 1903.

511. LIPPS, T. *Leitfaden der Psychologie,* Leipzig, Engelmann, 1903.

512. LIPPS, T. *Vom Fuehlen, Wollen und Denken. Versuch einer Theorie des Willens,* (2 Aufl.), Leipzig, Barth, 1907.

513. LIPPS, T. "Das Wissen von fremden Ichen," *Psychol. Untersuch.,* 1:694–722; 1907.

514. LISSAUER, H. "Ein Fall von Seelenblindheit nebst einem Beitrag zur Theorie derselben," *Arch. Psychiat. Neurol.,* 21:222–270; 1890.

515. LOEB, J. *Der Heliotropismus der Thiere und seine Uebereinstimmung mit dem Heliotropismus der Pflanzen,* Wurzburg, Hertz, 1890.

516. LOEWENFELD, V. *The Nature of Creative Activity,* New York, Harcourt, 1939.

517. LOEWENSTEIN, R. "Conflict and Autonomous Ego Development During the Phallic Phase," pp. 47–52. In: *The Psychoanalytic Study of the Child,* Vol. V, New York, International Universities Press, 1950.

518. LOEWY, M. *Die Aktionsgefuehle: Ein Depersonalisationsfall als Beitrag zur Psychologie des Aktivitaetsgefuehls und des Personlichkeitsbewusstseins,* Prag, Loewy, 1908.

519. LOEWY, P. "Die Beziehungen zwischen Psyche und Statik," *Z. Neurol. Psychiat.,* 65:141–191; 1921.

520. LOMBROSO, C. *The Man of Genius,* English translation, London, Scott, 1891.

521. LOMBROSO, C. *Crime: its Causes and Remedies,* Boston, Little Brown & Company, 1911.

522. LORENZ, K. "Der Kumpan in der Umwelt des Vogels. Der Artgenosse als ausloesendes Moment sozialer Verhaltungsweisen," *J. Ornith.,* 83:137–213; 1935.

523. LURIA, A. "Die Methode der abbildenden Motorik bei Kommunikation der Systeme und ihre Anwendung auf die Affektpsychologie," *Psychol. Forsch.,* 12:127–179; 1929.

524. MACCURDY, J. *The Psychology of Emotion,* New York, Harcourt, Brace, 1925.

525. MacCurdy, J. *Common Principles in Psychology and Physiology,* Cambridge, Harvard University Press, 1928.

526. MacNish, R. *Philosophy of Sleep,* Hartford, Andrus, 1845.

527. McCleary, R. "The Nature of the Galvanic Skin Response," *Psychol. Bull.,* 47:97–117; 1950.

528. McCulloch, W. "Machines That Think and Want," pp. 39–50. In: *Brain and Behavior,* ed. W. C. Halstead, Berkeley, University of California Press, 1950.

529. Maday, S. v. "Begriffsbildung und Denken beim Menschen und beim Pferde," *Arch. Psychol.,* 32:472–490; 1914.

530. Maier, N. and Schneirla, T. *Principles of Animal Psychology,* New York, McGraw-Hill, 1935.

531. Marbe, K. *Experimentell-psychologische Untersuchungen ueber das Urteil,* Leipzig, Engelmann, 1901.

532. Marbe, K. "Ueber das Gedankenlesen und die Gleichfoermigkeit des psychischen Geschehens," *Z. Psychol. Physiol.,* 56:241–263; 1910.

533. Marie, P. *Revision de la question de l'aphasie,* Semaine Médicale, 1906.

534. Marie, P. "Existe-t-il dans le cerveau humain des centres innés ou préformés du language?" *Presse méd.,* 30:177–181; 1922.

535. Martin, L. "Zur Lehre von den Bewegungsvorstellungen," *Z. Psychol. Physiol.,* 56:401–447; 1910.

536. Martin, L. "Die Projektionsmethode und die Lokalisation visueller und anderer Vorstellungsbilder," *Z. Psychol.,* 61:321–545; 1912.

537. Martin, L. "Quantitative Untersuchungen ueber das Verhaeltnis anschaulicher und unanschaulicher Bewusstseinsinhalte," *Z. Psychol. Physiol.,* 65:417–490; 1913.

538. Marx, N. "Beitraege zur Psychologie der Cocainomanie," *Z. Neurol. Psychiat.,* 80:550–559; 1923.

539. Maslow, A. and Mittelmann, B. *Principles of Abnormal Psychology: The Dynamics of Psychic Illness,* 2nd ed., New York, Harper & Brothers, 1951.

540. Massermann, J. *Principles of Dynamic Psychiatry: Including an Integrative Approach to Abnormal and Clinical Psychology,* Philadelphia, Saunders, 1946.

541. Maury, A. *Le sommeil et les rêves,* 3rd ed., Paris, Didier, 1865.

542. Mauthner, F. *Beitraege zu einer Kritik der Sprache. I. Bd. Zur Sprache und zur Psychologie,* (2 Aufl.), Stuttgart, Cotta, 1906.

543. MAUTHNER, L. "Pathologie und Physiologie des Schlafes," *Wien. klin. Wochenschr.*, 3:445–446; 1890.

544. MAUTHNER, L. "Zur Pathologie und Physiologie des Schlafes, nebst Bemerkungen ueber die 'Nona,' " *Wien. med. Wochenschr.*, 40:961, 1001, 1049, 1092, 1144, 1185; 1890.

545. MAYER-GROSS, W. "Ueber die Stellungnahme zur abgelaufenen akuten Psychose," *Z. Neurol. Psychiat.*, 60:160–212; 1920.

546. MEGGENDORFER, F. "Klinische und genealogische Untersuchungen ueber 'Moral Insanity,' " *Z. Neurol. Psychiat.*, 66:208–231; 1921.

547. MEINONG, A. "Ueber Gegenstaende hoeherer Ordnung und deren Verhaeltniss zur inneren Wahrnehmung," *Z. Psychol. Physiol.*, 21:182–271; 1899.

548. MEINONG, A. "Ueber Annahmen," *Z. Psychol.*, Suppl. Vol. II, Leipzig, Barth, 1902.

549. MENNINGER, K. *Love Against Hate*, New York, Harcourt, Brace, 1942.

549a. MERLAN, P. "Brentano and Freud," *J. History of Ideas*, 6: 375–377; 1945; and 10:451; 1949.

550. MESSER, K. "Experimentell-psychologische Untersuchungen ueber das Denken," *Arch. Psychol.*, 8:1–224; 1906.

551. MEUMANN, E. "Beitraege zur Psychologie des Zeitsinns," *Philosoph. Studien*, 8:431–509; 1892.

552. MEUMANN, E. "Beitraege zur Psychologie des Zeitsinns," *Philosoph. Studien*, 9:264–306; 1893.

553. MEUMANN, E. "Beitraege zur Psychologie des Zeitbewusstseins," *Philosoph. Studien*, 12:127–254; 1896.

554. MEYERSON, L., LADIEU, G., HANFMANN, E. and DEMBO, T. "Studies in Adjustment to Visible Injuries: Evaluation of Help By the Injured," *J. Abnorm. Soc. Psychol.*, 42: 169–192; 1947.
WHITE, R., WRIGHT, B. and DEMBO, T. "Studies in Adjustment to Visible Injuries: Evaluation of Curiosity By the Injured," *J. Abnorm. Soc. Psychol.*, 43:13–28; 1948.
LADIEU, G., ADLER, D. and DEMBO, T. "Studies in Adjustment to Visible Injuries; Social Acceptance of the Injured," *J. Soc. Issues*, 4:55–61; 1948.

555. MEYNERT, T. "Amentia, die Verwirrtheit," *Jahrb. Psychiat.*, 9:1–112; 1889–1890.

556. MICHOTTE, A. and PRUEM, E. "Etude expérimentale sur le choix volontaire et ses antécédents immédiats," *Arch. Psychol.*, 10:119–299; 1910.

557. MICHOTTE, A. and RANSY, C. "Contribution à l'étude de la mémoire logique," *Annales Louvain, Inst. sup. de philos.*, 1:3–95; 1912.

558. MILLER, G. *Language and Communication*, New York, Mc-Graw-Hill, 1951.

559. MILLER, N. and DOLLARD, J. *Social Learning and Imitation*, New Haven, Yale University Press, 1941.

560. MITCHELL, S. *Mary Reynolds, a Case of Double Consciousness*, Philadelphia, W. J. Dornan, 1889.

561. MITTELMANN, B. "Psychodynamics of Motility; Studies of Adults, Children and Infants." Paper at the American Psychoanalytic Meetings, Washington, 1952.

562. MOEBIUS, P. "Nietzsche" (3. Ausg.). In: *Ausgewaehlte Werke*, Leipzig, Barth, 1909.

562a. MOEN, P. *Diary*, London, Faber and Faber.

563. MONAKOW, C. v. *Die Lokalisation im Grosshirn und der Abbau der Funktion durch kortikale Herde*, Wiesbaden, Bergmann, 1914.

564. MORGENTHALER, W. *Ein Geisteskranker als Kuenstler. Arbeiten zur angew. Psychiatrie*, I, Bern, Bircher, 1921.

565. MOURGUE, R. "Disorders of Symbolic Thinking Due to Local Lesions of the Brain," *Brit. J. Psychol.* (Med. Section), 1:97–124; 1921.

566. MOURGUE, R. "Le syndrome clinique de la rigidité de cérèbre, etc.," *Schweiz. Arch. Neurol. Psychiat.*, 11:196–203; 1922.

567. MOWRER, O. H. and KLUCKHOHN, C. "Dynamic Theory of Personality," pp. 69–135. In: *Personality and the Behavior Disorders*, ed. J. M. Hunt, Vol. I, New York, Ronald, 1944.

568. MOWRER, O. H. *Learning Theory and Personality Dynamics*, New York, Ronald, 1950.

569. MUELLER, G. "Zur Analyse der Gedaechtnistaetigkeit und des Vorstellungsverlaufes," *Z. Psychol.*, Suppl. Vol. V, 1911; Suppl. Vol. VIII, 1913; Suppl. Vol. IX, 1917, Leipzig, Barth.

570. MUELLER, G. and SCHUMANN, F. "Ueber die psychologischen Grundlagen der Vergleichung gehobener Gewichte," *Pflüg. Arch. Physiol.*, 45:37–112; 1889.

571. MUELLER, G. and PILZECKER, A. "Experimentelle Beitraege zur Lehre vom Gedaechtnis," *Z. Psychol.*, Suppl. Vol. I, Leipzig, Barth, 1900.

572. MUENSTERBERG, H. *Psychologie und Wirtschaftsleben. Ein*

Beitrag zur angewandten Experimentalpsychologie, Leipzig, Barth, 1913.

573. MURALT, L. "Zur Frage der epileptischen Amnesie," *Z. Hypnot.,* 10:75–90; 1902.

574. MURPHY, G. *Personality: a Biosocial Approach to Origins and Structure,* New York, Harper, 1947.

575. NACHMANSOHN, M. "Concerning Experimentally Produced Dreams," pp. 257–287. In: Rapaport, D., *Organization and Pathology of Thought,* New York, Columbia University Press, 1951.

576. NATORP, P. *Allgemeine Psychologie nach kritischer Methode. I. Buch: Objekt und Methode der Psychologie,* Tuebingen, Mohr, 1912.

577. NAVILLE, P. "Mémoires d'un médecin aphasique," *Arch. Psychol.,* 17:1–57; 1918.

578. NIELSEN, J. *Agnosia, Apraxia, Aphasia,* New York, Hoeber, 1947.

578a. NIESSL V. MAYENDORFF. "Tastblindheit nach Schussverletzung der hinteren Wurzeln," *Z. Neurol. Psychiat.,* 39:24–29; 1918.

579. NOTHNAGEL, H. "Ein Fall von ploetzlicher Erblindung," *Wien med. Blaetter,* 11:609–611; 1888.

580. NUNBERG, H. "The Course of the Libidinal Conflict in a Case of Schizophrenia," pp. 24–59. In: *Practice and Theory of Psychoanalysis,* New York, Nerv. and Ment. Dis. Pub., 1948.

581. NUNBERG, H. "On the Catatonic Attack," pp. 3–23. In: *Practice and Theory of Psychoanalysis,* New York, Nerv. and Ment. Dis. Pub., 1948.

582. NUNBERG, H. "The Synthetic Function of the Ego," pp. 120–136. In: *Practice and Theory of Psychoanalysis,* New York, Nerv. and Ment. Dis. Pub., 1948.

583. OBERNDORF, C. "A Theory of Depersonalization," *Trans. Amer. Neurol. Assn.,* 59:150–151; 1933.

584. OBERNDORF, C. "Depersonalization in Relation to Erotization of Thought," *Int. J. Psychoanal.,* 15:271–295; 1934.

585. OBERNDORF, C. "The Genesis of the Feeling of Unreality," *Int. J. Psychoanal.,* 16:296–306; 1935.

586. OBERNDORF, C. "On Retaining the Sense of Reality in States of Depersonalization," *Int. J. Psychoanal.,* 20:137–147; 1939.

587. OEHRWALL, H. "Der sogenannte Muskelsinn," *Skand. Arch. Physiol.,* 32:217–245; 1915.

588. OESTERREICH, K. "Die Entfremdung der Wahrnehmungswelt und die Depersonalisation in der Psychasthenie," *J. Psychol. Neurol.*, 7:253–276; 1906, 8:61–97; 1906, 8:141–174, 220–237; 1907, 9:15–53; 1907.

589. OESTERREICH, K. *Die Phaenomenologie des Ich in ihren Grundproblemen*, Leipzig, Barth, 1910.

590. OESTERREICH, K. *Einfuehrung in die Religionspsychologie*, Berlin, Mittler and Sohn, 1917.

591. OESTERREICH, K. *Occultism and Modern Science*, New York, McBride, 1923.

592. OPPENHEIM, H. and KRAUSE, F. "Ein operativ geheilter Tumor des Occipitallappens des Gehirns," *Berlin Med. Gesellsch.*, 37:429–438; 1906.

593. ORTH, J. *Gefuehl und Bewusstseinslage*, Berlin, Reuther and Reichard, 1903.

594. ORTON, S. *Reading, Writing and Speech Problems in Children*, New York, Norton, 1937.

595. OTTO, R. *Das Heilige. Ueber das Irrationale in der Idee des Goettlichen und sein Verhaeltnis zum Rationalen*, (8th ed.), Breslau, Trewendt u. Granier, 1922.

596. PARRISIUS, W. "Kapillarstudien bei Vasoneurosen," *D. Z. Nervenk.*, 72:310–352; 1921.

597. PAVLOV, J. "Psychische Erregung der Speicheldruesen," *Ergebn. Physiol.*, 3:177–193; 1904.

598. PEAR, T. *Remembering and Forgetting*, New York, Dutton, 1922.

599. PENFIELD, W. and RASMUSSEN, T. *The Cerebral Cortex of Man*, New York, Macmillan, 1950.

600. PENFIELD, W. "Observations on the Anatomy of Memory," *Folia Psychiatrica, Neurologica et Neurochirurgica Neerlandica*, 53:349–351; 1950.

601. PENFIELD, W. "Memory Mechanisms," *Archives of Neurology and Psychiatry*, 67:178–191; 1952.

602. PETERS, W. "Zur Entwicklung der Farbenwahrnehmung nach Versuchen an abnormen Kindern," *Fortschr. Psychol.*, 3:150–166; 1915.

603. PFAENDER, A. *Zur Psychologie der Gesinnungen*, Halle, Niemeyer, 1913.

604. PFEIFER, R. "Die Lokalisation der Tonskala innerhalb der kortikalen Hoersphaere des Menschen," *Monat. Psychiat.*, 50:7–48, 99–108; 1921.

605. PFEIFER, R. and QUENSEL, F. "Ein Fall von reiner sensorischer Amnesie," *Z. Neurol. Psychiat.*, 81:311–330; 1923.

606. PFERSDORFF, K. "Die Gruppierung der sprachlichen Assoziationen," *Monat. Psychiat. Neurol.*, 31:233–250, 350–376, 488–504; 1912.

607. PFISTER, O. "Die psychologische Entraetselung der religioesen Glossolalie und der automatischen Kryptographie," *Jahrb. Psychoanal. Psychopath.*, 3:427–468, 730–794; 1911.

608. PFISTER, O. "Therapy and Ethics." In: *Searchlights on Delinquency*, ed. K. R. Eissler, New York, Int. Univ. Press, 1949.

609. PFISTER, O. *Zum Kampf um die Psychoanalyse*, Vienna, Internat. Psychoanalyt. Verlag, 1920.

610. PFUNGST, O. *Das Pferd des Herrn vom Osten (der kluge Hans)*, Leipzig, Barth, 1907.

611. PIAGET, J. *The Child's Conception of Causality*, London, Paul, Trench, Trubner; New York, Harcourt, Brace, 1930.

612. PIAGET, J. *The Language and Thought of the Child*, 2nd ed., London, Kegan Paul, 1932.

613. PIAGET, J. (1936). *The Origins of Intelligence in Children*, New York, International Universities Press, 1952.

614. PIAGET, J. *Le développement de la notion de temps chez l'enfant*, Paris, Presses Universitaires de France, 1946.

615. PIAGET, J. *La Représentation de l'espace chez l'enfant*, Paris, Presses Universitaires de France, 1948.

616. PIAGET, J. *Introduction à l'épistémologie génétique:* Vol. I, "La pensée mathématique," Paris, Presses Universitaires de France, 1950.

617. PIAGET, J. *Play, Dreams and Imitation in Childhood*, New York, Norton, 1952.

618. PICK, A. *Beitraege zur Pathologie und pathologischen Anatomie des Centralnervensystems*, Berlin, Karger, 1898.

619. PICK, A. "Ueber die Bedeutung des akustischen Sprachcentrums als Hemmungsorgan des Sprachmechanismus," *Wien. klin. Wochenschr.*, 13:823–827; 1900.

620. PICK, A. *Ueber Stoerungen der Orientierung am eigenen Koerper*, Arbeiten aus der deutschen psychiatr. Univ.-Klinik in Prag, Berlin, Karger, 1908.

621. PICK, A. *Zur Symptomatologie des atrophischen Hinterhauptlappens*, Arbeiten aus der deutschen psychiatr. Univ.-Klinik in Prag, Berlin, Karger, 1908.

622. PICK, A. *Ueber das Sprachverstaendnis*, Leipzig, Barth, 1909.

623. PICK, A. *Die agrammatischen Sprachstoerungen. Studien zur*

psychologischen Grundlegung der Aphasielehre, Berlin, Springer, 1913.

624. PICK, A. "Bewegung und Aufmerksamkeit," *Monat. Psychiat. Neurol.,* 40:65–87; 1916.

625. PICK, A. "Historische Notiz zur Empfindungslehre nebst Bemerkungen bezueglich ihrer Verwertung," *Z. Psychol. Physiol.,* 76:232–246; 1916.

626. PICK, A. "Kritische Bemerkungen zur Lehre von den Farbennennungen bei Aphasischen," *Z. Neurol. Psychiat.,* 32:319–325; 1916.

627. PICK, A. "Psychopathologie des Zeitsinns," *Z. Pathopsychol.,* 3:430–441; 1919.

628. PICK, A. "Stoerung der Orientierung am eigenen Koerper," *Psychol. Forsch.,* 1:303–319; 1922.

629. PICK, A. "Zur Lehre von der Halluzinationen," *Monat. Psychiat. Neurol.,* 52:65–76; 1922.

630. POETZL, O. and REDLICH, E. "Demonstration eines Falles bilateraler Affektion der Occipitallappen," *Wien. klin. Wochenschr.,* 24:517–518; 1911.

631. POETZL, O. "Experimentell erregte Traumbilder in ihren Beziehungen zum indirekten Sehen," *Z. Neurol. Psychiat.,* 37:278–349; 1917.

632. POPPELREUTER, W. *Die Stoerungen der niederen und hoeheren Sehleistungen durch Verletzung des Okzipitalhirns,* Bd. I, Leipzig, L. Voss, 1912.

633. POPPELREUTER, W. "Ueber den Versuch einer Revision der psychophysiologischen Lehre von der elementaren Assoziation und Reproduktion," *Monat. Psychiat. Neurol.,* 37:278–323; 1915.

634. POPPELREUTER, W. *Die psychischen Schaedigungen durch Kopfschuss im Kriege,* Leipzig, Voss, 1917.

635. POPPELREUTER, W. "Zur Psychologie und Pathologie der optischen Wahrnehmung," *Z. Neurol. Psychiat.,* 83:26–152; 1923.

636. PRATT, C. *The Logic of Modern Psychology,* New York, Macmillan, 1939.

637. PREUSS, K. T. "Der Ursprung der Religion und Kunst," *Globus,* 86:321–327, 355–363, 375–379, 388–392; 1904. 87:333–337, 347–350, 380–384, 394–400, 413–419; 1905.

638. PRINCE, M. and PETERSON, F. "Experiments in Psychogalvanic Reactions From Co-Conscious (Subconscious) Ideas in a Case of Multiple Personality," *J. Abnorm. Soc. Psychol.,* 3:114–131; 1908–1909.

639. PRINCE, M. *The Dissociation of a Personality*, New York, Longmans, 1920.

640. PRINZHORN, H. *Bildnerei der Geisteskranken*, Berlin, Springer, 1923.

641. PRINZHORN, H. "Der Psychiater und die Psychoanalyse," *Z. Neurol. Psychiat.*, 80:1–9; 1923.

642. RADL, E. *Untersuchungen ueber den Phototropismus der Tiere*, Leipzig, Engelmann, 1903.

643. RAEHLMANN, E. "Physiologisch-psychologische Studien ueber die Entwicklung der Gesichtswahrnehmungen bei Kindern und bei operierten Blindgeborenen," *Z. Psychol. Physiol. Sinnesorg.*, 2:53–96; 1891.

644. RAIMANN, E. "Ueber Glykosurie und alimentaere Glykosurie bei Geisteskranken," *Z. f. Heilk., Abt. f. interne Med.*, 23:145–208; 1902.

645. RANK, O. *Das Inzest-Motiv in Dichtung und Sage. Grundzuege einer Psychologie des dichterischen Schaffens*, Leipzig and Wien, Deuticke, 1912.

646. RANK, O. *The Myth of the Birth of the Hero*, New York, Brunner, 1952.

647. RANK, O. "Perversion und Neurose," *Int. Z. Psychoanal.*, 8:397–420; 1922.

648. RANK, O. *The Trauma of Birth*, New York, Harcourt, Brace, 1929.

649. RANSCHBURG, P. *Das kranke Gedaechtnis*, Leipzig, Barth, 1911.

650. RAPAPORT, D., GILL, M. and SCHAFER, R. *Diagnostic Psychological Testing*, 2 vols., Chicago, Year Book Publishers, 1945–1946.

651. RAPAPORT, D. "Principles Underlying Non-Projective Tests of Personality," *Annals New York Acad. Sci.*, 66:643–652; 1946.

652. RAPAPORT, D. "Technological Growth and the Psychology of Man," *Psychiatry*, 10:253–259; 1947.

653. RAPAPORT, D. Review: Sartre's *The Psychology of Imagination, Psychoanal. Quart.*, 18:389–390; 1949.

654. RAPAPORT, D. *Emotions and Memory*, 2nd ed., New York, International Universities Press, 1950.

655. RAPAPORT, D. "On the Psychoanalytic Theory of Thinking," *Int. J. Psychoanal.*, 31:1–10; 1950.

656. RAPAPORT, D. "The Autonomy of the Ego," *Bull. Menninger Clin.*, 15:113–123; 1951.

657. RAPAPORT, D. "The Conceptual Model of Psychoanalysis," *J. Personal.*, 20:56–81; 1951.

658. RAPAPORT, D. *Organization and Pathology of Thought,* New York, Columbia University Press, 1951.

659. RAPAPORT, D. "States of Consciousness, a Psychopathological and Psychodynamic View," pp. 18–57. In: *Problems of Consciousness,* Transactions of the Second Conference, New York, Josiah Macy, Jr. Foundation, 1951.

660. RAPAPORT, D. "On the Psychoanalytic Theory of Affects." (In press: *Int. J. Psychoanal.,* 1953.)

661. RAPAPORT, D. "Projective Techniques and the Theory of Thinking," *J. Proj. Tech.,* 16:269–275; 1952.

662. REDLICH, E. and BONVICINI, G. "Ueber das Fehlen der Wahrnehmung der eigenen Blindheit bei Hirnkrankheiten," *J. Psychiat. Neurol.,* 29:1–133; 1909.

663. REDLICH, E. and DORSEY, J. "Denial of Blindness by Patients With Cerebral Disease," *Arch. N. P.,* 53:407–417; 1945.

664. REICH, W. *Charakteranalyse,* Vienna, Selbstverlag des Verfassers, 1933.

665. REICHARDT, M. "Theoretisches ueber die Psyche," *J. Psychol. Neurol.,* 23:168–184; 1918.

666. REIK, T. *Der eigene und der fremde Gott. Zur Psychoanalyse der religioesen Entwicklung,* Vienna, Internat. psychoanal. Verlag, 1923.

667. REIK, T. *The Psychological Problems of Religion,* New York, Farrar, 1946.

668. REISS, E. "Ueber erbliche Belastung bei Schwerverbrechern," *Klin. Wochenschr.,* 1:2184–2187; 1922.

669. RIEGER, C. "Ueber Apparate in dem Hirn," *Arbeit psychiat. Klinik. Wuerzburg,* 5. Heft, I–VIII, 197, Jena, Fischer, 1909.

670. RIKLIN, F. *Hebung epileptischer Amnesien durch Hypnose,* (Diss.) Zurich, 1903.

671. RIKLIN, F. "Zur Anwendung der Hypnose bei epileptischen Amnesien," *J. Psychol. Neurol.,* 2:28–30;1903.

672. RITTERSHAUS, E. "Die Komplexforschung," *J. Psychol. Neurol.,* 15:184–220; 1910, 16:1–43; 1910.

673. RITTERSHAUS, E. "Die 'Spuren interessebetonter Erlebnisse' und die 'Komplexforschung,'" *Z. Neurol. Psychiat.,* 8: 273–283; 1911.

674. RODENWALDT, E. "Aufnahme des geistigen Inventars Gesunder als Masstab fuer Defektpruefungen bei Kranken," *Monat. Psychiat. Neurol.,* 17:17–83; 1905.

675. ROETHLISBERGER, F. and DICKSON, W. *Management and the Worker,* Cambridge, Harvard University Press, 1939.

676. ROFFENSTEIN, G. "Experiments on Symbolization in Dreams," pp. 249–256. In: Rapaport, D., *Organization and Pathology of Thought*, New York, Columbia University Press, 1951.

677. ROMEIS, B. "Quantitative Untersuchungen ueber die Wirkung von Thyroxin, Dijodtyrosin, Jodothyrin und Jodthyreoglobulin," *Klin. Wochenschr.*, 1:1262; 1922.

678. RUEDIN, E. *Ueber die klinischen Formen der Seelenstoerungen bei zu lebenslaenglicher Zuchthausstrafe Verurteilten*, Muenchen, Wolf, 1909.

679. RUNZE, G. "Psychologie der Religion," pp. 93–180. In: *Die Funktionen des normalen Seelenlebens. Vol. II. Handbuch der vergleichenden Psychologie*, ed. C. Kafka, Muenchen, Reinhardt, 1922.

680. SADGER, J. *Die Lehre von den Geschlechtsverirrungen (Psychopathia sexualis)*, Wien, Deuticke, 1921.

681. SALOMON, E. "Motorische Aphasie mit Agrammatismus und sensorischagrammatischen Stoerungen," *Monat. Psychiat. Neurol.*, 35:181–208, 216–275; 1914.

682. SALOMON, E. "Die Lokalisation des Depeschenstils," *Monat. Psychiat. Neurol.*, 45:221–228; 1919.

683. SANDER, F. "Experimentelle Ergebnisse der Gestaltpsychologie," *Ber. Kong. exper. Psychol.*, 10:23–87; 1928.

684. SARTRE, J. *The Psychology of Imagination*, New York, Philosophical Library, 1948.

685. SCHAFER, R. "A Study of Personality Characteristics Related to Hypnotizability." Master's Thesis, University of Kansas, 1947.

685a. SCHAFER, R. "A Study of Thought-Processes in a Word-Association Test," *Character and Personality*, 13:212–227; 1945.

686. SCHAFER, R. *The Clinical Application of Psychological Tests*, New York, International Universities Press, 1948.

687. SCHEERER, M. "Problems of Performance Analysis in the Study of Personality," *Annals New York Acad. Sci.*, 46:653–678; 1946.

688. SCHELER, M. "Formalismus und materiale Wertethik," *J. Phaenomenol.*, 1:1913, 2:1916.

689. SCHELER, M. *Wesen und Formen der Sympathie*, 5th ed., Frankfurt a.M., Schulte-Bumke, 1948.

690. SCHILDER, P. *Selbstbewusstsein und Persoenlichkeitsbewusstsein*, Berlin, Springer, 1914.

691. SCHILDER, P. "Zur Kenntniss symbolaehnlicher Bildungen im

Rahmen der Schizophrenie," *Z. Neurol. Psychiat.*, 26: 201–244; 1914.

692. SCHILDER, P. *Wahn und Erkenntnis*, Berlin, Springer, 1918.

693. SCHILDER, P. and BAUER, J. "Ueber einige psychophysiologische Mechanismen functioneller Neurosen," *Dtsch. Nervenk.*, 64:279–299; 1919.

693a. See Reference 270.

694. SCHILDER, P. "Ueber Halluzinationen," *Wien. klin. Wochenschr.*, 33:53–54; 1920.

695. SCHILDER, P. "Ueber Gedankenentwicklung," *Z. Neurol. Psychiat.*, 59:250–263; 1920. Also: "On the Development of Thoughts," pp. 497–518. In: Rapaport, D., *Organization and Pathology of Thought*, New York, Columbia University Press, 1951.

696. SCHILDER, P. "Ueber Identifizierung, auf Grund der Analyse eines Falles von Homosexualitaet," *Z. Neurol. Psychiat.*, 59:217–249; 1920.

697. SCHILDER, P. "Zur Theorie der Entfremdung der Wahrnehmungswelt," *Allg. Z. Psychiat. Neurol.*, 76:766–773; 1920.

698. SCHILDER, P. and DIMITZ, L. "Encephalitis epidemica des Jahres 1920," *Z. Neurol. Psychiat.*, 68:299–340; 1921.

699. SCHILDER, P. "Ueber die kausale Bedeutung des durch Psychoanalyse gewonnen Materiales," *Wien. klin. Wochenschr.*, 34:355–393; 1921.

700. SCHILDER, P. "Vorstudien zu einer Psychologie der Manie," *Z. Neurol. Psychiat.*, 68:90–135; 1921.

701. SCHILDER, P. "Bemerkungen ueber die Psychologie des paralytischen Groessenwahns," *Z. Neurol. Psychiat.*, 74:1–14; 1922.

702. SCHILDER, P. "Einige Bemerkungen zu der Problemsphaere: Cortex, Stammganglien—Psyche, Neurose," *Z. Neurol. Psychiat.*, 74:454–481; 1922.

703. SCHILDER, P. *Ueber das Wesen der Hypnose*, Berlin, Springer, 1922. English: *The Nature of Hypnosis*, New York, International Universities Press, 1953.

704. SCHILDER, P. "Das Unbewusste," *Z. Neurol. Psychiat.*, 80:96–116; 1922.

705. SCHILDER, P. "Zur Pathologie des Ichideals," *Int. Z. Psychoanal.*, 8:322–325; 1922.

706. SCHILDER, P. *Das Koerperschema*, Berlin, Springer, 1923.

707. SCHILDER, P. *Seele und Leben*, Berlin, Springer, 1923.

708. SCHILDER, P. "Ueber den Wirkungswert psychischer Erleb-

nisse und ueber die Vielheit der Quellgebiete der psy-chischen Energie," *Arch. Psychiatrie,* 70:1–15; 1924.

709. SCHILDER, P. "Ueber den Wirkungswert psychischer Erleb-nisse und ueber die Vielheit der Quellgebiete der psy-chischen Energie," *Arch. Psychiat. Nervenk.,* 70:1–15; 1924.

710. SCHILDER, P. "Zur Lehre von den Amnesien Epileptischer, von der Schlafmittelhypnose und vom Gedaechtnis," *Arch. Psychiat. Nervenkr.,* 72:323–325; 1924.

711. SCHILDER, P. "Zur Psychologie epileptischer Ausnahmezu-staende (mit besonderen Beruecksichtigung des Ge-daechtnisses)," *Allg. Z. Psychiat.,* 80:33–39; 1924.

712. SCHILDER, P. "Hypnosis Combined With Narcotics," *Wien. klin. Wochenschr.,* 38:1213–1214; 1925.

713. SCHILDER, P. and POLLAK, E. "Ueber die Bedeutung extra-pyramidaler Apparate f. die Umsetzung des Bewe-gungsentwurfes in die Handlung," *Jahrb. Psychiat. Neu-rol.,* 44:37–54; 1925.

714. SCHILDER, P. and HOFF, H. "Cerebellar Imitation Test," *Dtsch. Nervenkr.,* 90:284–295; 1926.

715. SCHILDER, P. and HOFF, H. "Neue Beobachtungen ueber Imi-tationsphaenomene," *Dtsch. Nervenkr.,* 93:161–173; 1926.

716. SCHILDER, P. and SUGAR, N. "Zur Lehre von den schizophre-nen Sprachstoerungen," *Z. Neurol. Psychiat.,* 104:689–714; 1926.

717. SCHILDER, P. and POLLAK, E. "Zur Lehre von den Sprach-antrieben," *Z. Neurol. Psychiat.,* 104:480–502; 1926.

718. SCHILDER, P. and KAUDERS, O. *Hypnosis,* Trans. Rothenberg, S., Nerv. and Ment. Dis. Monogr. Series, #46, 1927.

719. SCHILDER, P. "Ueber Gleichgewichtsstoerungen," *Jahrb. Psy-chiat. Neurol.,* 45:160–186; 1927.

720. SCHILDER, P. "Zentrale Bewegunsstoerungen mit besonderer Beruecksichtigung der Sprache," *Wien. med. Wochen-schr.,* 77:635–668; 1927.

720a. SCHILDER, P. "Der Begriff der Demenz," *Wien. med. Wo-chenschr.,* 78:936–938; 1929.

721. SCHILDER, P. *Gedanken zur Naturphilosophie,* Wien, Spring-er, 1928.

722. SCHILDER, P. and HOFF, H. "Zur Kenntniss der Symptoma-tologie vestibulaerer Erkrankungen," *Dtsch. Nervenkr.,* 103:176–188; 1928.

722a. SCHILDER, P. and HOFF, H. "Eine neue Tasttaeuschung und ihre Beziehung zum Koerperschema," *Z. Psychol. Phy-siol. Sinnesorgane,* 60:284–289; 1929.

723. SCHILDER, P. and EISINGER, K. "Traeume bei Labyrinth-laesionen," *Monat. Psychiat. Neurol.*, 73:314–329; 1929.

724. SCHILDER, P. "Ueber das Hypnose-Erlebnis der Schizophrenen," *Z. Neurol. Psychiat.*, 120:700–707; 1929.

725. SCHILDER, P. and PARKER, S. "Das Koerperschema im Lift," *Z. Neurol. Psychiat.*, 128:777–783; 1930.

726. SCHILDER, P. and KANNER, L. "Movements in Optic Imagination of Movements," *J. Nerv. Ment. Dis.*, 72:489–517; 1930.

727. SCHILDER, P. "Unity of Body, Sadism and Dizziness," *Psychoanal. Rev.*, 17:114–122; 1930.

728. SCHILDER, P. "Vestibulo-Optik und Koerperschema in der Alkoholhalluzinose," *Z. Neurol. Psychiat.*, 128:784–791; 1930.

729. SCHILDER, P. (1931) *Brain and Personality,* 2nd ed., New York, International Universities Press, 1951.

730. SCHILDER, P. and BROMBERG, W. "On Tactile Imagination and Tactile After-Effects," *Arch. N. P.*, 28:37–51; 1932.

731. SCHILDER, P. and BROMBERG, W. "Death and Dying: Comparative Study of Attitudes and Mental Reactions Toward Death and Dying," *Psychoanal. Rev.*, 20:133–185; 1933.

732. SCHILDER, P. "Experiments on Imagination, After-Images and Hallucinations," *Amer. J. Psychiat.*, 13:597–611; 1933.

733. SCHILDER, P. "Das Koerperbild und die Sozialpsychologie," *Imago,* 19:367–376; 1933.

734. SCHILDER, P. "Paraphrenie, Narkolepsie, Hypophyse," *Wien. med. Wochenschr.*, 83:326–327; 1933.

735. SCHILDER, P. and BROMBERG, W. "Psychologic Considerations in Alcoholic Hallucinosis—Castration and Dismembering Motives (Zerstueckelungsmotiv)," *Int. J. Psychoanal.*, 14:206–224; 1933.

736. SCHILDER, P. "Vestibular Apparatus in Neurosis and Psychoses," *J. Nerv. Ment. Dis.*, 78:1–137; 1933.

737. SCHILDER, P. "Self-Consciousness and Optic Imagination in a Case of Depression," *Psychoanal. Rev.*, 21:316–328; 1934.

738. SCHILDER, P. and ROSS, N. "Tachistoscopic Experiments on the Perception of the Human Figure," *J. Gen. Psychol.*, 10:152; 1934.

738a. SCHILDER, P. and WECHSLER, D. "The Attitudes of Children Toward Death," *J. Genet. Psychol.*, 46:406–451; 1934.

739. SCHILDER, P. and PARKER, S. "Acoustic Imagination and

Acoustic Hallucination," *Arch. N. P.*, 34:744–757; 1935.

740. SCHILDER, P. (1935) *The Image and Appearance of the Human Body,* New York, International Universities Press, 1950.

741. SCHILDER, P. and CURRAN, F. "Paraphasic Signs in Diffuse Lesions of the Brain," *J. Nerv. Ment. Dis.*, 82:613–636; 1935.

742. SCHILDER, P. and WECHSLER, D. "What Do Children Know About the Interior of the Body?" *Int. J. Psychoanal.*, 16:355–360; 1935.

743. SCHILDER, P. "Analysis of Ideologies as Psychotherapeutic Method, Especially in Group Treatment," *Amer. J. Psychiat.*, 93:601–617; 1936.

744. SCHILDER, P. and BENDER, LAURETTA. "Suicidal Preoccupations and Attempts in Children," *Amer. J. Orthopsychiat.*, 7:225–234; 1937.

744a. SCHILDER, P. "The Psychological Implications of Motor Development in Children," *Institute of the Woods Schools,* 4:38–59; 1937.

745. SCHILDER, P. "The Child and the Symbol," *Scientia,* 64:21–26; 1938.

746. SCHILDER, P. "The Social Neurosis," *Psychoanal. Rev.,* 25:1–19; 1938.

747. SCHILDER, P., FINGERT, H. and KAGAN, J. "The Goodenough Test in Insulin and Metrazol Treatment of Schizophrenia," *J. Gen. Psychol.,* 21:349–365; 1939.

748. SCHILDER, P. "Cultural Patterns and Constructive Psychology," *Psychoanal. Rev.,* 27:159–177; 1940.

749. SCHILDER, P. *Goals and Desires of Man,* New York, Columbia University Press, 1942.

750. SCHILDER, P. *Mind: Perception and Thought in Their Constructive Aspects,* New York, Columbia University Press, 1942.

751. SCHILDER, P. "On the Development of Thoughts," pp. 497–518. In: Rapaport, D., *Organization and Pathology of Thought,* New York, Columbia University Press, 1951.

752. SCHILDER, P. "Studies Concerning the Psychology and Symptomatology of General Paresis," pp. 519–580. In: Rapaport, D., *Organization and Pathology of Thought,* New York, Columbia University Press, 1951.

752a. SCHILDER, P. *Psychoanalysis, Man and Society,* New York, Norton, 1951.

753. SCHMIDT, W. *Der Ursprung der Gottesidee,* I, Muenster, Aschendorff, 1912.

754. SCHNEIDER, C. *Tierpsychologisches Praktikum in Dialogform,* Leipzig, Veit, 1912.

755. SCHNEIDER, K. "Bemerkungen zu einer phaenomenologischen Psychologie der invertierten Sexualitaet und erotischen Liebe," *Z. Neurol. Psychiat.,* 71:346–351; 1921.

756. SCHNEIDER, K. "Pathologische Beitraege zur psychologischen Phaenomenologie von Liebe und Mitfuehlen," *Z. Neurol. Psychiat.,* 65:109–140; 1921.

757. SCHNEIDER, K. "Zur Psychologie und Psychopathologie der Reue," *Monat. Krim.-Psychol. Strafrechtsref.,* 13:40–46; 1922.

758. SCHRENCK-NOTZING, A. VON. *Phenomena of Materialization,* New York, Dutton, 1920.

759. SCHROEDER, J. "Ueber gedankenfluechtige Denkhemmung," *Z. Neurol. Psychiat.,* 2:57–76; 1910.

760. SCHROETTER, K. "Experimental Dreams," pp. 234–248. In: Rapaport, D., *Organization and Pathology of Thought,* New York, Columbia University Press, 1951.

761. SCHROTTENBACH, H. "Studien ueber den Einfluss der Grosshirntaetigkeit auf die Magensaftsekretion des Menschen," *Z. Neurol. Psychiat.,* 69:254–302; 1921.

762. SCHULTZ, J. *Die seelische Krankenbehandlung (Psychotherapie),* 3rd ed., Jena, Fischer, 1922.

763. SCHUMANN, F. "Beitraege zur Analyse der Gesichtswahrnehmungen," *Z. Psychol.,* 23:1–32; 1900, 24:1–33; 1900, 30: 241–291, 321–339; 1902, 36:161–185; 1904.

764. SCHUMANN, F. *Psychologie des Lesens,* Leipzig, Barth, 1907.

765. SCHUMANN, F. "Untersuchungen ueber die psychologischen Grundprobleme der Tiefenwahrnehmung. I. Die Repraesentation des leeren Raumes im Bewusstsein. Eine neue Empfindung," *Z. Psychol.,* 85:224–244; 1920.

766. SCHURTZ, H. *Altersklassen und Maennerbuende,* Berlin, Reimer, 1902.

767. SCHUSTER, P. "Zwangsgreifen und Nachgreifen, zwei posthemiplegische Bewegungsstoerungen," *Z. Neurol. Psychiat.,* 83:586–609; 1923.

768. SCHWARZ, G. "Ueber Rueckfaelligkeit bei Umgewoehnung, I und II," *Psychol. Forsch.,* 2:86–158; 1927, 18:143–190; 1933.

769. SEARS, R. *Survey of Objective Studies of Psychoanalytic Con-*

cepts, New York, Social Science Research Council, Bulletin #51, 1943.

770. SEIFERT, F. "Zur Psychologie der Abstraktion und der Gestaltauffassung," Z. Psychol. Physiol., 78:55–144; 1917.

771. SELZ, O. Die Gesetze des geordneten Denkverlaufes, Stuttgart, Spemann, 1913.

772. SELZ, O. "Komplextheorie und Konstellationstheorie," Z. Psychol. Physiol., 84:211–234; 1920.

773. SEMON, R. Mneme, New York, Macmillan, 1921.

774. SENDEN, M. Raum- und Gestaltauffassung bei operierten Blindgeborenen vor und nach der Operation, Leipzig, Barth, 1932.

774a. SHAKOW, D. The Nature of Deterioration in Schizophrenic Conditions, New York, Nerv. and Ment. Dis. Pub., 1947.

775. SHELDON, W., et al. The Varieties of Human Physique, New York, Harper, 1940.

776. SHELDON, W. The Varieties of Temperament: a Psychology of Constitutional Differences, New York, Harper, 1942.

777. SHELDON, W., et al. Varieties of Delinquent Youth, New York, Harper, 1949.

778. SHERRINGTON, C. "Experiments on the Value of Vascular and Visceral Factors for the Genesis of Emotion," Proc. roy. soc. med., 66:390–403; 1900.

779. SHERRINGTON, C. The Integrative Action of the Nervous System, New York, Scribner, 1907.

780. SIEMERLING, E. Ein Fall von sogenannter Seelenblindheit (nebst anderweitigen cerebralen Symptomen), Berlin, Schumacher, 1890.

781. SILBERER, H. "Bericht ueber eine Methode, gewisse symbolische Halluzinations-Erscheinungen hervorzurufen und zu beobachten," J. Psychoanal., 1:513–525; 1909. Also: "Report on a Method of Eliciting and Observing Certain Symbolic Hallucination-Phenomena," pp. 195–207. In: Rapaport, D., Organization and Pathology of Thought, New York, Columbia University Press, 1951.

782. SILBERER, H. "On Symbol-Formation," pp. 208–233. In: Rapaport, D., Organization and Pathology of Thought, New York, Columbia University Press, 1951.

783. SOMMER, R. "Dreidimensionale Analyse von Ausdrucksbewegungen," Z. Psychol. Physiol., 16:275–297; 1898.

784. SPECHT, W. Ueber die Aufmerksamkeit, Leipzig, Barth, 1909.

785. SPITZ, R. and WOLF, K. "The Smiling Response: a Contribution to the Ontogenesis of Social Relations," Genet. Psychol. Monogr., 34:57–125; 1946.

786. SPITZ, R. "Purposive Grasping," *Personal.*, 1:141–148; 1951.

787. STAERCKE, A. "Psychoanalysis and Psychiatry," *Int. J. Psychoanal.*, 2:361–415; 1921.

788. STARBUCK, E. *Religionspsychologie, empirische Entwicklungsstudie religioesen Bewusstseins*, Leipzig, Klinkhardt, 1909.

789. STAUFFENBERG, J. VON. "Klinische und anatomische Beitraege zur Kenntnis der aphasischen, agnostischen und apraktischen Symptome," *Z. Neurol. Psychiat.*, 39:71–213; 1918.

790. STEFFENS, L. "Ueber die motorische Einstellung," *Z. Psychol.*, 23:241–308; 1900.

791. STEINACH, E. "Willkuerliche Unwandlung von Saeugetier-Maennchen in Tiere mit ausgepraegt weiblichen Geschlechts-charakteren und weiblicher Psyche. Eine Untersuchung ueber die Funktion und Bedeutung der Pubertaetsdruesen," *Arch. Physiol.*, 144:71–108; 1912.

792. STEINS, E. *Werke I: Kreuzeswissenschaft. Studien ueber Johannes a Cruce*, Louvain, Nauwelaerts, 1950.

793. STEKEL, W. *Onanie und Homosexualitaet*, Berlin und Wien, Urban und Schwarzenberg, 1917.

794. STEKEL, W. *Die Geschlechtskaelte der Frau*, Berlin und Wien, Urban und Schwarzenberg, 1919.

795. STEKEL, W. *Conditions of Nervous Anxiety and Their Treatment*, New York, Dodd, Mead and Company, 1923.

795a. STEKEL, W. "The Polyphony of Thought," pp. 311–314. In: Rapaport, D., *Organization and Pathology of Thought*, New York, Columbia University Press, 1951.

796. STEKEL, W. *Impotence in the Male. The Psychic Disorders of Sexual Functions in the Male*, New York, Boni and Liveright, 1927.

797. STENGEL, E. and STEELE, G. "Unawareness of Physical Disability (Anosognosia)," *J. Ment. Sci.*, 92:379–388; 1946.

798. STERBA, R. "Zur Problematik der Sublimierungslehre," *Int. Z.*, 16:370–378; 1930.

799. STERBA, R. *Introduction to the Psychoanalytic Theory of the Libido*, New York, Nerv. and Ment. Dis. Pub., 1942.

800. STERN, C. and W. *Psychologie der fruehen Kindheit*, Leipzig, Barth, 1921.

801. STERN, C. and W. *Die Kindersprache. Eine psychologische und sprachtheoretische Untersuchung*, Leipzig, Barth, 1922.

802. STERN, E. "Beitraege zur Psychologie und Psychopathologie des Selbstwerterlebens," *Z. Pathopsychol.*, 3:500–553; 1919.

803. STERN, E. "Zur Gleichfoermigkeit des psychischen Geschehens," *J. Psychol. Neurol.*, 25:105–128; 1920.

804. STERN, G. *Meaning and Change of Meaning*, Goeteborg, Elanders, 1931.

805. STERN, W. "Ueber verlagerte Raumformen," *Z. angew. Psychol.*, 2:498–525; 1909.

806. STERN, W. "Personalistik der Erinnerung," *Z. Psychol.*, 118: 350–381; 1930.

807. STERN, W. *General Psychology From the Personalistic Standpoint*, New York, Macmillan, 1938.

808. STEVENS, S. *Handbook of Experimental Psychology*, New York, Wiley, 1951.

809. STORCH, A. "Zur Psychologie und Psychopathologie des Selbstwerterlebens," *Arch. ges. Psychol.*, 37:113–128; 1918.

810. STORCH, A. *The Primitive Archaic Forms of Inner Experience and Thought in Schizophrenia*, New York, Nerv. and Ment. Dis. Pub., 1924.

811. STRANSKY, E. *Ueber Sprachverwirrtheit*, Halle, Marhold, 1905.

812. STRANSKY, E. "Angewandte Psychiatrie, Motive und Elemente zu einem Programmentwurf," *Allg. Z. Psychiat.*, 74:22–53; 1918.

813. STRANSKY, E. "Ausnahmezustand und Normalseelenzustand," *Z. Neurol., Psychiat.*, 43:351–358; 1918.

814. STRANSKY, E. "Keine Bedenklichkeit der angewandten Psychiatrie," *Z. Neurol. Psychiat.*, 69:327–331; 1921.

815. STRATTON, G. "Eye-Movement and the Aesthetics of Visual Form," *Philosophische Studien*, ed. Wundt, 20:336–359; 1902.

816. STRATTON, G. "Retroactive Hypermnesia and Other Emotional Effects on Memory," *Psychol. Rev.*, 26:474–486; 1919.

817. STRAUSS, A. and WERNER, H. "Finger Agnosia in Children, With Brief Discussion on Defect and Retardation in Mentally Handicapped Children," *Amer. J. Psychiat.*, 95:1215–1225; 1939.

818. STRICKER, S. *Studien ueber Sprachvorstellungen*, Wien, Braunmueller, 1880.

819. STRUEMPELL, A. "Ueber die Stoerungen der Bewegung bei fast vollstaendiger Anaesthesie eines Armes durch Stichverletzung des Rueckenmarks," *Deutsch. A. Nervenheilk.*, 23:1–38; 1902.

820. STUMPF, C. *Tonpsychologie*. I. Leipzig, 1883. II. 1890.

821. STUMPF, C. "Zur Methodik der Kinderpsychologie," *Z. paedag. Psychol.*, 2:1–21; 1900.

822. STUMPF, C. "Ueber Gefuehlsempfindungen," *Z. Psychol.*, 44: 1–49; 1906.

823. STUMPF, C. "Verlust der Gefuehlsempfindungen im Tongebiete (musikalische Anhedonie)," *Z. Psychol. Physiol.*, 75:39–53; 1916.

824. STUMPF, C. "Empfindung und Vorstellung," *Akad. d. Wiss. Philos. Kl.*, Berlin, Abhandl., 3–116; 1918.

825. SULLIVAN, H. *Conceptions of Modern Psychiatry*. Reprinted from: *Psychiatry*, Vol. III, No. 1, 1940, and Vol. III, No. 2, 1945.

826. TARCHANOFF, J. "Ueber galvanische Erscheinungen in der Haut des Menschen usw.," *Pfluegers Arch. ges. Physiol.*, 46:46–55; 1890.

827. TARDE, G. *Les lois de l'imitation*, Paris, Alcan, 1895.

828. TEUBER, H. and BENDER, MORRIS. "Disturbances in Visual Perception Following Cerebral Lesions." (Paper read at the 12th International Congress of Psychology, Edinburg, Scotland, July 1948.)

829. TEUBER, H. and BENDER, MORRIS. "Psychopathology of Vision," pp. 163–192. In: *Progress in Neurology and Psychiatry*, New York, Grune and Stratton 1949.

830. TEUBER, H. "Neuropsychology," pp. 30–52. In: *Recent Advances in Diagnostic Psychological Testing: a Critical Summary*, Springfield, Illinois, Charles C. Thomas, 1950.

831. TEUBER, H., BATTERSBY, W. and BENDER, MORRIS. "Performance of Complex Visual Tasks After Cerebral Lesions," *J. Nerv. Ment. Dis.*, 114:413–429; 1951.

832. THORPE, W. "The Modern Concept of Instinctive Behavior," *Bull. Animal Behaviour*, 7:12; 1948.

833. TINBERGEN, N. *The Study of Instinct*, Oxford, England, Clarendon Press, 1951.

834. TISCHNER, R. *Einfuehrung in den Okkultismus und Spiritismus*, Muenchen, J. F. Bergmann, 1921.

835. TITCHENER, E. *Lectures on the Elementary Psychology of Feeling and Attention*, New York, Macmillan, 1908.

836. TROEMNER, E. *Das Problem des Schlafes. Biologisch und psychophysiologisch betrachtet*, Wiesbaden, Bergmann, 1912.

837. TROEMNER, E. *Hypnotismus und Suggestion*, Leipzig und Berlin, Teubner, 1913.

838. TROTTER, W. and DAVIES, H. "Experimental Studies in the Innervation of the Skin," *J. Physiol.*, 38:134–146; 1909.

839. UEXKUELL, J. *Theoretical Biology*, New York, Harcourt, Brace, 1926.

840. UEXKUELL, J. and KRIZAT, G. *Streifzuege durch die Umwelten von Tieren und Menschen*, Berlin, Springer, 1934.

841. UEXKUELL, J. *Umwelt und Innenwelt der Tiere*, Berlin, Springer, 1909.

842. UNDERWOOD, B. J. *Experimental Psychology, an Introduction*, New York, Appleton-Century-Crofts, 1949.

843. URBANTSCHITSCH, V. *Ueber subjektive optische Anschauungsbilder*, Wien, Deuticke, 1907.

844. VAN VALCKENBURG, C. "Zur fokalen Lokalisation der Sensibilitaet in der Grosshirnrinde des Menschen," *Z. Neurol. Psychiat.*, 24:294–312; 1914.

845. VERAGUTH, O. *Das psychogalvanische Reflexphaenomen*, Berlin, Karger, 1909.

846. VIERKANDT, A. "Die Anfaenge der Religion und Zauberei," *Globus*, 92:21–25, 40–45, 60–65; 1907.

847. VIGOTSKY, L. "Thought and Speech," *Psychiatry*, 2:29–54; 1939.

848. VILLEY, P. *Le monde des aveugles. Essai de psychologie*, Paris, Flammarion, 1914.

849. VINACKE, W. *The Psychology of Thinking*, New York, McGraw-Hill, 1952.

850. VOGT, C. and O. *Allgemeine Ergebnisse unserer Hirnforschung*, Leipzig, Barth, 1919.

851. VOGT, C. and O. "Zur Kenntnis der pathologischen Veraenderungen des Striatum und der Pathophysiologie der hierbei auftretenden Krankheitserscheinungen," *Sitzungsber. d. Heidelberg. Akad. d. Wiss., Math.-naturw. M.-B. 14, Abt.*, 1919.

852. VOGT, C. and O. "Zur Lehre der Erkrankungen des striaeren Systems," *J. Psychol. Neurol.*, 25:627–846; 1920.

853. VOGT, C. and O. "Erkrankungen der Grosshirnrinde," *J. Psychol. Neurol.*, 28:1–171; 1922.

854. VOLD, M. "Einige Experimente ueber Gesichtsbilder im Traume," *Z. f. Psychologie u. Physiologie der Sinnesorgane*, 13:66–74; 1897.

855. VOLD, M. *Ueber den Traum*, Bd. 1, 2, Leipzig, Barth, 1910, 1912.

856. VOLKELT, H. *Ueber die Vorstellungen der Tiere. Ein Beitrag zur Entwicklungspsychologie*, Leipzig, Engelmann, 1914.

857. Vossler, K. *The Spirit of Language in Civilization,* London, Kegan Paul, 1932.

858. Waelder, R. "The Problem of Freedom in Psychoanalysis and the Problem of Reality-Testing," *Int. J. Psychoanal.,* 17:89–108; 1936.

859. Washburn, M. *Movement and Mental Imagery,* Boston, Houghton Mifflin, 1916.

860. Wasielewsko, W. *Telepathie und Hellsehen. Versuche und Betrachtungen ueber ungewoehnliche seelische Faehigkeiten,* Halle, Marhold, 1922.

861. Weber, E. *Der Einfluss psychischer Vorgaenge auf den Koerper, insbesondere auf die Blutverteilung,* Berlin, Springer, 1910.

862. Weichbrodt, R. "Der Selbstmord," *Abh. Neurol. Psychiat. Psychol. Grenzgeb.,* 27:1–44; 1923.

863. Weinstein, E. and Kahn, R. "Syndrome of Anosognosia," *Arch. N. P.,* 64:772–791; 1950.

864. Weisenburg, T. and McBride, K. *Aphasia,* New York, The Commonwealth Fund, 1935.

865. Weiss, E. and English, O. *Psychosomatic Medicine,* Philadelphia, Saunders, 1949.

866. Weitzenhoffer, A. "The Production of Antisocial Acts Under Hypnosis," *J. Abnorm. Soc. Psychol.,* 44:420–422; 1949.

867. Weizsaecker, V. "Neuere Forschungen und Anschauungen ueber Reflexe und ihre physiologische Bedeutung," *Klin. Wochenschr.,* 1:2217–2220; 1922.

868. Weizsaecker, V. "Ueber die Sensibilitaet, insbesondere den Drucksinn, vom physiologischen Gesichtspunkte aus," *Klin. Wochenschr.,* 2:2109–2112; 1923.

869. Wells, F. "The Systematic Observation of the Personality in Its Relation to the Hygiene of Mind," *Psychol. Rev.,* 21: 295–333; 1914.

870. Werner, H. *Comparative Psychology of Mental Development,* rev. ed., New York, Follett, 1948.

871. Werner, H. and Wapner, S. "Sensory-Tonic Field Theory of Perception," *J. Personal.,* 18:88–107; 1949.

872. Werner, H. and Kaplan, E. *The Acquisition of Word Meanings: A Developmental Study,* Monographs for the Society for Research in Child Development, Inc., Vol. XV, No. 1, 1950.

873. WERNER, H. and WAPNER, S. "Toward a General Theory of Perception," *Psychol. Rev.*, 59:324–338; 1952.

874. WERNICKE, C. *Der aphasische Symptomencomplex. Eine psychologische Studie auf anatomischer Basis*, Breslau, Cohn und Weigert, 1874.

875. WERTHEIMER, M. and KLEIN, J. "Psychologische Tatbestanddiagnostik," *Arch. Kriminalanthropol.*, 15:72–113; 1904.

876. WERTHEIMER, M. "Experimentelle Studien ueber das Sehen von Bewegung," *Z. Psychol.*, 61:161–265; 1912.

877. WERTHEIMER, M. *Productive Thinking*, New York, Harper, 1945.

878. WESTPHAL, K. "Haupt- und Nebenaufgaben bei Reaktionsversuchen," *Arch. Psychol.*, 21:219–434; 1911.

879. WEXLER, M. "The Structural Problem in Schizophrenia: The Role of the Internal Object," pp. 179–201. In: *Psychotherapy With Schizophrenics*, eds. E. Brody, and F. Redlich, New York, International Universities Press, 1952.

880. WHITE, R. "A Preface to the Theory of Hypnotism," *J. Abnorm. Soc. Psychol.*, 36:477–505; 1941.

881. WHITE, R. *The Abnormal Personality, a Textbook*, New York, Ronald, 1948.

882. WHITE, R., WRIGHT, B. and DEMBO, T. "Studies in Adjustment to Visible Injuries: Evaluation of Curiosity by the Injured," *J. Abnorm. Soc. Psychol.*, 43:13–28; 1948.

883. WHORF, B. "Four Articles on Metalinguistics," Foreign Service Institute, Department of State, Washington, 1950.

884. WIENER, N. *Cybernetics, or Control and Communication in the Animal and the Machine*, New York, John Wiley and Sons, 1948.

885. WILBRAND, H. *Die Seelenblindheit als Herderscheinung und ihre Beziehungen zur Alexie und Agraphie*, Wiesbaden, Bergmann, 1887.

886. WILBRAND, H. "Ein Fall von Seelenblindheit und Hemianopsie mit Sections Obduktionsbefund," *Dtsch. Nervenkr.*, 2:361–387; 1892.

887. WILBRAND, H. and SAENGER, A. *Die Neurologie des Auges: ein Handbuch fuer Nerven- u. Augenaerzte, Bd. VIII: Die Erkrankungen der Sehbahn vom Tractus bis in den Cortex*, Wiesbaden, Bergmann, 1917.

888. WILSON, A. "A Case of Double Consciousness," *Lancet*, 2:227; 1903, *J. Ment. Sci.*, 49:640–658; 1903.

889. WITASEK, S. *Grundlinien der Psychologie*, Leipzig, Duerr, 1908.

890. WITKIN, H. "Perception of Body Position and of the Position of the Visual Field," *Psychol. Monogrs.*, 63:1–46; 1949.

891. WOLFF, W. *The Expression of Personality*, New York, Harper, 1943.

892. WOODGER, J. *Biological Principles*, London, Kegan Paul, 1929.

893. WOODWORTH, R. *Experimental Psychology*, New York, Henry Holt, 1938.

894. WUNDT, W. *Hypnotismus und Suggestion*, Philosoph. Studien, 8, Leipzig, Engelmann, 1893.

895. WUNDT, W. *Principles of Physiological Psychology*, New York, Macmillan, 1904.

896. WUNDT, W. *Voelkerpsychologie*, 1–10, 2nd ed., Leipzig, Engelmann, 1904.

897. WUNDT, W. *Grundriss der Psychologie*, 9 Aufl., Leipzig, Engelmann, 1909.

898. WUNDT, W. *Elements of Folk Psychology*, New York, Macmillan, 1916.

899. YACORZYNSKI, C. *Medical Psychology. A Basis for Psychiatry and Clinical Psychology*, New York, Ronald Press, 1951.

900. YERKES, R. and HUGGINS, G. "Habit Formation in the Crawfish, Camburus Affinis," *Psychol. Rev.*, Monogr. Suppl. #17, 565–577; 1903.

901. YERKES, R. "The Intelligence of Earthworms," *J. Animal Behaviour*, 2:332–352; 1912.

902. YOUNG, P. C. "Experimental Hypnotism: a Review," *Psychol. Bull.*, 38:92–104; 1941.

903. YOUNG, P. T. *Emotion in Man and Animal*, New York, Wiley, 1943.

904. ZIEHEN, T. *Leitfaden der physiologischen Psychologie in 15 Vorlesungen*, (8 Aufl.), Jena, Fischer, 1908.

905. ZIEHEN, T. "Ueber die raeumlichen Eigenschaften einiger Empfindungsgruppen," *Fortschr. Psychol.*, 1:227–337; 1912.

NAME INDEX

SUBJECT INDEX